CW01096244

A
HISTORY Of
SOUTH CROFTY
MINE

J. A. Buckley

DYLLANSOW TRURAN

Other mining titles by the author:

Tudor Tinbounds (1987)
A Miner's Tale: Story of Howard Mankee (1988)
Geevor Mine (1989)
Cornish Mining: Underground (1989)
Cornish Engine Houses (Ed) (1989)
Cornish Mining: Surface (1990)
The Cornish Mining Industry (1992)
Bailiff of Blackmoor (1994)
South Crofty Underground (1995)
Geevor Mine Underground (1996)
Wheal Jane Underground (1997)

First published in 1982
Dyllansow Truran

This edition published
Dyllansow Truran
Croft Prince, Mount Hawke, Truro, Cornwall TR4 8EE

Copyright J. A. Buckley © 1997

ISBN - 1 85022 115 4 (cased)

ISBN - 1 85022 116 2 (paperback)

Printed and bound in Cornwall by
R. Booth (Bookbinder) Ltd. & Troutbeck Press,
Antron Hill, Mabe, Penryn TR10 9HH

Main text set in 10/12 point Times Roman

Contents

The author & publishers gratefully acknowledge the generosity of the late
J H Trounson for the use of photographs from his collection.

All colour photographs including covers
Copyright P R Deakin FRPS © 1997

Reproduction of the Tributer's pay slip on page 32 by kind permission of the
Cornwall County Record Office Truro.

Line drawings by Alan Reynolds Copyright Dyllansow Truran © 1997

The publishers have made every effort to contact copyright holders of
photographic material used in this book and will gladly acknowledge any errors
in future editions.

Illustrations

LINE DRAWINGS

PHOTOGRAPHS

Acknowledgements
First Edition

There are many people without whose help this book would not be completed, and the author expresses his gratitude to them. The staff at Tehidy Mineral Office, Camborne, gave every assistance to me; Miss Angela Broome and H.L. Douch of the Royal Institution of Cornwall; the staff at the Cornish Record Office; Terry Knight and Mrs B. Olds at the Local Studies Library Redruth; Oliver Padel at the Institute of Cornish Studies, all gave invaluable help in locating records and interpreting them. Joe Thomas of Redruth School, Douglas Smith of Holmans, Justin Brooke of Marazion, Jack Trounson of Redruth and Dr. Ken Hoskin of the Camborne School of Mines all gave me great encouragement by their desire to help locate and understand information used in this book. The late Dr. A.K. Hamilton Jenkin was a constant source of enthusiastic help, his knowledge and understanding of the subject being without equal. Many others, like Frank Hutchins, Ross Polkinhorne, G.C. Pengilly and H.R.M. Hodding contributed comments or advice to the author.

I would like to gratefully acknowledge the help given me by the staff of South Crofty Mine. G.W. Curtis, R.J. Fullard, John Lewis, John Penberthy and John Toman have all exercised patience in bringing me up to date with the present (1980) techniques used, machinery employed and understanding of the distribution of ore throughout the property. Many of the office staff assisted my search for old ledgers and records, and some, particularly Mike Williams and Mark Olliff tolerated my presence in their offices for inconveniently long periods. The late Ted Rowe spent much time answering my questions and volunteering unsolicited information.

My greatest debt of gratitude must go to the miners who gave help in my search for facts. The vast amount of information supplied by these men, sometimes from their fathers and grandfathers who worked at Crofty, enabled me to gain a clear picture of the mine back to the late years of the last century. A great deal of material in the form of old pay slips, photographs and other material has been loaned to me for use here. Fred Sedgemore, Willie Nettle, Bill Gronnert, Howard Vigus, Harold May, Jimmy Collins, Reggie Moyle, Howard Mankee, Ron Opie, Fred Calf and Martin Crothers are just a few of the miners who have supplied me with an abundance of stories and facts. Some still work at the mine, others are now retired, and many of them are now dead.

Finally, my special thanks must go to Mrs Sue Stone, who spent over 60 hours typing and re-typing my original almost illegible manuscript.

To J.H. Trounson I am indebted for loaning me so many of the photographs used. to R.E. Earl who assisted me with his camera and Dan Fossey for his drawings. I am grateful to the RIC for the use of the Henderson MSS, and to the CRO for the use of their vast collection of MSS.

For this new edition of the book I must thank Jenny Hinton and Emma White for typing the manuscript and making many corrections. Once again I acknowledge the generosity of the late Jack Trounson for loaning photographs used in both editions of the book. Thanks to Paul Deakin for his more recent photographs, and to Alan Reynolds for so skillfully drawing the maps. I am particularly grateful to my wife, whose help and support over the last three years of rewriting and editing this book, has been invaluable. Once again it is the miners to whom I express my greatest debt.

JAB November 1997

Introduction

South Crofty Mine lies at the centre of a metalliferous district which has seen mining for a variety of metals over many centuries. The present mine sett contains the workings of some thirty 18th century and well over a dozen 19th century mines, including some of the largest and most important tin and copper mines of the last 250 years. Dolcoath, North and South Roskear, Carn Brea, Tincroft, Cooks Kitchen and East Pool were among the largest copper producers of the 18th and early 19th centuries and the greatest tin mines of the 19th and early 20th centuries.

The current mine workings lie along the northern side of a line of granite hills including Carn Brea, Carnarthen and Carn Entral, and stretch over a distance of some 2.2 miles, from near the centre of Camborne to the Tolskithy valley. The present, relatively small underground workforce breaks a greater tonnage of tin ore than any other Cornish mine has ever produced.

At the end of the 20th century South Crofty is the sole surviving mine out of the thousands which have operated over the last few hundred years. It is no exaggeration to say that mining has taken place at South Crofty, under many different names, since Tudor times, and there is a continuous record of mining there since the 1670s. The mine has been involved in every change in the condition and fortune of the Cornish mining industry during the last three centuries. The many booms and depressions, expansions and disasters, technological improvements and economic revolutions have all left their marks upon the story of South Crofty Mine. The mine's successful survival is due to the skill and tenacity of its workforce and the strength and persistence of its lodes.

Chapter One:
Penhellick Vean Mine

Camborne and Illogan parishes have been at the centre of the Cornish tin industry since medieval times, and during the 17th century several mines, which now comprise South Crofty became very important tin producers.

At the heart of the 20th century mine is the ancient tenement of Penhellick Vean, in the parish of Illogan. This small holding, originally part of Tehidy Manor, occupies the area to the south-west of Pool crossroads where the tenements (or estates) of Treloweth, Trevenson and Tregajorran Wollas meet it. Being surrounded by several busy mines, 18th century Pool quickly grew into a populous village. Blacksmiths shops, carpenters shops, rope walks, candle making factories, grocery stores and public houses soon formed the centre of a burgeoning community. Beneath the village the workings of the 'the poole' and 'Penhellick work' were removing increasing tonnages of ore. To the north,south, east and west of Pool a large number of mines and tin streams operated.

During the late medieval period Penhellick Vean became alienated from Tehidy Manor, due to marriage settlements, and by the 16th century the two estates of Trevenson and Penhellick Vean were divided between three landowning families, the Vyvyans, Praeds and the Angoves. The mineral ownership was also divided, but not equally (Praed [GHW] CRO Truro).

Most of the earliest references to tin production were to working the alluvial deposits along the stream, which runs through Pool from Carnarthen Moor to Trevenson Moor and Halgoss. There are references in the Penwith and Kerrier Stannary records, of 1507, to such activity between Trevenson and Treloweth, close to Pool School, and further downstream, at Halgoss near Tehidy (British Library Additional Ms. 24746). The Red River which runs through Brea and Tuckingmill, and the stream through Tolskithy, were also extensively streamed for tin, the earliest references being to damage caused by tinners to Church land prior to 1237, and to tinners damaging the river banks close to Carn Brea Village in 1301 (Assize Rolls Crown Pleas No. 118).

There is a large corpus of information to support the belief that by the latter part of the Tudor period tin mining was widespread in the Camborne and Illogan area (*Topographical & Historical Description of Cornwall* (1584) John Norden; HB 5/165 RIC, Truro). By the time that the Praed family purchased Penhellick Vean and Trevenson, both shode mining and exploration of gossan lodes beneath the surface were carried out in the Red River Valley, and along the stream that runs through Pool. Tolcarne Mine, to the south of Camborne, was mentioned by Norden, in the late 16th century and the Vyvyan papers from that period show it was an important mine. Woon Antron, at Troon, Treslothan Mine and Carnkie Bal were all reported to be important throughout the 16th century, both Carnkie Bal and Woon Antron contributing to Camborne Church in the 1540s. Mines Royal records show that copper mining was also signified in Illogan Parish in the 1560s and 1580s (*Elizabethan Copper: The History of Mines Royal*, M. B. Donald (London 1967)). There is a lease agreement, dated 1588, between the Cranes of Camborne and the Bassets of Tehidy, which was concerned with, "Two stamping mills ... water courses, letes and buddels", used in connection with tin streaming at Brea. Brea tenement stretched from the present village, right along the eastern side of the Red River Valley, and included Brea Croft, where the engine houses of old Cook's Kitchen can still be seen, as well as New Cooks Kitchen Shaft and the present mine offices. Its eastern boundary was along Dudnance Lane, the other side of which was the tenement of Dudnance, and its northern boundary lay along the main road between Tuckingmill and Dudnance Lane (HB/5/11 RIC Truro).

By the reign of Elizabeth 1, the search for tin on Trevenson Estate was general. The 1542 description of Trevenson's Bounds, refers to a 'blowing house' close to the Red River at the western end of Trevenson, and by the end of the century mentions of tin working in the lease agreements there were common. John Angove of Trevenson leased his third of the estate to one "Richard Kearne (Carne) alias Tresillian", in March 1592, and the agreement included, "All tolle tynne and tynne works already founde and hereafter to be founde in and upon the p(re)mysses w(i)th free lib(er)tie ingres egres & regres to digge delve & serch for tynne w(hi)ch so had founde & wroughte the same ... (HB 5/165 RIC Truro).

On the eastern side of Penhellick Vean, at Tregajorran Wollas, which lies to the south of the main road and to the east of Carn Brea Lane, mining was also taking place. A document dated October 6th 1675, that related to the lease of Tregajorran Wollas by Francis Basset to John Rogers, mentions, "all tynn, toll tynn & tynn works & mines of mettall now found or wrought in or upon the said tenement". In 1699 an agreement was made between Francis Basset and Reginald Angove that reserved to the Basset's, "all tyn, toll tyn, tyn works and tyn mines and all other mines for mettalls." (HB 5/148: HB 5/149 RIC Truro).

These tin workings were right on the border with Penhellick Vean. Tregajorran Mine, also called 'the poole', was worked throughout the second half of the 17th century (Tehidy Lease Agreement 1698).

Along the southern boundaries of Penhellick Vean, in Penhellick Veor, records show that mining was well advanced by the end of the 17th century. The Radnor

Court Rolls give many details of the development of mining at Penhellick. One of the October 1663 presentments for the Manor of Treloweth says, "We present so muche tinne to be wrought in Gew (Geau, in Penhellick) as that same thereof is 3 gallons, the lord's part one gallon & sold unto Stephen Mitchell for £1 7s 0d". An October 1664 presentment refers to "Some tinne to be wrought by William Lanyon on the borders of Penhellick in holing against John Pawle in Mr Basset's ground and encroaching there." Clearly, John Pawle was mining on Basset's land, on the western side of Dudnance Lane, and Lanyon had encroached outside Penhellick. There is another reference to this encroachment in 1666, and at that time William Lanyon was said to be mining "in Penhellick side of the lane in holing against Richard Pawle". By 1678 the records show that John Lanyon was "putting downe a shaft in Penhellick to stop men working in Mr Basset's land", where Penhellick miners had "digged up some tyn stuff", an account of which was to be given at the next court (HU13 (1625-1763) CRO Truro).

The shallow workings were worked intermittently at that time as is indicated by references to particular workings in Penhellick being "still at work" or starting to work again. The mine on the boundary of Penhellick Veor is identified in the 1683 records as being situated "in the Tyn Croft at Penhellick". The field of that name is shown in the Lanhydrock Atlas of 1696, alongside Dudnance Lane, at the present western entrance to Pool Market. The presentment mentions £30 worth of "tyn stuff" sold in May 1682, that had been mined at Tyn Croft (HU13 (1625-1763) CRO Truro).

Between 1682 - 92 there are several references to mining at Tyn Croft, the Round, the Gew, and Penhellick House's "Orchard Moor". Mention is also made of Horse Field and The Meadow being used to store tin stuff. The burrows were spreading across the present site of Home World and Texas stores 300 years ago. All of the above fields can be located on the 1696 Atlas (Copy at RIC Truro).

Workings on Brea tenement, known as Wheal-an-Gare and John Pawle's Mine, were to form part of Cooks Kitchen and New Cooks Kitchen in the 18th and 19th centuries. Both mines were called Brea Mine in the early 18th century. Just along the lane one-hundred yards, the field called Long Close was being worked for copper by the early 18th century, and no doubt, like its immediate neighbours, still produced some tin.

During the 1600s Penhellick Vean was divided between the Vyvyans of Trelowarren, the Praeds of Trevethow and the Angoves of Trevenson House. After the Civil War and the Restoration, things eventually settled down in Cornwall, and some of the ancient shallow mines were revived together with newer operations, like the ones at Penhellick Veor. It was at that time that the three mineral-lords, Vyvyan, Praed and Angove leased Penhellick Vean sett to the adventurers of Penhellick Vean Mine. It is very probable that they were substantial shareholders in the adventure, as this was commonly the case, and certainly all three families were involved in mining during the 17th, 18th and 19th centuries (DDHL (2) 135 (1681-94) CRO Truro). Both Penhellick Vean Mine and Tregajorran Mine were visited in about 1670, by a famous botanist and mineral collector called Richard Dyer of Oriel College, Oxford. He made a collection of interesting specimens from mines all over the country, and most of his tin and copper samples came from Cornwall.

Dyer's collection eventually came into the possession of John Poynter MA, who listed the specimens from Illogan thus: "No 15. Oar from Tregajorran Mine in Luggan Parish, Cornwall. No 16. Oar from Penhallock-Vein Mine in Luggan Parish, Cornwall." (Rich.Dyer Matric. 1669. Fellow of Oriel, 1673) (*Early Science in Oxford* Vol. 3, pp 497-9, R. T. Gunther).

We have little information on the extent of the 16th century Penhellick Vean Mine workings, but we can gain some idea from the shallow workings that are shown on later plans, and from what can be seen of them when they are occasionally uncovered. The principal lode of this sett was called 'Penhelik' Lode, the name by which it was known throughout the 1700s, and it was first worked only 15 feet below the surface, at a point a short distance west of the Basset Arms. The main workings were concentrated behind the Basset Arms, and they are shown on a map of Penhellick Vean in the Praed family papers, from about 1740. The line of Pool Adit is shown, and the part running behind the Basset Arms towards what is now Station Road, is called 'Old Works'. There are three shafts shown, and one of them was later called Serpell's Shaft, after the tenants of the shops that were directly in front of it. In the winter of 1977-78, whilst Station Road was dug up for new storm drains, some of the old, shallow workings were uncovered about 12 feet down. The levels driven in the late 1600s and early 1700s were around the 100 foot mark, and the Pool Adit, begun after 1710, was driven through Penhellick Vean at a depth of about 120 feet, in order to allow the mine to work deeper. The workings close to the surface very likely date from late Tudor or early Stuart times. It would appear that both Reeves' and Pryces' Lodes were worked at Penhellick Vean from that period, as gossan lodes. (Kerrier District Council Plans & Report (1978)).

The final years of the 17th century were marked by several developments which revolutionised mining in Cornwall. The water wheels described by Carew, which were usually between 12' and 15' in diameter, were replaced about the turn of the century by much larger over-shot wheels which could operate tiers of pumps, and effectively unwater mines many fathoms deeper than hitherto. Pryce, in his *Mineralogia Cornubiensis* 1778 wrote:

"About four score years back (1690s), small wheels of twelve or fifteen feet diameter were not the best machinery for draining the mines, and if one or two were insufficient, more were often adopted to that purpose, all worked by the same stream of water."

Pryce further stated in 1778, that the engineer and copper smelting agent, John Coster was responsible for the introduction into Cornish mines of those large over-shot water-wheels, which by the latter part of the 1700s rivalled for efficiency the steam engines of that period. During the early 1700s he worked locally, and was closely connected with Penhellick Vean Mine and the adjacent Pool Mine. He leased the Lenobrey (St.Agnes) smelting house near Porthtowan and apparently tried copper smelting there is 1721. He also leased several sets of stamps in that area.

Of no less significance was the introduction in the late 1680s of gunpowder. Thomas Epsley was brought from Somerset by the Godolphins to teach their miners at Breage and Germoe the art of 'shooting the rocks'. He arrived at Breage in June 1689, and by December of that year he was killed at the mine, apparently as a result of a gunpowder explosion. Although his death underlined the dangers of blasting, the great value of this new technique was not lost on the miners throughout West Cornwall, and the practice soon spread to the mines at Pool (Breage Burial Registers 1689).

The slow laborious method of hewing the rock by means of gads, plugs and wedges, and the less common methods of 'firesetting' and lime-blasting, soon gave way to this new technique, which despite its dangers, made development many times easier.

Early in the 1700s, the steam engineer Newcomen, encouraged by the interest of Sir Sidney Godolphin, the principal government minister and largest Cornish mine-owner, developed the ideas patented by Savory in the previous century. Godolphin brought in tax concessions to the renascent Cornish mining industry, and indirectly Newcomen's steam pumping engines were eventually enabled to compete effectively with the cheaply run water-wheels of John Coster. Early in the 18th century one of Newcomen's engines was erected at Wheal Vor.

The new methods of pumping water from greater depth; blasting through rocks at greater speeds; the improved milling techniques; valuable assistance from the Government on reduced coal charges from Welsh ports, prepared the way for expansion at Pool and the rest of Cornwall. The Bassets were quick to seize the opportunity. The mine they owned at Trevenson, and the adjacent Penhellick Vean Mine, were to be transformed from small, barely economical operations to sharers in a boom that was to make the fortunes of the Basset family, and keep men in work here for almost a century without letup.

In 1710 the Bassets obtained from the mineral lords a lease to work the above setts, and the lease details are interesting.

"9 March 1710 Articles of agreement between Sir Richard Vyvyan of Trelowarren Bart, John Praed of Trevethowe Esq., & Abel Angove of Illogan Gent., of the one part and Francis Basset of Tehidy of the other.

Whereas Sir R Vyvyan, John Praed and Abel Angove are seized of Penhellick Vean in Illogan viz $1/4$ Sir R Vyvyan, $1/2$ John Praed, and the residue A.Angove of Trevenson in Illogan, viz $1/3$ in each with all mineral rights to both estates -they lease the above to Francis Basset and give him licence to dig for tin and copper. Francis Basset promises to deliver to the landlords the 9th part of all ore he shall raise in Penhellick Vean, and $2/3$ of the 6th part of ore raised in Trevenson and he also undertakes to carry the half of all the copper ore taken in Penhellick Vean and $1/3$ part of all copper ore taken from Trevenson to a quay belonging to John Praed called Lelant Quay in order to have it shipped. John Praed agrees however that in case there should be no ship at the quay. Mr Basset shall carry off his ore to another quay."

According to Celia Fiennes, who journeyed through these parts in the last decade of the previous century, some small amount of copper smelting took place at St Ives, but it would seem from the above agreement, that is was usual to send the copper ore to Bristol or Wales for smelting. Any small quantity of tin that might be mined would probably be smelted at the 'blowing house' at the western end of Trevenson. Certainly it is apparent from the above agreement that Penhellick Vean Mine was to be worked as part of the Basset owned Pool Adit. The Penhellick Vean sett, which then was taken by Pool Adit, was to be worked by several almost independent undertakings as the 18th century progressed. Pool Adit was sometimes worked under the name Pool Mine, as this was the mine to which the adit was originally driven.

Chapter Two:
Penhellick & Pool Mines 1710-1787

R epresenting the interests of the Bristol Copper Smelters at Pool was John Coster and his was one of the signatures on the 1710 lease agreement. It is apparent that he was closely involved in all aspects of this new undertaking of the Bassets. Certainly, his large over-shot water-wheels were used in the early 1700s at Pool Mine, and they are shown by the main pumping shaft on Doidge's1737 Tehidy Manor map. With the daily footage increased by the use of gunpowder, the Bassets could undertake the driving of an adit from the Red River Valley, just below Tuckingmill. This adit would give Pool and Penhellick Vean Mines a drain 120 feet deep throughout their main workings. It was driven east, and followed a copper lode into the old Trevenson workings, and then under the main road into Penhellick Vean Mine near to Burgess' Shaft. Before this it had to pierce an extraordinarily hard 'irestone' dyke. Over half a century later, Pryce, in his *Mineralogia Cornubiensis* (page 148), whilst describing the relative costs in adit driving, said about the Pool Adit, "The greatest expense for the ground discovered, that I ever heard of in driving an adit, was in the old Pool, two miles off (from Redruth), where Mr Basset paid five and thirty pounds(£35) per fathom for the driving of several fathoms, through irestone stratum; which great price answered so badly for the contractors, that they were very much injured by the undertaking"

Cornish Miners also called these 'irestone' dykes, 'iron bars' or just 'bars', because of their excessive hardness. This particular dyke, although giving the miners and the adventurers much trouble, did not alter the great profitability of the adit in general. For a while the adventurers were discouraged, and the ground was so hard that nearly a century later it had become a byword for impervious rock, and William Phillips, in 1802, remarked that the dyke turned the "edge of every tool, so that it was found impossible to drive a hole deep enough to blast with gunpowder. The miners, therefore were compelled little by little to pick through that part of it, in doing which the seat-board (croust seat) was not once moved forward during the space of twelve months." (Trans. Geolog. Soc. (London) Vol. II p133).

Once the adit was completed to the main workings, the water-wheels, which powered tiers of pumps, were able to bring the water up to the adit level so that it ran away into the Red River. Although these efficient Coster engines could then take the greater part of the water, horse-whims and rag-and-chain pumps were still used to supplement the main pumps and also to bring the water up from

15

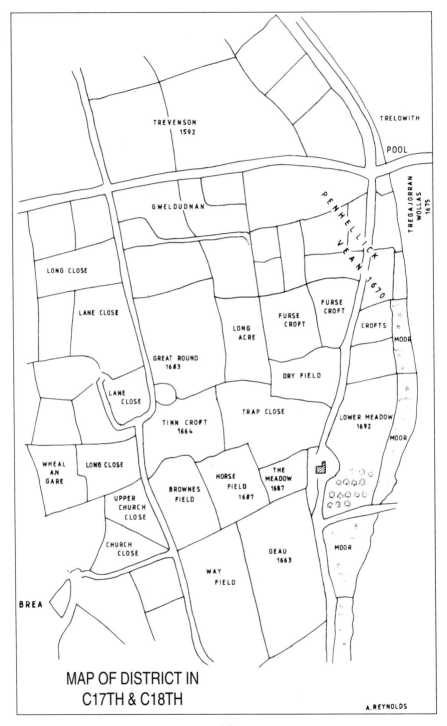

TREVENSON
1592

TRELOWITH

POOL

GWELDUDNAN

PENHELLICK VEAN 1670

TREGAJORRAN WOLLAS 1675

LONG CLOSE

LANE CLOSE

FURSE CROFT

FURSE CROFT

CROFTS

MOOR

LONG ACRE

GREAT ROUND
1683

DRY FIELD

LANE CLOSE

TRAP CLOSE

LOWER MEADOW
1692

TINN CROFT
1664

MOOR

WHEAL AN GARE

LONG CLOSE

HORSE FIELD
1687

THE MEADOW
1687

BROWNES FIELD

UPPER CHURCH CLOSE

CHURCH CLOSE

GEAU
1663

MOOR

WAY FIELD

BREA

MAP OF DISTRICT IN
C17TH & C18TH

A.REYNOLDS

1. *Richard Trevithick's birthplace. The picture was taken in the 1880s. The house, now 35 Station Road, was originally Penhellick Vean Farm, and Trevithick's father rented it, together with several acres, from Tehidy Manor. Palmers engine house can be seen in the background, with the small headgear of Bickfords Shaft in the right background. Palmers 60" engine was erected in 1862 and continued in use until 1908. Notice the tin streamers in the foreground, where Crofty Close now stands.*

2. *Two machinemen using a Stephens Imperial bar-and-arm rock drill. The photograph was taken in February 1910, at Palmers section, on the 170 fm level. Note, the primitive water-laying arrangement, where water was sucked from a bucket to be sprayed onto the face.*

cisterns at the very bottom of the mine. To ensure a good water supply for these pumps the Bassets inserted a head-weir in the Red River above Brea Adit (Betty Adit). They had constructed a leat that stretched from this head-weir, ran along the eastern side of Brea Village, along the cliff top, crossing what is now Tincroft Road and the railway, across Brea Croft, where old Cook's Kitchen engine houses now stand, and into the tenement of Dudnance, just to the east of Wheal Dudnance Mine. From there it carried the water, on launders, across the main Pool-Tuckingmill road to the water engines constructed by John Coster. This water was used by Penhellick Vean Mine after it had gone over the wheels on the northern side of the road. It was returned to the Red River by way of the Pool Adit (Doidge Tehidy Manor Map).

All of this worked well, and the lodes discovered by the driving of the Pool Adit were to prove some of the richest shallow lodes ever mined in Cornwall. The Adit cauntered two lodes known as Wheal Crofty Lodes, Cherry Garden.Lode, Trevenson Lode, Wheal Vernon Lode, Wheal Knight Lode and Wheal Horse Lode. It also gave easier access to Penhellick Lode, Wheal Dudnance Lode and Old Pool Lode. It must be stated, however, that these lodes were not always the ones known by these names later in the 19th century. The famous Reeve's Lode was named in the 1830s after an important adventurer in East Wheal Crofty; before that it was worked under other, older names. The Penhellick Lode worked in the late l9th century by South Wheal Crofty, and the Dudnance Lode worked at the same time, are both different lodes from those with the same names a century earlier.

Pryce stated that by 1720, within a decade of the amalgamation of Pool and Penhellick Vean Mines, the Adit which had been conceived as a means to better work them, was itself the most profitable venture hereabouts. Penhellick Mine, as it was generally called in the 18th century, was worked as a section of Pool Adit, but the setts were later worked on the line of the Adit as separate ventures.

As the Bassets were the principal adventurers in both undertakings it did not cause great problems, but after more then two centuries, it needs a very careful examination of the agreements to determine with any accuracy the demarcation between the various undertakings.

The accounts for the early and mid-1700s show that the expenses and returns for Trevenson and Penhellick Vean were kept separate in both the Pool Mine Cost Books, and those for Pool Adit. Although for all practical purposes these points held true, there are numerous departures from them, and frequently agreements seem to indicate that the names Pool Mine, which at first referred to 'the poole' at Tregajorran, later became attached to Trevenson workings.

Between 1710 and 1730 Pool Adit, Pool Mine and Penhellick Mine together, accounted for copper of enormous value. With their workings very shallow, being

17

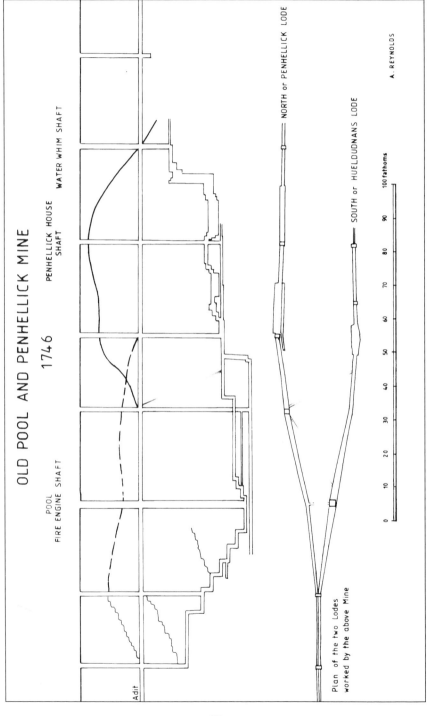

OLD POOL AND PENHELLICK MINE

1746

POOL
FIRE ENGINE SHAFT

PENHELLICK HOUSE
SHAFT

WATER WHIM SHAFT

Adit

Plan of the two Lodes
worked by the above Mine

NORTH or PENHELLICK LODE

SOUTH or HUELDUDNANS LODE

A. REYNOLDS

0   10   20   30   40   50   60   70   80   90   100 fathoms

sometimes above the adit level of 120 feet below surface, with water available to drive the machinery relatively cheaply, the Bassets were home and dry financially. Nearby at Dudnance, cobolt was mined, and this also was of high value. Behind the Penhellick Mine, across the croft, Brea Mine and Wheal-an-Gare Mine were restarting as Cook's Kitchen. Throughout this area mining for copper expanded although tin remained constant.

The map drawn in 1737 by William Doidge, for the Bassets of Tehidy, gives much detail that is of interest to us. Although Penhellick Vean was not included in the manor, there is sufficient on the map to tell us the position in 1737. The Brea leat is shown, as is the length of the launder between the end of the leat, in Dudnance tenement, and the large water-wheels at the centre of the Pool Adit. The line of Pool Adit is shown, with the workings indicated along its entire length. At Crofty, on Penhellick Vean sett, workings were shown right across the northern part of the sett, just south of the main road. The Adit ran from John's Shaft along the back of the houses, behind the Basset Arms (then in existence) to the mine called 'poole work'. The Adit cauntered lodes that mostly ran in a more northerly direction than the Adit, so the drives and stopes of those ancient workings ran just south of west toward Dudnance sett. The map shows the field that gave Longclose Mine its name, but although it is not specifically described as a mine, it was by that time producing large quantities of copper. Between 1743-55 it gave its adventurers profit of about £19,000 (Tehidy Accounts).

A map in the Praed family papers dated 1740 shows "The Copper Mines" along the line of Pool Adit, where it crosses the main road from Trevenson to Penhellick Vean, just clipping the north-east corner of 'Gwealdudnan'. Five shafts are shown to the north of the road, two in Dudnance and two in Penhellick Vean. There are also the three shafts at the back of the Basset arms which are described as 'Old Works'. It is apparent from this map, as it is from other records, that although Penhellick Mine and Pool Mine (Trevenson Mine) were run as one mine, they remained distinct. The details of those workings, corresponds exactly with the section and lode plan of Pool Mine by Borlase in 1746-58 (*Natural History of Cornwall* (1758) William Borlase).

Dudnance sett was worked under the names Wheal Dudnance, Pool Mine and Pool Adit, with lease agreements drawn up to carefully distinguish between the workings of each.

Between December 1739 and November 1742, 2,700 tons of copper, and a small quantity of tinstuff were produced by Pool Adit, and sold for over £20,000 giving a profit of £10,199. Among the numerous valuable parcels of copper ore sold in 1739-41, were several small parcels of 'tinstuff'. "1740 August 22nd Henry Proviss for parcel of Tinstuff - £15 0s 0d". In the Tehidy Accounts costs column for September 15th 1740, "Mr Bennet $1/2$ of Tinstuff sold Proviss £6 13s 4d." Just below that entry it tells us that dues of £1 13s 4d were paid on that small parcel of tin. Another entry later on in 1740 says, "Capt Tresadern for a parcel of Tinstuff - £44 8s 10³/₄d". During that same period nearly £9,000 worth of copper was sold by Pool Adit, giving a profit for the year of £5,863 9s 6¹/₂d (Tehidy Accounts).

During 1741 £6,495 was returned being made up of £24 14s 3d, for "Candles and drawing", £53 16s 9¹/₂d, for tinstuff, including £18 6s 8d, "for Penhellick Tinstuff", and the other £6,420 from copper.

The 'Costs Account' has some interesting entries which prove that Pool Adit was divided into sections that approximated to the areas of the old mines being worked:

"August 4th Poundage to the Takers	£202	12	11
July Month	£132	15	0¹/₂
John Luke for dressing Oar	£17	17	0
August Cost for Pool Adit	£83	19	5¹/₂
August Cost for Trevenson and Wh. Dudnance	£33	3	7
August Cost for Penhellick	£26	11	0
September Cost for Trevenson	£121	8	4
September Cost for Penhellick	£47	14	7
"October 10.30 Two Horses	£10	10	0
October Cost for Trevenson	£144	16	3
October Cost for Penhellick	£55	18	11
"November 19th Capt. Tresadern for Candles	£2	16	0
Poundage to the Takers	£320	14	5¹/₂
November Cost in Penhellick	£28	4	8
November Cost in Trevenson	£226	18	3¹/₂

(Tehidy Accounts 1741)

It appears from that section of cost accounts, that Wheal Dudnance was worked from Trevenson, Penhellick section was kept separate so far as costs were concerned, and this is interesting, as the cost books for the 19th century, East Wheal Crofty, tended to lump all the costs together, whilst separating returns - for the purpose of paying the correct dues. The profit for 1741 was over £3,180.

In 1741, under pressure from the powerful copper lobby, the London government once again came to the rescue of the Cornish mines, when it remitted the duty on coals "expended in workings fire engines". Borlase commented that without this assistance, the Newcomen engines erected at Dolcoath, Bullen Garden and Pool Mine, would never have been contemplated. He says that after that date, engines with cyclinder capacity of up to 6 foot were built, and many were erected by Joseph Hornblower and his family. In his Natural History of Cornwall (1758), Borlase gives a drawing of the engine at Pool Mine, and shows it to have been a 36" engine. He indicated that this engine was erected in the mid-1740s.

Pool Adit produced ore of £4,255 in 1742, including four parcels of tinstuff to the value of £74. Costs in Penhellick section were given at £50; whereas those in Trevenson were £497.

In February 1743 the lease to work Trevenson and Penhellick Vean setts on the line of the Pool Adit was renewed. John Edwards acted as trustee for the grantors of the lease, and together the Bassets, Sir Francis Vyvyan, William Markworth Praed and Abel Angove, were all in the position of grantors, being mineral-lords, and representatives of the adventurers of the mine, as well as prominent adventurers themselves (Tehidy Mine Sett Agreement).

By the year 1744 the adventurers in Pool Mine, and Pool Adit, were in a position to take advantage of the cheaper Welsh coal. They clearly did not intend to remove their water engines, but saw that if they were to go deeper they would need steam power to pump out the water. The transactions between the adventurers and the Coalbrookdale Co., who manufactured the Newcomen engines, show how vague the demarcation was between Pool Adit and Old Pool Mine. The main source of our information on these Newcomen engines is the Accounts Book of Thomas Goldney, a Bristol merchant-banker with shares in the Coalbrookdale Co. He lived from 1694-1768, and we are indebted to him for his carefully kept records.

At the end of December 1744 Goldney delivered to Thomas Lanyon for Abel Angove & Co., of "Trevenson in the parish of Logan", a bored cylinder weighing 43cwt., a bottom, and five barrels, costing in all £120. The weight of the cylinder indicates a diameter of about 40". On February 2nd 1745 this cylinder was sent back to Coalbrookdale having been found to be faulty. At that time another consignment was sent down to Pool, this time being addressed to Sir Francis Vivian & Co., and subsequent entries show that this was to the same company. In October of that year more pitwork was sent to Pool, together with a 60cwt cylinder to replace the faulty one. During 1746 more pit-barrels were sent, together with other fittings including pipes. This lot totalled £801.

These entries for 1744 call the mine delivered to 'Trevenson Mine'; those for 1745 call it either 'Trevenson Mine' or 'Pool Adit'; and when in 1748 a 60" engine was delivered to Thomas Lanyon, each reference was to 'Pool Adit'. This 60" engine weighed 90cwt, and cost £198. With all of its related pieces of machinery and pitwork the cost totalled £875.00. More deliveries were made from Coalbrookdale in 1751. Borlase, who visited the mine and viewed the engines in about 1746, called the mine either 'the Pool (mine),' or 'Pool Adit'.

The above indicates that at least two Newcomen engines were working at Pool Adit and Pool Mine by 1750. For a complete description of Pool Mine between 1746-50, let us turn again to Borlase, who used Pool Mine as an example of a typical Cornish Mine of that period (*Natural History of Cornwall* (1758) William Borlase).

Borlase says that the workings described are shown as they were in 1746. He does not include all Pool Adit in his descriptions, but concentrates on what he called Pool Mine at the eastern side of Trevenson and Penhellick Vean. On the section (fig. 1) he shows that the depth at that time was about 330 feet below the surface, approximately 210 feet below adit. The nine shafts in use, were sunk on the two main lodes being worked, "North, or Penhellick Lode", which was worked within 15 feet of the surface at Penhellick Shaft, and "South or Hueldudnans Lode", which was first discovered about 30 feet down. These two lodes were the original lodes worked by the Penhellick Vean Mine in the 1600s and perhaps earller.

From the west, the shafts were (1) Black-ore Shaft, sunk on both lodes; (2) House Shaft, also sunk on both lodes, at the point where they separate; (3) Fire-engine Shaft, sunk on Wheal Dudnance Lode; (4) North House Shaft, sunk on Penhellick Lode; (5) Little North House Shaft, also sunk on Penhellick Lode; (8) Roskear Shaft, at the extreme eastern end of the area worked, on Penhellick Lode; (9) Grey-ore Shaft, on Wheal Dudnance Lode. An examination of the plan will show how the two lodes stood in relation to each other.

At the top of Fire-engine Shaft, also called Summer Pole or Poole Shaft, the 36" engine already referred to, stood. This was a Newcomen engine supplied by the Coalbrookdale Company. The cylinders up which the water was pumped were described by Borlase as "some iron, some of brass". A drift to carry the water from the northern lode to the bottom of Fire-engine Shaft was shown on the plan and section of the mine. Other drifts carried water into the 'dippas' or pits, from whence 'force-pumps' were used to lift it. In pursuit of the lode downwards, 'little winds' or 'small shafts' were sunk, so that the lode was followed down in a series of big steps, following the lode on strike until it got richer in the bottom of the drive, then down in a winds for a couple of fathoms, and so on. In the case of Pool Mine this method was pursued from the western end of the workings near to House Shaft, and then by a series of winds and drives along the wide section of Hueldudnans Lode until the bottom of Fire-engine Shaft was reached. "From whence the water of the whole mine there gathered together by various drifts and landers (launders) or gutters of wood, is drawn up to the main adit."

In lifting water up relatively small distances, apart from the 'force-pumps', there were 'rag and chain pumps'. Borlase said that these were used extensively at Pool Mine, especially when winzes were sunk in pursuit of the lode.

"Another water-engine which the Cornish use is the rag and chain; it consists of an iron chain with knobs of cloth (fenc'd and stiffen'd with leather) betwixt two and three feet asunder; the chain is turned round by a wheel of two or three feet diameter, furnished with iron spikes which inclose and keep steady the chain, so that it may rise through a wooden pump of about six or eight inches bore, and twelve or fifteen feet long, and by means of the leather knobs bring up with it a stream of water answerable to the diameter of the pump, and in quantity according to the circumvolutions of the wheel in any given time. This engine is worked usually by hand (as at Pool Mine), but where plenty of water can be had ... much more effectually and frugally by small water-wheels". (Borlase p.171).

At Water-Whim Shaft a large over-shot wheel of the Coster type was used to pump water up the shaft. At that time, before the Carnkie Leat was built to supplement Brea Leat, the water engines at Pool Mine and Penhellick Mine had an unreliable supply. After 1754, when the Carnkie Leat was joined to their supply, and water was more readily available from Tregajorran, this was not quite the problem, although the enormous wheels at Cook's Kitchen took precedence over Pool Mine. Borlase described the effectiveness of these water-wheel engines, and said it was "An engine whose power is answerable to the diameter of the wheel, and the length of the bobs fastened to its axis by large iron cranks; a perpendicular rod of timber to each end of the bobs, works a piston in a wooden, or (which is far better) a brass hollow cylinder, and the quantity of water exhausted will be in proportion to the bore of the cylinder, and the number of times which the piston moves up and down in any given space".

Horse-whims were also used, where two horses, fastened to the end of a transverse beam provided power to hoist 'kibbles' full of water up the shafts. These were only practical where the shafts were vertical.

Borlase showed that most of the stoping was done by 'pares' of about 12 men, and that at Pool Mine, although back stoping appears to have taken place, mostly it was underhand stoping, working away on a dozen or so large steps (benches). Where the stope was worked out, they placed stull pieces covered with fir planks, and threw the 'deads' upon them. With copper, a lot of the sorting of ore from 'deads' was done underground.

Borlase said that the lodes in Pool and Penhellick Mines tended to get richer as they went eastward, although there were exceptions, as at that time, in 1746, there were rich deposits at the western end, where the two lodes ran together. Whilst the miners were engaged in pursuing the lodes by driving and sinking, the "Chief miners (called Captains) took the bearing of the lodes with a well appoved needle (which they call dialling the ground), and sink another shaft". So after establishing through 'dialling' the exact position and direction of the drive, a new shaft is sunk ahead of the miners, so that air is available when needed, and better access also. Sometimes at Pool Mine, "there are three shafts or more sinking on the lode at one time".

The responsibility of the mine-captains at that time was not merely to do survey work, but also to have overall control of the workforce.

"That the common labourers may be employed without confusion in breaking and raising the ore, the captains see that they be properly disposed in the several parts of the mine that they have necessary tools and implements ready provided; they are to examine, and provide for its security; see that the adit be sound and clear, that the shafts, hollows and looser parts of the mine, be well propped with timber; that they are to see that proper communications be made and maintained between the several works of the mine (footnote: Horizontal planks were to be used to make the levels for this purpose); more expecially are they to inspect the ores, insist that they be speedily broken, as carefully separated from the deads and from each other and as honestly brought up for the owner's use, as may be. But, indeed, their chief care, and what required their constant skill and attention, is the management of the water, which in the Cornish mines is generally very troublesome, every cranny that is cut throwing forth its water into the cavity where the miners work. To obviate this inconveniency the captain should be a kind of engineer, and well know how to collect, divert, and conduct, as well as raise the water. It is not expected indeed that the captains of mines should know how to build, repair or rectify the several engines; for such purposes there is a professed undertaker, or engineer, but the Captain is to take care that the engineer has immediate notice as soon as anything goes amiss, that he has proper materials, and without delay attends to remedy the disorder. In order to do this, the water must be convey'd over and beside the passages, and cross the openings of the mine by side drifts and gutters, so that all that possibly can, may run off by the common drain (the adit); what is below that level must be collected and drawn up to the adit. Where there are two lodes (as here at Pool Mine) there must be ducts of communication, which serve to convey the water of the North Lode (Penhelik) into the cistern made in the South Lode (Hueldudnans)".

Borlase then described the Newcomen 'fire engine' that drained the main workings at Pool and Penhellick. He dealt at length with the basic principles of the Newcomen engine, and discussed the relative merits of it. He does not comment upon the engines used by Pool Adit, which apparently, from the Coalbrookedale records, were of larger size. Thus in the mid-1740s, Pool Mine (including Penhellick Mine), was served by a 36" steam engine, and a large over-shot wheel engine, together with numerous 'force pumps' and 'rag and chain' pumps. Pool adit, considerably richer at that period, had the benefit of two large steam engines and numerous pumps of the smaller variety.

From the time of the original driving of Pool Adit, the owners of the ancient workings to the south of Crofty saw the potential of going deeper. Throughout the area called Brea Croft, in that part of Brea tenement that stretched to the main road at Tuckingmill, and in Penhellick Veor (Great Penhellick), usually

24

nowadays called just Penhellick, adits were started to explore the existing workings at greater depth. As early as 1730 Brea Mine had an adit driven in from the Red River, shown on the 1737 Doidge map as 'Brea Audit', and within a decade a network of adits, that amounted to cross-cuts, were driven to join both this adit and the deeper Pool Adit.

In 1740 Abel Angove of Trevenson, and Benjamin Hocking of Illogan, applied for and received permission to continue an adit that had already been started in the north-east corner of Penhellick Veor, close to Penhellick Vean, not far from where Palmer's Shaft now is. Angove and Hocking were to continue this adit across Penhellick through what became Tincroft Mine, to within "five land goads of ground to the extent thereof on the south" (a land goad was 5 yards).

Apart from its obvious value as an adit, it proved, like so many of those ancient shallow adits, a reliable means of exploring the ground for tin and copper. Surprisingly, with the whole area geared to copper production, and the occasionsl parcel of tinstuff being incidental, this particular adit was to go through an area that was extraordinarily rich in tin.

Originally this mine was called New Penhellick, to distinquish it from Penhellick Mine, and on some of the accounts for Basset adventures, the old Penhellick Vean Mine, by then universally known as Penhellick Mine, was called 'Old Penhellick'. By the early 1750s the new mine was frequently called 'Penhellick alias Tincroft', or 'Tincroft alias Penhellick'. This did not persist however, and by the 1760s the mine was generally known as just Tincroft Mine, as it has been ever since (Tehidy Accounts).

Between April 1751 and June 1753 Tincroft sold £890 8s 10d. worth of ore, and almost all of it was tin. It is of interest to note, that the accounts for that period have caused considerable confusion among researchers. Both pages, the returns and the costs, are headed by the title, 'Old Penhellick', and then in the rest, 'Penhellick alias Tincroft', is found. Subsequent pages indicate that the accounts are actually for 'New Penhellick', and a closer examination of the word 'Old', at the top of those two pages show that they were both added by a later hand.

The great advantage that Pool Adit gave the workings at Penhellick Vean, from the early years of the 18th century, can be guaged by the small-scale and largely ineffectual activities of those mines which lay too far south of the adit to benefit immediately. Wheal-an-Gare, which operated in the 1600s, was virtually at a standstill by the time of the Pool Adit boom; Brea Mine remained a shallow, uneconomical mine until it eventually linked up with extensions to Pool Adit, as did Dudnance and Long Close. Surface activity at Penhellick Veor had not been very productive either. A lease agreement dated 1747 (19 George II Jan 20), between the late Earl of Radnor's steward, John Laroche, and Abel Angove and

25

Ben. Hocking, refers to leases and sub-leases for the purpose of mining for tin and copper at Penhellick Veor, that go back to 1713. From the tenor of the document it appears that no one had been particularly successful there (Lanhydrock Accounts CRO).

In 1742 further agreements were made over the supply of water from Brea Leat. It appears that Pool and Penhellick Mines had close connections with various streaming operations on the river above Brea. Certainly, the systems of stamps, leats and buddles at Carnarthen were extensive. The water-wheel engine at Penhellick Mine, as well as the other equipment there, was in constant need of a reliable supply of water. Despite the introduction of steam, and eventually in our day, electricity, this leat continued until the 1980s to be an important source of water for South Crofty Mill. (Tehidy Proposal and Memorandum Books).

In 1751 the Pool Adit lease was renewed. John Rashleigh of Menabilly acted as trustee for the underage John Pendarves Basset, and the Praeds and Angoves were also signatories.

"Whereas an Addit running East or West or near there abouts was and hath been driven by Francis Basset Esquire, deceased, late father to the said John Pendarves Basset ... in length 300 fathoms or thereabouts (to be the same more or less) and extending itself beyond the said tenement of Trevenson into and through a tenement called Penhellick Vean the lands of inheritance of the said Sir Francis Vyvyan said Will. Markworth Praed and said Abel Angove" (Tehidy Mine Leases).

In his 'Account Current of all my Adventures', Sir Francis Basset left an accurate and informative picture of the importance of Pool Adit during the mid-1700s. Between the years 1747-56, Pool Adit alone netted the Bassets over £111,000 clear profit. From a peak of £11,409 profit in the years 1747-48, the figures dropped ever so slightly, until by the year 1756, it was down to an annual profit of £10,199. On just this one adventure Sir Francis averaged over £11,000 income per year. If we compare these figures with those of the mighty Dolcoath during that same period, we find that the Bassets' profit from Dolcoath totalled £18,220 over ten years, that she averaged £1,822 and her highest year's profits were £3,715, in 1756. Although there was clearly a difference in the share held by Sir Francis Basset in these two adventures, nevertheless, we can appreciate the relative size and importance of Pool Adit at that time (Tehidy Accounts).

During the ten years covered by those accounts, Pool Mine (together with Penhellick Mine) and small undertakings of the Bassets on Penhellick Vean and Dudnance setts, lost steadily. It would appear from these accounts, and other agreements, as well as copper return records from that period, that the association between Pool Mine and Penhellick Mine was loosening. By 1753 'New

Penhellick alias Tincroft' had appeared in the accounts, and like the older Penhellick, was losing money for the Bassets. This position was maintained by Tincroft, until Sir Francis invited other adventurers in to share the burden, and eventually the mine was turned to profitability.

On the costs pages, which show the loss on the unprofitable adventures, we find that over that same ten year period, between 1747-56, Old Pool totalled a loss to the Bassets of £953, which averaged out at about £95 loss per annum; Old Penhellick adventure, which appears to be the old Penhellick Mine, now dealt with separately again, lost a total over those ten years of £8,190, averaging £819 per annum. 1752, with a loss of £1,357 19s 7³/₄d., was its worst year.

During that period the profit from Pool Adit reached its peak. After the 1760s her production dipped, following the fortunes of Old Pool, which by the 1740s was past its best. As far as Penhellick Mine was concerned, the Bassets and the other adventurers must have been far from happy. No doubt the sett itself continued to contribute to the profitability of Pool Adit, but both Old Pool and Penhellick Mines were failing to return copper in sufficient quantities to justify their continued existence. Nevertheless, their adventurers continued to speculate in the hope that the lodes might prove richer at depth.

In 1754 the Bassets built the long leat from Carnkie along the bottom of Carn Brea through Tregajorran and Penhellick to Cook's Kitchen. The older leat from Carnarthen and Brea Adit, was linked to the new one near to Cook's Kitchen on Brea Croft. These two water supplies brought power to the famous over-shot wheels at Cook's Kitchen Mine; the water engine at Long Close Mine; and various operations throughout Trevenson, before going over Penhellick Mine engine, beside the main road, and into the Pool Adit. Water from this leat was also used by Tincroft and Tregajorran Mines, the latter allowing the water thereafter to be used by Penhellick engine (Tehidy Memorandum Book).

In January 1757, on behalf of the adventurers of Penhellick Mine, John Vivian, an adventurer and agent of Penhellick and Pool Mines, was granted part of the sett of Penhellick Vean. The sett applied for seems to exclude the extreme western end of Penhellick Vean, where Pool Adit enters the sett, leaving that for Pool Adit to work (Tehidy Memorandum Book).

On August 2nd 1759 Walter Reed and John Vivian applied to the Bassets on behalf of the other adventurers at Pool Mine and Penhellick Mine, for use of "Tregajorran water, and all such water as can be spared from Long Close engines for three months". They stated that they were willing to pay £20 per month for the use of it. The following July they negotiated a fuller agreement, which involved the use of water from Dolcoath Adit, after it had gone through Brea, Trevenson (west) Tolvaddon, Trevenson Moor (east), and back up the valley toward Pool Village from whence it was carried to Penhellick Mine (Tehidy Memorandum Book).

Another agreement concerning the supply of water to Penhellick engine, was made in 1762, and again it concerned water that had previously been used by the water engine at Tregajorran Mine. The Bassets already received money from the water coming out of Tregajorran Adit and used by Old Pool and Penhellick Mines, now they were to get more from the re-use of the water from the engine of that mine. in June 1762 a new agreement was made for the water from Long close engine, which once again was to be carried along the old Brea leat (Tehidy Memorandum Book).

From the considerable quantity of water involved in these various agreements it is apparent that despite the introduction of at least three powerful Newcomen steam enginges more than a decade earlier, along the length of Pool Adit, water engines still had a large part to play in unwatering the workings here. It would appear from the records, that although Old Pool still used water for various purposes after the introduction of steam engines, it was at Penhellick Mine that use of the large overshot water engines, first introduced by John Coster at the beginning of the century, persisted.

The copper returns for Basset's 'Scattered Mines' during the years 1768-75 show that by then Old Penhellick Mine, working the sett of the Penhellick Vean Mine of the 1600s was again independent. The sett was still mined by Pool Adit and Old Pool, but the small operations known as 'Penhellick', 'East Penhellick' and 'West Penhellick', were also selling small parcels of copper.

"1768 Aug.25 Penhellick 2 Tons at £13 6s 6d. Value £26 13s 0d Purchased by Cornish Copper Company.

1770 Sept.28 East Penhellick 10¹/₂ Tons at £3. Value £31 10s Purchased by Corn. Copper Co.

1771 Nov.22 East Penhellick 6 Tons at £7 6s 6d. Value £43 19s. Purchased by English Copper Company.

1771 June 27 East Penhellick 3¹/₄ Tons at £6 2s. Value £19 3s 5d. Purchased by Patten & Company.

1774 Oct. 4 East Penhellick 3 Tons at £2 10s 6d. Value £7 13s. Purchased by Freemans and Company.

1774 Nov. 1 West Penhellick 3³/₄ Tons at £5 5s 6d Value £19 19s 4d. Purchased by Roe & Co.

1775 Nov. 21 Penhellick 4¹/₄ Tons at 16/6 Value £3 10s 6d. Purchased by Lockwood".

(Teh. Manor Copper Sales Records).

How independant of each other or of the Bassets these were, we do not know, but the Tehidy and Praed tenants leases for the late 1700s and early 1800s make it plain, that these small mines were within a short distance of each other, along the southern side of the main Pool to Tuckingmill road. The following extracts from Tehidy Manor tenants agreements between the years 1772 and 1826, serve to show how closely the above operations, variously called 'East Penhellick', 'West Penhellick', and 'Penhellick', were to each other, if not actually different names for the same tiny operation.

"August 7th 1772. Henry Eddy (Eudy) Illogan, Tinner. Tenant of West Counting House on Tenement of Penhellick, Illogan".

"August 7th 1772. Tenant Henry Eudy (Eddy), Yeoman. 1/4 part of West Counting House in tenement of Penhellick, Illogan and land adjoining ..."

"Sept. 4th 1772. Tenant Henry Eudy (Eddy), Yeoman. 1/2 part of house called East House, lately used as a warehouse for East Penhellick Mine, part of leat of Penhellick".

"Sept. 18th 1772. Henry Eudy (Eddy) 1/4 of house called West Accounting House, with piece of land adjoining, and 1/4 of house called East Accounding House, late used as warehouse for East Penhellick Mine, all in leat of Penhellick.

"Sept. 18th 1772. Owners Humphry Markworth Praed of Trevethowe Esq., Tenant Henry Eddy, Illogan, Innkeeper. Part of house called East House lately used as warehouse for Penhellick Mine. Also part of stable and gardens in Penhellick, adjoining the road to Redruth".

"July 1st. 1826. William Burgess tenant. Moiety of house formerly the Counting House of Penhellick Mine, now called the School House, with meadow behind bounded on West by Dudnance tenement and on the north by the road from Camborne to Pool".

"July 1st. 1826. Tenant Cornelius James, Blacksmith. Moiety of house in village of Pool part of tenement of Penhellick Vean. House was formerly a stable belonging to adventurers of Penhellick Mine" (Tehidy Leases).

It is quite apparent from those quotations, that the "Accounting Houses" referred to, were sometimes different names for the same building, and sometimes buildings that were immediately adjacent to each other. At any rate the buildings called "West Accounting House", the "Counting House of Penhellick Mine" and the "School House", all stood to the south of the present No. 61 Trevenson Road, at the north-west corner of Penhellick Vean tenement and sett.

Among the tenants agreements referred to, were others that described the holding at Penhellick Vean of Richard Trevithick's father, also called Richard. "1767 September 10th. Richard Trevithick, Illogan, Tinner. 4th part of house built by John Trevithick. 2 fields adjoining about 5 acres part of tenement of Penhellick Vean, Illogan, with common pasture on Illogan Downs". Another dated April 1st 1768, described the holding as 5 fields, and one for 1802 shows that the Trevithick family holding as 5 fields and one for 1802 shows that the Trevithick family holding included land behind the old offices of South Crofty. At that time Pool had a couple of blacksmith's shops, a malthouse, two inns, the Basset Arms and the Plume of Feathers, a foundry, and numerous other small business. There was a small hamlet that stretched across from the south-eastern corner of Penhellick Vean, into the tenement of Tregajorran where Carn Brea Lane turns towards Wilson Way. It probably gave rise to the belief among many that Trevithick was born at Tregajorran. Penhellick Vean Farmhouse lies some 200 yards from Lower Tregajorran tenement (Tehidy Leases).

In 1780 and 1781, the setts of Trevenson and Penhellick Vean were renewed through the agency of Sir Francis Basset's steward, Thomas Kevill (1736-98). Sir Richard Vyvyan of Trelowarren was also a party to the agreement, as were the "adventurers of Pool Adit Mine". On July 11th 1781 the Pool Adit adventurers agreed to work Trevenson and Penhellick Vean setts as before, limiting their exploitation to so many fathoms on either side of the point that the Adit intersected the lodes (Tehidy Mine Leases).

In 1780 Boulton and Watt, the famous engineers, and 'saviours' through their highly efficient steam pumping engines, of Cornish mining, built one of their engines at Pool Mine. This engine had a 60" diameter cylinder, and was much more effective that the one it replaced. The adventurers at Pool Mine agreed to pay Boulton and Watt the saving in the costs of coal, between the old Newcomen engine, and their new engine. Each year this was calculated by working out the cost in fuel against the work done. James Watt and his partner also became adventurers of Pool Mine, with a 1/32nd holding.

Some time before this association began, enormous copper deposits were found on Anglesey, North Wales. These massive finds of copper ore, near to the surface and easily worked, spelt disaster for Cornish copper mining. The price of copper dropped rapidly and even the richest mines were forced to close. In 1787 Pool Adit, then known as Trevenson Mine, closed. It had become to expensive to search for copper at the depths to which Pool Mine and Pool Adit were then workings. After nearly a century of continuous working the mines around Crofty were almost all closed.

In the late 1790s the Birmingham based manufacturing industry, instigated an offical enquiry into the still rising price of copper. Among those mines that the resultant report showed to have been working was one called 'Cherry Garden Mine'. In 1790 Joseph Vivian and his fellow adventurers had taken out a lease on the south-western part of Great Trevenson sett, between Tuckingmill and Trevenson Engine Shaft. Although this was part of the old Trevenson Mine (Pool Adit), the operation was generally known as 'Cherry Garden', as this was also the name given to the lode they were working. On December 25th 1798 Vivian and his partners were granted the sett that formed part of "Great Trevenson in the parish of Illogan" including the whole of the western end of that tenement. It is interesting, that the area then to be worked, presumably in conjunction with Cherry Garden was the area that included the eastern extensions of the Wheal Crofty lodes. This lease was granted to "Josepth Vivian on behalf of himself and Partners in Eastern Wheal Crofty Mine", for 21 years, and the agreed dues were $^1/_2$ of $^1/_7$th.

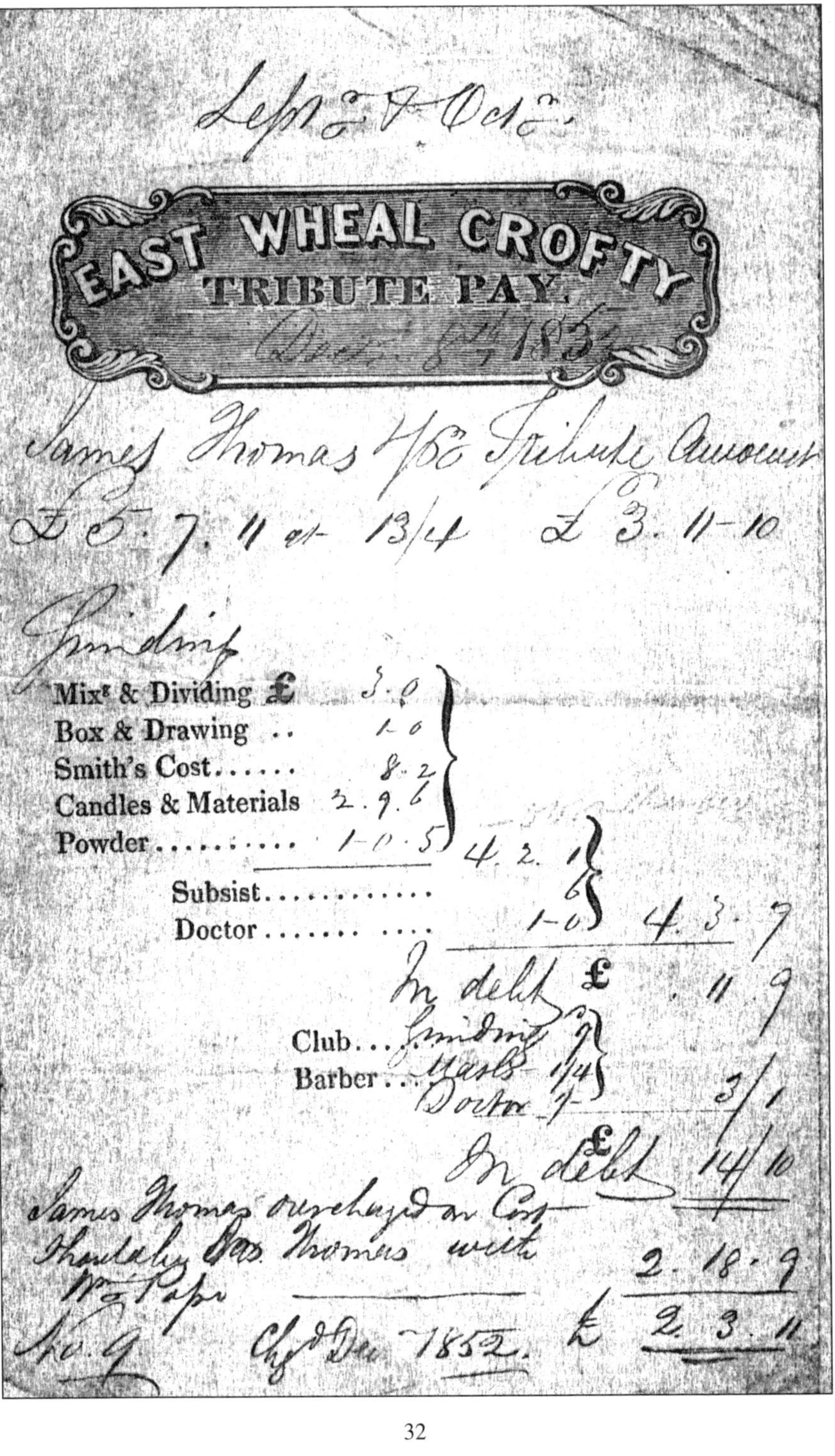

Sept.r & Oct.r

EAST WHEAL CROFTY
TRIBUTE PAY.

Dec.r 8.h 1852

James Thomas 4/6 Tribute Amount

£ 5. 7. 11 at 13/4   £ 3. 11 - 10

Grinding

Mix.s & Dividing £	3. 0			
Box & Drawing ..	1. 0			
Smith's Cost.....	8. 2			
Candles & Materials	2. 9. 6			
Powder...........	1 - 0. 5	4. 2. 1		
Subsist...........		1 - 0	6	
Doctor.......		1 - 0	4. 3. 9	

In debt £   . 11. 9

Club... Grinding
Barber.. Wash 1/4   3/1
Doctor 1/

In debt £ 14/10

James Thomas overcharged on Cost
Thursday Jas. Thomas with
W.m Paps   2. 18. 9
No 4   Ch.d Dec.r 1852   £   2. 3. 11

3. A McCullock-Holman rock drill, first used at South Wheal Crofty in the early 1880s. This extremely heavy, reciprocating, bar-and-arm machine, was very successful, and helped to establish Holman Bros as internationally known manufacturers of rock drills.

4. *Cornish steam stamps in 1907, with Californian stamps being erected on the extreme right of the picture. The 40" engine operated 32 heads of stamps, and those to the left continued production whilst the others were removed to give space for the 40 battery Californian stamps. The modern stamps were the first local, commercial users of electricity.*

5. *Captain Jack Penhall and his miners about to descend Palmers Shaft in 1904. Penhall was principal agent at Crofty from early 1900 until September 1904, when he became manager of Carn Brea Mines, the second largest tin mine in Cornwall.*

6. *Seventeenth century workings below Station Road, Pool. In the winter of 1977-78, during trenching for storm drains, these old mine workings were discovered within 12 feet of the road surface. The photograph shows Rod Lyon, a Kerrier official, examining an ancient 'stull piece' (timber support).*

Chapter Three:
East Wheal Crofty

When the 18th century ended the copper mines between Pool and Tuckingmill were mostly inactive from the effects of the copper price crisis. Only informal mining continued in most mines, with tributers working shallow parts of the mines on their own behalf. Even big, rich mines like Dolcoath had either closed altogether, or at least suspended operations until the price increased. By the late 1790s Anglesey copper had declined sufficiently for the copper price to rise once again to a point where it became economical to continue deep mining for it.

Trevenson Mine had closed down as early as 1787, in reaction to the crisis, but despite the gradually increased price, which rose from £80 - £90 in 1791 to £128 in 1799, the fortunes of this mine, and her near neighbour, Pool Mine, did not much improve. There was a little activity at the extreme western end of the sett, on Cherry Garden Lode, at the turn of the century. Despite this situation, within a decade or so, local mines were to experience a greater period of productivity than during the Pool Adit boom nearly a century earlier.

WHEAL CROFTY
Wheal Crofty was a mine which operated throughout the first half of the 1700s, but became unworkable as its depth increased and it could no longer cope with the water. It worked the area around the old Tolgarrack Quarry, more recently used as a Council refuse tip. Although it was never a particularly notable mine, it was shown in the 1819 map of the mining area by Richard Thomas. According to Thomas, it ceased operating about 1750-60. His map shows the old mine astride the deep adit from Dolcoath and Cook's Kitchen, and right over two rich copper lodes that ran slightly north of east. The New Deep Dolcoath Adit, which was partially driven by Richard Trevithick senior, lay to the west of Wheal Crofty.

Its only real claim to fame was provided by experiments at the mine, to obtain copper from copper-rich water by immersing iron bars. The iron bars were dissolved by the copper-rich acids in the water, leaving the copper in a solidified state. Pryce, in his *Mineralogia Cornubiensis, 1778*, described the experiments and commented: "An attempt of this kind was some years past made in Huel-Crafty, but without success."

Despite the new potential for deeper mining in that area, provided by the driving in the 1760s and '70s of the Dolcoath New Deep Adit, it was not until about 1816 that the lodes there were again exploited in earnest.

NORTH ROSKEAR

In 1816 the Pendarves family began to develop the setts of several old mines, under the general title of North Roskear Mine. These stretched from the Red River (and the Great Crosscourse), for a mile westward on the course of the principal lodes. The most easterly of these old mines was Wheal Crofty. The new venture had almost immediate success. Particularly in the Wheal Crofty sett were the lodes rich, and they proved even more so as they neared the Great Crosscourse. Clearly, Edward Pendarves and the other North Roskear adventurers wished to take full advantage of their discovery, and they applied for the sett to the east of the Great Crosscourse.

Although a small sett was granted them by the mineral-lord, Lord de Dunstanville, he and others (including apparently some of the North Roskear adventurers), also wished to work these valuable lodes (Tehidy Mines Leases). By 1822 Lord de Dunstanville, together with the wealthy Praed family, and the Reynolds of Trevenson, had formed a company which they called East Wheal Crofty, because it lay to the east of the old Wheal Crofty Mine, whose lodes they were to exploit as they ran eastward.

Two years later, on June 23 1824, Edward Pendarves, on behalf of the North Roskear adventurers, was granted the sett at the extreme western end of Great Trevenson.

"On the west to join the lands of Edward William Wynne Pendarves Esq., and from thence east 30 fathoms to a stone post set up near a cross course, on the south to join Wheal Susan sett, on the north to join the Portreath Great Road leading to Tolvaddon Down in the Parish of Illogan." (Tehidy Mine Leases).

Pendarves and the North Roskear adventurers had wished to work the new sett from the easterly drives in the Wheal Crofty section of North Roskear. They would merely continue operations underground. Lord de Dunstanville and his partners had more ambitious plans.

EAST WHEAL CROFTY

Precisely when the new mine came into existence is not known, but certainly by 1822 copper ore was being raised and sold by East Wheal Crofty. The new company took over the sett, equipment, buildings and machinery of the old Trevenson Mine, and the Trevenson Engine Shaft formed its organisational centre. The mine required immediately to replace worn out and inadequate pumping and winding engines. Lord de Dunstanville held a major share in the mine, as he had in Trevenson Mine, and the other adventurers had to pay for the transferred assets of Trevenson Mine out of the copper returns for the first decade. As the company became established, so Lord de Dunstanville reduced his share holding, so that the costs and risks of the venture were more evenly spread. (East Wheal Crofty Reports 1822-54). Shares in the new company were advertised for sale and 17 per cent of the shares were on the market in May of 1823. (West Briton May 9 1823).

Revenue from ore sold in the first half of 1822 gave East Wheal Crofty cash to the value of £245 8s ld. They paid to Lord de Dunstanville 20/48ths, or £102 5s. This rate continued until the summer of 1830 - (apart from one period when it rose to 20/47ths), - during which time they paid to the Bassets £1,446 13s l0d. Between 1830-36 their holding dropped to 26/94ths, and earned £2,175; between 1836 - 42 their holding dropped to 16/94ths and earned for the Bassets £6,640. These early returns show that the reopening of the old Trevenson workings had been worth the cost. It is of interest that the small sett at the extreme western end of Trevenson, which was worked from North Roskear, was at that time called West Wheal Crofty (EWC Reports).

In 1825 there began a national economic crisis, which resulted in the temporary closure, during 1827, of East Wheal Crofty. It took until 1831 for the mine to recover completely from the depression, and in that year there was a renewal of the sett held by East Wheal Crofty. The agreement was dated January 1 1831, and was taken out in the name of William Reynolds of Trevenson House, Illogan. As well as holding 6/94th share in EWC, and thus being a considerable shareholder, William Reynolds was also the mine's principal agent, its purser, and Lord de Dunstanville's agent. The 1831 agreement stated that East Wheal Crofty could work that part of Great Trevenson, being 'two-thirds of the whole', with the exception of that portion to the west granted to Edward Pendarves. With the new lease in hand a new company was formed to work East Wheal Crofty. The Basset share was reduced, the Praed share increased, and other adventurers from further afield bought into the company (EWC Reports).

A list of adventurers and their shares for the years 1834-35 shows that Lord de Dunstanville held 17/94ths; James Praed 16/94ths; W.T. Praed 6/94ths; Vere Fane 4/94ths; R.G.V. Fane 2/94ths; Mr Booth 4/94ths; Philip Reeve 4¹/₂/94ths; Mr and Mrs Daubuz 11/94ths; William Reynolds 6/94ths; Foxes & Portreath Co., 6/94ths; there were also a score of smaller adventurers who held between them about 24/94ths (EWC Reports).

A plan of East Wheal Crofty dated 1833 showed the extent of the new mine. Three setts to the south of the main road were added to the Trevenson sett already worked, so that with them Crofty had become a large undertaking. Penhellick Vean and Dudnance setts had been worked by the 18th century Pool Adit (Trevenson) and Pool Mines, but to these was then added Longclose Mine, which itself had enjoyed a long and distinguished life during the previous century. The workings along the length of Pool Adit are shown as being from the 43 fathom level and upward. In Penhellick Vean, the areas of the old Penhellick Vean Mine

(17th century) and the Penhellick Mine (18th century) are shown as being worked, and the workings around Palmer's Shaft, then called Boundary Shaft, which lay just outside Penhellick Vean were shown as 48 fathoms below adit. Robinson's Shaft was shown as about 12 fathoms below the shallow adit level, and Phillip's Shaft was at the adit level. The old 18th century shafts at Penhellick Mine are called 'School House Shaft' (Burgess's), and Treglown's Shaft (Tredinnick's). The 17th century shaft behind the Basset Arms was shown as Serpell's Shaft. Pryce's Shaft, which probably marks the place where that lode was first worked from, is shown just beside Pool Health Centre.

The Cost Book for 1834 gives a very good account of the state of the mine, the extent of its workings, the depth at which the lodes were pursued, and pay and conditions of those employed. If we examine carefully some of the details from the May 1834 accounts, we shall be able to understand better how this mine was run 160 years ago.

The mineral lords were principally the Bassets (Trevenson/Longclose setts), the Vyvyans, Praeds and Robartes (Penhellick Vean and Dudnance setts). Captain Nicholas Tredinnick was the manager, and he received the sum of £10 14s 0d per month. The engineer in charge of the engines, an 80" at Trevenson , and a 36" at Longclose Engine Shaft, together with a 26" whim engine, was James Mayne who also was paid £8 4s 0d per month.

The emphasis at that time was on expansion. Throughout the mine men were employed in reconditioning existing plant, replacing worn-out plant, building new engine-houses, expanding the copper dressing floor, and generally equipping the mine for greater production and a more efficient operation. East Wheal Crofty had become the owner of a very large sett, and she intended to sink down on the proven lodes to a much greater depth than previously contemplated.

Thomas Lean's *Steam Engines in Cornwall* (1839), says that in 1834 East Wheal Crofty had two steam pumping engines of 80" and 36" diameter cylinders at Trevenson and Longclose. He also refers to their 26" whim engine. His figures for the quantity of water pumped per minute at East Wheal Crofty, indicates that these two engines did a massive unwatering job during 1833-34. The monthly average reached a maximum in March 1833, of 577 imperial gallons per minute, and in February 1834, of 545 gallons a minute. The highest monthly average in the succeeding years until 1837 were never more than 214 gallons. Lean, who received 7s 6d almost ever other month from East Wheal Crofty, for inspecting and reporting on their engines, gave the 80" engine's stroke as 10' in the cylinder and 7' in the pump; the 36" engine he gave as 8' in the cylinder and 7' in the pump; the 26" whim engine he gave as 5' in the cylinder and 5' in the crank.

The May 1834 Cost Book entries show that underground also, much of the work was preparing to sink deeper, clearing and securing existing shafts for pit-work, manways and hoisting, and clearing and securing recently unwatered levels, to make them safe for reworking.

"8 men. John Jenkin - Clearing & Securing Pool Engine

	fm.	ft.	in.			£	s	d
Shaft under 43 level	4	3	0	at	£3	£13	10s	0d
Putting in Launders at the 43 level	55	0	0	at	2s 3d	£6	3s	0d
Cutting ground in Engine Shaft						£4	0s	0d
Attendances Stem						£1	10s	0d
						£25	3s	9d
				Less Costs		£5	11s	7d
				Club			2s	0d
				(8 men's) pay		£19	10s	2d

8 men. James Botteral - Sinking Trevenson Engine

	£	s	d
Shaft	£12	0s	0d
Putting in new lifts	£10	0s	0d
Repairing Shaft £8 - Watching engine 30s	£9	10s	0d
	£31	10s	0d
Less Costs	£10	1s	3d
Club		2s	0d
(8 men's) pay	£21	6s	0d

"4 men Chris Bennetts - Clearing Longclose

	fm.	ft.	in.			£	s	d
Engine Shaft	5	0	0	at	£1	£5	0s	0d
	5	0	6	at	£1 7s	£6	17s	3d
Timbering Shaft	12	0	0	at	12s 6d	£6	5s	0d
						£18	2s	3d
				Less Costs		£1	0s	8d
				Club			1s	0d
				(4 men's pay)		£17	0s	7d

"4 men. John Richards - Clearing 36 level east of Pool on Middle Lode. Securing level

	£	s	d
	£18	16s	9d
Less Costs	£4	17s	5d
Club		1s	0d
(4 men's pay)	£13	18s	4d

The accounts also refer to Joseph Roberts and 5 men "cutting down and securing" Roberts' Shaft, and Benjamin Blewitt and 2 others "clearing Dudnance South Shaft."

Almost all of the stoping and development at Crofty in 1834 was confined to the levels above the 43 although plans were going on to work the lodes in depth. The area between Trevenson Engine Shaft and the Old Pool workings was being stoped and explored throughout. The descriptions in the Cost Book, show the extent of this and the varying prices paid to the tutworkers for ground broken.

William Arthur and 3 others. Driving on the 43 level west of Pool on North Lode.

fm.ft. in.	at	Total	Costs	Club	Pay
6 1 7	£2.15s	£17 4s 6d	£3 6s 7d	ls 0d	£13 16s 11d

Stephen Arnan and 5 others. Driving on the 43 level north of Praed's Shaft on Caunter Lode.

fm.ft. in.	at	Total	Costs	Club	Pay
5 3 8	£7	£39 5s 7d			
2 0 0	£2. 15s	£5 10s 0d			
		£44 15s 7d	£8 10s 7d	£1s 6d	£36 6s 6d

Chris Paull and one other. Driving on 25 level North Lode, west of School House Shaft.

fm.ft. in.	at	Total	Costs	Club	Pay
1 3 6	75s	£5 10s 10d	£2 0s 2d	6d	£3 10s 2d

John Trezona and 5 others. Driving on 43 level west of Crosscut on Caunter Lode.

fm.ft. in.	at	Total	Costs	Club	Pay
3 3 9	£7 10s	£27 3s 9d			
Sundry Work		4s 2d			
		£27 7s 11d	£8 14s 0d	ls 6d	£18 12s 5d

John Terrill and 5 others. Driving 43 level east of Crosscut on Caunter Lode.

fm.ft. in.	at	Total	Costs	Club	Pay
3 0 0	£8	£24 0s 0d			
4 0 8	£3 15s	£15 8s 4d			
Sundry Work		3s 0d			
		£39 11s 4d	£8 17s 7d	ls 6d	£30 12s 2d

Thomas Vivian and 5 others. Driving 35 level west of Praeds Shaft on Caunter Lode.

fm.ft. in.	at	Total	Costs	Club	Pay
7 4 10	55s	£21 9s 3d			
Stoping on contract		£8 0s 0d			
Sundry work		3s 0d			
		£29 12s 3d	£8 11s 5d	ls 6d	£20 19s 4d

Joseph Kerby and 5 others. Driving 25 level east of School House Shaft.

fm.ft. in.	at	Total	Costs	Club	Pay
3 0 0	£7	£21 0s 0d			
1 10	£6	£1 16s 8d			
Taking over sides		£1 0s 0d			
		£23 16s 8d	£7 3s 4d	ls 6d	£16 11s 10d

At the same time Richard Gribble was driving the Deep Adit in Longclose, Henry Collins was driving the 43 level east of Pool Engine Shaft, William Ivey was driving the 35 level east of Ivey's Rise, and James Dunstone was driving the 60 level east of Trevenson Shaft. Each of the above tutworkers operated with a six man 'pare', John Clymons, sinking a winze under the 20 level on the North Lode, John Vellanoweth rising over 35 level and William Murrall driving the 35 level east of Pool on the School House Lode, all worked in 'pares' of four men.

There were several hundred workers at East Wheal Crofty in 1834, with over 140 tutworkers (piece workers) and probably an equal number of tributers (paid a proportion of the ore they raised).

The returns of 1834 from ore sold in the beginning of June, reflected the healthy state of this still developing mine.

Penhellick Vean	£748 8s 11d	Dues 1/18	£41 11s 7d
Dudnance	£70 6s 2d	1/24	£2 18s 7d
Longclose & Road	£93 17s 0d	1/24	£3 18s 2d
Trevenson	£4792 8s 5d	1/15	£319 9s 10d
	£5705 0s 6d		£367 18s 2d

Profit:- £961 17s 1d

By June 1834 Trevenson Engine Shaft was being sunk below the 60 level, Praeds Shaft was sinking below the 43 level, and Longclose Engine Shaft was being cleared and secured. An engine house was also being built at Longclose, for a new steam whim.

In Dudnance section a disused shaft was being cleared for use. Men were engaged in removing old ladders, and fixing and dividing the shaft. At Mayne's Shaft work was going on to clear the shaft under the adit, and at the same time new 'tram roads' were being laid. The rate was 2s per fathom, and in laying 13½ fathoms the trackmen earned £1 7s 0d.

During July, work continued in sinking the various engine shafts, and also in sinking a whim shaft at Trevenson. At Holmans's Shaft the 55 level was being cleared ready for driving. Work continued on building engine houses.

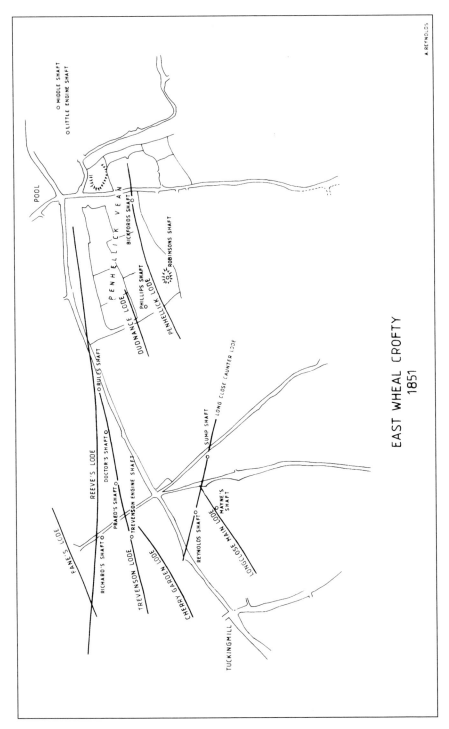

EAST WHEAL CROFTY
1851

In July 1834 the Williams Brothers of Scorrier bought 1/94 share in E.W.C.

In the summer of 1834 an unusual accident happened at Crofty, an account of which was given by W.J. Henwood in 'Metalliferous Deposits of Cornwall & Devon' (1843).

"At East Wheal Crofty, in the summer of 1834, during a severe thunderstorm, a flash of lightning struck the iron wire (knocker line) by which signals are made to the surface by the workmen underground. One of the labourers, who at depth of about 70 fathoms was at the same instant in the act of making a signal, received a shock which rendered him insensible for a short time … (his) was the only injury sustained in the mines."

Throughout that winter, work continued to deepen the shafts; clear and secure those abandoned and previously flooded and put in new ladderways and pitwork. The list of shafts in use in the mid-1830s is astonishingly long. Trevenson Engine Shaft, Pool Engine Shaft, Longclose Engine Shaft, Dudnance Engine Shaft, Trevenson Whim Shaft, Longclose Whim Shaft ("Whim Round"), Praed's, Holman's, Lean's, Burgess', Flat Rod, Pryce's, Tredinnick's, Mayne's, Tregonning's, Robert's, Doctor's, Reynold's, Kirkness', Petherick's, Dudnance Whim, Rodda's, Richard's, Gilbert's, Valley, (Fanes Lode), Rule's, Palmer's, Robinson's, Phillips, Rutter's, John's and James' Shafts. Thirty-two shafts in use, and very probably others not mentioned by name, but only as 'new shaft'. Of these, to start with, only Trevenson and Longclose Engines Shafts were used for pumping, but many of the others were used for hoisting. Among the whims referred to are 'Sims Whim', 'Steam Whim,' 'Horse Whim' and 'Dick's Whim.'

During the early months of 1835 Rodda's Shaft was secured to just below the 16 fathom level below adit, Doctor's Shaft was sinking below the 60 level, drives were being pushed west of Pool Engine Shaft on the 70 level, a footway down Holman's Shaft had been completed from the surface to the 60 level, Kirkness' Shaft was sunk below the 24 and a 'New Shaft' had been sunk from the surface to the 43 level which still remained the depth of most development.

During the summer of that year, the northern lode, now called Fane's Lode, was being opened up. The Deep Adit at Valley Shaft, on Fane's Lode, was driven eastward from the shaft. Throughout the mine, and particularly on Reeve's Lode, rich ore was being produced at an impressive rate. The returns and profits also showed a marked improvement. On Reynold's Lode in the vicinity of Holman's Shaft, on Reeve's Lode throughout its length and on Tyringham's Lode near to Rule's Shaft, fruitful work was being done. On the lodes in Penhellick at one end of the mine, and Longclose and Cherry Garden at the other, the search for copper was prosecuted with vigour.

At the close of the year, Tredinnick's Shaft, which was until 1834 called Treglown's Shaft and was used by the Old Pool and Penhellick miners working on the Pool Adit, was sunk below the 10 fathoms level. This shaft had been renamed by East Wheal Crofty after the manager, Nicholas Tredinnick. Apart from the main engine shafts, almost every shaft on the mine was named after officials and adventurers at East Wheal Crofty. Many old shafts, like Tredinnick's, were renamed during this period, so that it is often impossible to determine with accuracy which shaft is which when older records are consulted. The same is true of the lodes. Reeve's Lode had been worked for over a century by Trevenson Mine (Pool Adit), Old Pool Mine and even mines to the west of the Great Crosscourse. But when East Wheal Crofty began to work it they named it after one of their agents and adventurers, Philip Reeve. Fane's Lode was renamed after Vere Fane, also an agent and important adventurer at the mine. Other lodes, like Penhellick Lode, were not necessarily the lodes known by the same names during the 1700s. Some like Cherry Garden Lode, kept their original identities.

By the Spring of 1836 the prosperity of Crofty was reflected in the increased rate at which the manager was paid, and also the number of mine captains employed. In May 1834 Nicholas Tredinnick was paid £10 14s 0d per month, and his two mine-captains, John Lean and Hugh Tregonning, were paid £8 4s 0d. In March 1836 Captain Tredinnick's wage was increased to £12 16s 0d a month, and William Rutter was also listed as a mine captain. The ordinary captain's rate remained as it had been. The surveyor at that time, Nicholas Rule, was paid £2 12s 6d a month. Throughout 1836 development, returns and profits continued at a very healthy rate.

During the 1837 the new Hayle to Portreath Railway opened its branch-line to East Wheel Crofty. It ran from the main line at Cook's Kitchen, across Brea Croft, past New Cook's Kitchen, next to where Longclose Mine stood at that time, and crossed the main road at the top of East Hill. Its terminus was by Trevenson Engine Shaft. Its arrival at Crofty marked the zenith of the mine's fortunes. Statistics produced for that year by Sir Charles Lemon M.P., F.R.S., show that East Wheal Crofty employed a total of 1,004 people made up of 456 men, 404 women and 144 children. The mine produced 8,134 (21 cwt) tons of copper ore, which sold for £40,185 during 1837, and made a profit for the year of £6,073 13s 3d. At that time Dolcoath employed 590 workers, and sold 2,962 tons of copper ore for £13,787, which is a fair indication of the new importance of East Wheal Crofty. The April 1837 accounts inform us that Crofty paid an annual rent of £28 for Tolvaddon Stamps; during the subsequent years this was to rise considerably.

Despite the general high productivity there were problems in the southern sections. The returns for Penhellick Vean and Dudnance had begun to drop sharply. In May and June 1837 the mine actually sustained a loss of £118 11s 1d.

Although these two sections did not improve immediately, by the able redistribution of his work-force, Tredinnick managed to return the mine to profitability, although at a more modest rate that previously. (The profit for 1836 was nearly £16,000).

In October 1837, James Sims was paid £23 2s. toward the cost of erecting a new 22" steam engine. This whim engine was considered one of the finest of the day, and was a model of efficiency. It had an upright engine attached by bevel gearing to a couple of 48" diameter winding drums that were horizontal, and so arranged that it could hoist from two shafts at the same time. Its gearing mechanism enabled the engine to draw at the correct speed for the crooked shafts at which it worked, and also helped in pulling up or lowering down heavy loads. The whim drew kibbles of wrought iron construction by means of chains, and each kibble could hoist about a quarter of a ton of ore.

During 1838 the returns for copper remained steady. The profits and dividends, although lower than during 1836, still maintained a healthy condition for the size of the mine.

1839 found the copper production further reduced, and the Dudnance section producing nothing for months at a time. The profits fell to a level where less than £500 was being made most months. The divident was lower than for some time. A hopeful sign which might have appeared at the time as significant was the occasional sale of tin by East Wheal Crofty. In December 1839 they sold £23 10s 1d worth.

The returns and profits remained steady in 1840, despite a loss of £660 during May and June. Only £83 worth of copper was raised from Dudnance section during 1840, but Gilbert's Shaft in Dudnance section was being deepened.

The September 1840 accounts show that James Richards and Francis Gilbert had replaced Lean and Tregonning as mine-captains. Their pay remained at £8 4s 0d per month. J.J. Reynolds was still clerk, but in that month he received the high rate of £8 12s 0d. William Burgess was paid £8 4s 0d, John Phillips, the surveyor, £3 3s 0d and Thomas Lean the engine reporter was paid 7s 6d. In December 1840 he was paid £2 5s 0d for reporting on Longclose Engine.

The 1840 Illogan Tithe Map shows that the mines to the south of the main road which formed East Wheal Crofty's southern sections, were still regarded by the parish authorities as individual mines. Longclose Mine, Dudnance Mine and Penhellick Mine, were all shown under their 18th century names.

In 1841 the returns and profits took another upward swing, with the output of September and October reaching £7,735, which was the highest figure since

43

December 1836. At Trevenson Engine Shaft sinking had commenced below the 130 level, and John Trevithick was driving a cross-cut north of the shaft on that level.

On February 17 1842 an earthquake shook the district. Throughout the area between Helston and Newquay there were reports of severe shaking and some slight damage to property. W.J. Henwood had been carrying out experiments at Crofty, and he has on hand to get first accounts of the effects underground. The shafts and stopes shook violently, and rocks fell onto stulls with great noise and commotion, causing the miners to abandon their work places for fear they might collapse. The interruption of work, however, was only a short one, and soon the miners were back in their stopes, and Henwood was able to continue his experiments on the affects of the lodes at EWC upon the flow of electricity.

In 1842, the results of a Parliamentary Commission of enquiry into the working conditions of young people, was published. One of the mines which the investigators visited was East Wheal Crofty. They were impressed with the way it was run, and seemed to agree with the opinion of the Stannary Court officials who regarded EWC as a 'model' mine. The Report contained descriptions of the methods used to take air into ends, the various kinds of work done in the dressing of copper, - each stage of which involved the use of youngsters - statistics on accidents, wages, educational standards, how many of each sex were employed, and what the capabilities of the children were. The miners' "Club" was also discussed in the Report, as were almost all aspects of mining at EWC.

Ventilation was particularly discussed, as this obviously bore upon the health of those young boys working underground. In this connection 'special contrivances' were used to better facilitate the movement of air in the ends. At EWC, an agent said air was taken in, "by shafts, trapdoors and winzes, 15 fathoms apart; also airpipes, waterfalls, etc. for ends not relieved by winzes. Waterfall, where applicable is best." (Page 738).

The Commissioners were impressed by the fact that Capt. Tredinnick was the only manager of a Cornish Mine who kept a complete accidents record. During 1840 there were 95 accidents at Crofty that required two or more days off work. There was one fatal accident, described as "death by falling" and three other serious accidents, all broken legs and all of them in January. These more serious accidents required six, fourteen and eighteen months off work respectively. The average time lost per accident in 1840 was 8.9 days, not counting the three serious accidents referred to. The number of men employed underground at that time was 586 and the total number of workers at EWC was 919. The miners' 'Club' was at that time in a healthy state, and was described thus:

"The Club belonging to the mine has £1,500 in the savings bank in the name of Lady Basset as Trustee, to defray the expenses of which the men pay 4d in the pound from their earnings, which enables us to add £60 or £70 per year to the amount in the bank and also to give monthly pay to all widows whose husbands met with their deaths in this mine, so as to keep them from parochial relief. Every man, whilst off work, occasioned by hurt received in the mine was paid 1s per day, and very boy 6d per day; if families are distressed we relieve them according to the extent of the case." (Nicholas Tredinnick's statement).

In the eighteen months between January 1840 and June 1841, £301 4s 2d was paid out by the 'Club', of which about £100 was given over that period to seven widows of men killed at the mine; £9 6s was paid to cover the expenses at three burials; £10 was paid to assist those distressed by fever; £35 was spent for bedding for large, poor familes of miners' and at Christmas 1840, £146 was given to the families of injured miners.

The Report's tables showed that in 1841 there were 586 men underground and 33 boys below the age of 18. Of these 33, 4 were 12 years old, 6 were 14, 7 were 15, 7 were 16, and 6 were 17 years old. These youngsters invariably went underground with their fathers, bothers and uncles. The evidence indicates that they were well looked after, and brought on gradually. Most of the mine-captains and managers had been sent underground at any early age to learn mining. Josiah Thomas of Dolcoath, was sent down when he was 15 years old by his father, who was then manager of that great mine. That tradition is one that we see examples of at Crofty even now.

There were boys and girls from the age of 8 who worked on the surface assisting in copper dressing. Apart from the 4 boys underground, there were 30 below the age of 13 working on the surface, and 14 girls. There were also 29 girls below the age of 18. The Report described the work these hefty young 'bal-maids' carried out. After the large rocks had been broken by men with 'ragging' hammers (sledgehammers), girls of 16 or over would 'riddle' or 'griddle' the ore by means of sieve-like apparatus. Girls of a similar age would then 'spal' the stone to the size of a man's fist by use of a smaller sledgehammer called a 'spalling hammer.' This was done inside 'spalling sheds' at EWC, but at other mines it was often outside. Next, girls of 15 would break the ore smaller by use of light hammers, calle 'Cobbing' hammers. They reduced it to gravel size, and usually worked inside sheds, seated on the floor. After the 'cobbing' came the 'bucking' operation, where by skillful use of a flat 'bucking' hammer, the gravel sized ore was further reduced to sand. The work was well paid and the older girls and women who carried it out received 10d or 1s per day. Most of the work done by hammers was eventually done by steam driven crushers, but there was a tendency to avoid 'stamping' copper ore, as the very fine pulp disappeared too easily up the smelters' chimney.

Working closely with the above operatives were a small army of little boys and girls who were engaged in washing the ore in troughs, picking out the worthless from the valuable, and wheel-barrowing the broken stuff for re-working or re-examination. The vast complex between the western end of Dudnance and Tehidy Mill, was covered by many acres of 'spalling' sheds, settling pits, water-stamps, leats, buddles of enormous variety and complexity, and a host of other machinery, that employed many hundred of people of all ages. East Wheal Crofty was just one of many mines and streaming operations centred at Tuckingmill and Tolvaddon. At that time however, she was the most important. Crofty's youngsters were better paid than the average worker in these parts. An 18 year old boy miner averaged 10s per week, whereas a 12 year old got 3s 6d. Even on the surface some youngsters were paid as much as 9s 6d a week, although a little 8 year old girl only received 1s 3d. There were 200 adult women employed at Crofty in 1840.

Attention was paid in the Report to the educational standard attained by Crofty's children. There were 75 of them at Sunday School, and the survey showed that most could read and write a little. Many of the adults could manage to write their names, and read an easy book. Throughout the area there were parochial schools that taught the basics. At Brea, Tuckingmill, Pool and elsewhere the chapels and private individuals took the children of miners into their schools. 'Reading and Writing', 'Reading and Religion', and 'Writing and Summing', were the usual descriptions the proprieters gave of their curricula.

The Report mentioned that 'crowst' time was 10 a.m., that Crofty's copper ore in 1840-41 averaged nearly 10% pure copper, and that the deepest working level was the 130 - against Dolcoath's depth which was 190 fathoms below adit. The total fatal accidents in Cornish Mines was given as 75 for the year 1840, one of which occurred at East Wheal Crofty.

Meanwhile, as that report was being published, things did not look so good at the Mine, 1842 began badly and got worse. Although January and February showed a small profit it was wiped out by the loss sustained in March and April. The returns were down also, and only picked up again in the late summer. May and June showed a small profit and July and August an almost equal loss. From September to December the figures all showed a marked improvement. Once again Dudnance was a great disappointment to the adventurers, producing only about £150 worth of copper for the whole year. Over £75 worth of tin was raised in the autumn of 1842.

Late in 1842 production at Penhellick Vean began to rival Trevenson. South-east of Pryce's Shaft activity was concentrated around James's Shaft, where tutworkers under the direction of Edward Jeffery were driving the 60 level west of James's. Tonnage from that area had been creeping up for several years.

Returns and profits continued to rise in the early part of 1843, with Penhellick producing an even larger share of the returns. Dudnance was still a disappointment, with only a slightly increased return of £170 worth of copper. July and August showed a loss of £70 15s 4d, as Trevenson's production slipped, but things had picked up again by the end of the year. Several small parcels of tin were mined during the year.

During September 1844, there was a very serious accident at the mine, when a miner called Jenkin was killed by an old pump rod falling in the shaft. Jenkin appears to have been knocked off the ladder road and fell to his death.

In Penhellick section a new shaft, referred to as 'Penhellick Shaft' was being sunk under the adit. In December 1844 a shaft simply called 'New Shaft in Penhellick' was having the adit connected to it on its eastern side. Very probably these are references to the same shaft. Phillips' Shaft, named after John Phillips the Surveyor, was being deepened during 1844.

In November 1844 the Bickford family of Tuckingmill, famous as the developers of the safety fuse, applied for a share in East Wheal Crofty. They did this as prospective 'in' adventurers. That is, they intended to secure their position as fuse suppliers to the mine.

G.D. Johns and John Rule had taken over as pursers on the death in May 1844 of William Reynolds. Johns was to receive £50 per annum, and Rule £70. At the same time the adventurers showed their appreciation for the way the mine was managed, by increasing yet again the monthly renumeration of the manager, Captain Nicholas Tredinnick to £15 19s 0d.

The Mine's production, which had been low at the beginning of 1844, gradually rose until it was quite healthy by the end. The profits were also very good, particularly in proportion to the tonnage. In the November and December 1844 accounts, a profit of £2,388 is shown on copper and tin returns of only £6,794. The early months of 1845 show the same high proportion or profits to income. Several valuable sales of tin and 'Black Jack' were sold during 1844-45 and in the August returns for 1844 there is included £358 from Tincroft adventurers, which was for ore they had gained through following the lode over the boundary into Penhellick Vean sett.

The Basset agent's report for the latter part of 1845, dated January 1846, and signed by Charles Thomas, stated that although there was considerable work going on in Trevenson, particularly on Reeve's Lode, which neared both boundaries on the 130 level, the best prospects were on Penhellick Lode. He estimated that there was £15,000 worth of ore on Penhellick Lode, but unfortunately, the lode ran into Tincroft sett as it went westward. Much development was taking place on Reeve's Lode from Rule's Shaft, Praed's Shaft and Engine Shaft, which was then 162 fathoms below adit. From Cherry Garden

Shaft the old Cherry Garden Lode was being explored at greater depth than hitherto.

Thomas said that the mine was being run efficiently, had good prospects, especially in the Penhellick section, and that apart from Longclose pumping engine, the machinery was in good order. The hoped for return was projected as:

Longclose   £300
Trevenson   £600
Penhellick   £1,300

By June 1846 the ore from Reeve's Lode had improved, and with it the prospects for Trevenson section. On the Longclose Caunter Lode, the Engine Shaft, which was vertical, was sunk below the 70 fathom level. In Penhellick section, Robinson's vertical shaft was sinking 3 fathoms below the 24 level. In the extreme south-west corner of Longclose sett, a new shaft was proposed to explore the Copper Tankard Lode. There were 143 tutworkers and 80 men on tribute.

By the autumn of 1846 the expectations or rich rewards from Reeve's Lode were being realised and the lode was followed to Great Crosscourse, where West Crofty had found rich tin ore. A cross-cut was being driven north from Praed's Shaft on the 60 level, for a distance of some 500 feet, to explore for more copper in the north of the sett.

On Cherry Garden Lode values of up tp £30 per fathom were found, but nearby, on Longclose Caunter Lode, and the Longclose South Caunter Lode there was great disappointment. Robinson's Shaft was sunk down to 35 fathoms below adit, and the new Copper Tankard Shaft was sunk to adit level. In October 1846 there were 212 miners on tutwork or tribute. The profit for the last two months of 1846 was £665.

By the mid-1840s in Penhellick section work was concentrated in the south-east of the sett. Where Reeve's Lode enters the sett in the north-west corner, Trevenson miners were operating, and as the lode is a north dipper, it went into the northern section as it got deeper. Between the area of the old Penhellick Mine and the newer workings between Robinson's and Palmer's there was a large area of unexplored ground. Elsewhere in Penhellick Vean, James's, Bickford's and Palmer's Shafts were all down to the 60 level; Evans's, Pryce's and Phillip's shafts were still quite shallow, and Robinson's was at the 35 fathom level where it stayed for nearly 60 years.

In Dudnance section, apart from work through Robinson's Shaft, operations were concentrated on the three shallow shafts to the west, called Tregonning's,

7. Arsenic calciners in the 1920s. These five calciners were an important part of Crofty's plant. Arsenic accounted for a significant proportion of the mine's profits until the 1940s, and the calciners continued in use until well after the Second World War.

8. *Robinsons Shaft engine house and compressor building in 1906. The modernisation of the mine began in earnest in 1902, and by 1908 the buildings centred on Robinsons Shaft formed a very modern and well-equipped mine.*

9. *Commencing to sink New Cooks Kitchen Vertical Shaft in 1907. The shaft was sunk in stages during the next 80 years until it reached its present depth just below the 420 fm level, 778m from surface.*

10. Robinsons engine house in September 1904. The building was erected to house the 80"
engine bought from Tregurtha Downs Mine a couple of years earlier. It finally stopped
pumping in 1955 after working almost continuously for 101 years.

Stainby's and Gilbert's. During the 1840s Dudnance section produced very little, but always seemed to have better prospects ahead.

In January of 1847 concern was expressed at the ground worked away between North Roskear and East Wheal Crofty. The small undertaking started by Edward Pendarves in 1824, and called West Wheal Crofty, was also concerned about the possibility of flooding if the workings to the west were abandoned. The vague boundaries between these setts should be fixed more clearly, it was stated.

In Penhellick, 1847 began with mixed blessings. The copper values for Penhellick and Dudnance were very promising, but East Pool pumping engine had stopped and the deeper levels at Penhellick were flooded. In April it was decided to ask the mineral lords for a reduction in the dues because of the flooded eastern section.

Meanwhile work continued throughout the western and northern sections. On Reeve's Lode, at Doctor's Shaft on the 103 level, the lode was 5 feet wide. A cross-cut was driven north from Petherick's Shaft to explore new ground, and the Trevenson Engine Shaft was being sunk to the 167 fathom level through hard elvan. Tredinnick Shaft had been temporarily halted, and the results on the Cherry Garden Lode had been mixed.

Throughout the Longclose section prospects appeared bad, despite activity on both cauntering lodes, the Copper-Tankard adit drives (now north and south), and the Longclose Main Lode being followed west from Mayne's Shaft. In Dudnance the future once again seemed hopeful.

Although the eastern part of Penhellick was flooded, the shallower workings at Robinson's were well above the water, and there the values remained high. The profit for January and February 1847 was £15 6s 8d. The company then had a balance in hand of £3002 1s 9d. There were 126 tutworkers, 92 on tribute and 6 described as stoping.

By the end of July the Penhellick workings were drained and work was resumed. East Pool's engine was again pumping and the threat to the bottoms was past. On the 60 level, drifting east fronm Bickford's Shaft, the miners were within 80 yards of the East Pool boundary. A cross-cut was being driven north from Robinson's on the 35 level. On this level east of Gilbert's Shaft, a cross-cut was driven 70 yards northward without striking a lode.

In the early months of 1848 the sinking of the Trevenson Engine Shaft continued, and the 173 level was reached. Activity along Reeve's Lode was general. Work continued also in the deeper levels at Penhellick. There was a slight improvement in the employment situation with 110 tutworkers and 95 tributers, totalling 205.

During the summer of 1848 the Trevenson section's prospects looked less hopeful as the sinking of the engine shaft was stopped and the overall workforce dropped again to 195. Doctor's Shaft was sunk to the 130 level.

The end of 1848 found the mine in a not very healthy condition, with one section up and another down. James Lanyon's report indicated that work was slowly progressing on Reeve's Lode, Cherry Garden Lode, the various Longclose Lodes, and those in Dudnance and Penhellick. There were 94 miners on tut and 105 on Tribute, making 199 altogether.

During 1849 the trend toward the predominance of the southern sections was marked. Despite widespread activity on Reeve's Lode, on the 36 and 60 levels at Tredinnick's Shaft, and Praed's Shaft, on the 110 level, east of Rule's Shaft, and the 120 and 130 levels east of Doctor's Shaft, the general prospects did not seem good. The December report did indicate better ore on Reeve's Lode on the 80, 110 and 120 levels, but this was not typical.

The Longclose reports were only 'hopeful', whereas the Dudnance section work continued only at the higher levels, 12 level, west of Robinson's and 25 level, which was within 3 fathoms of Tincroft boundary.

In Penhellick section development was continuing at a good pace with the prospects bright. James's Shaft had been sunk to 66 fathoms below adit by March of 1849, and drives on lode were extending from Bickford's Shaft on the 70 level and Palmer's Shaft on the 80. Both of these drives were going eastward. In June, despite the report stating that again Penhellick prospects were good, East Wheal Crofty in general was not! The report announced the intention of of the management to lay men off. In the March of that year there had been 116 tutworkers, and 77 tributers. By June the tutworkers had decreased to 104, and the tributers increased to 95. On September 1849 the tutworkers were down to 92 and the tributers up to 101, and by December the figures were given as tutworkers 80, tributers 90 and stopers 20. What sort of work agreement these 'stopers' had we cannot say, but presumably there was a difference between the conditions of employment of the tutmen, who were paid so much per fathom broken and trammed back to the shaft; the tributers who were paid a percentage (between 9s 6d and 13s 6d in the pound during that period at Crofty) of the value of the ore once it was raised to the surface, and the stopers who were apparently employed at a rate that was entirely to the advantage of the company. This is implied in the parlous state of the mine when they were taken on and when financial considerations dictated lay-offs. Their numbers kept the work force to its pre-crisis level.

By early 1850, with returns from the Penhellick and Dudnance sections good, the company accounts could stand a slightly higher percentage of tutworkers.

James's Shaft was sunk to 88 fathoms below adit by August 1850. In Trevenson the ore values were showing improvement on the 130 level. By the end of the year James Lanyon was delighted to be able to announce development going forward on several lodes in all sections of the mine. He mentioned Reeve's, Fane's, Cherry Garden, and the Longclose South Caunter Lodes with some hope, and reckoned that the prospects were so good that returns would soon cover the recent loss. Ominously, the workforce was dropping severely!

Lanyon's prediction was frustrated by a situation over which he had no control. In May 1851 water again began to inundate the deeper workings in the Penhellick section of East Wheal Crofty. This time it was not the East Pool engine, but the Tincroft one that had stopped. All of the eastern workings below the 80 and 90 levels were now threatened with this water.

The October 1851 Report was most distressing, Lanyon said that the mine, "is in a critical condition, laying off 26 tutmen in 3 months. The Mine has not paid regular dividents since December 1846. The balance was £2,986, and this varied from £1,700 to £2,350 at the end of April 1849, when a divident was declared of £470, which was not warranted by the state of the mine. At the end of February last the balance was reduced to £592; to this was added the club, amounting to £1,230 making £1,822; to the end of August last this was reduced to about £800; the loss during the present 2 months will reduce it to about £500."

It was proposed that the mine take up the Trevenson Engine, which was "under water and useless". Surprisingly, while the company was rocking to its foundations, the sinking of Longclose Engine Shaft, in the poorest section of the mine continued, and by October had reached 91 fathoms below adit. There were then 136 men on either tribute or tut.

The bottom of the pit was reached in March 1852, when James Lanyon announced that all of the money had gone. Even the men's 'club' money had been spent by the struggling company. £1,230 contributed at a rate of a few coppers each contract day by the miners, to guard against death or injury, had been spent by the managers in an effort to keep going. A further call on the adventurers was made and paid by them. The mine was given at least a short breathing space.

With this injection of cash from the adventurers, the mine once again pushed ahead with development. On Fane's Lode the 60 level was driven eastwards to within 20 yards of Trevenson House. Longclose Engine Shaft was sunk to 106 fathoms below adit, and the 115 level was driven under it. In Penhellick, only tributers were working, as the bottoms were still flooded back to east Pool. Throughout the whole of EWC there were only 54 on tutwork and 70 on tribute. Lanyon, the Basset Agent, concluded his July 1852 report by saying, that in consequence of the "late accident", and the falling off of returns, the "present prospects do not warrant expectation of meeting the costs."

Just how serious the "late accident" was we do not know. It is implied that the accident affected production, and it is partly blamed for the financial position at that time, but there is no mention of a severe "run of ground", or breakage in machinery, and so it must be assumed that it was the misfortune that befell the manager. Early in 1852 Capt. Tredinnick was underground, when he "was seized with paralysis". As a result of this stroke he was unable to continue in his position of manager, and the adventurers had to find a replacement.

Whilst this situation upset the normal running of the mine, another, potentially as serious broke out. At the point on the Great Crosscourse where Reeve's Lode intersects it, the Crosscourse splits, leaving an area of disputed ground between the two arms. North Roskear Mine and East Wheal Crofty seemed set for a protracted legal row over the ground, when to the surprise of many, EWC appointed North Roskear's manager, Capt. Joseph Vivian, to replace Tredinnick. He decided the dispute in Crofty's favour.

1853 was a disastrous year all round. Longclose Engine Shaft was holed through to the 115 level, and James's Shaft reached the 100 level, but the former section was depressingly poor, and the latter was still flooded in its deeper levels. Prospecting in the rest of the mine proved fruitless and there was general gloom. At the beginning of the year the workforce had been increased 30% to 160, the bulk of these being tributers, but despite the appearance of greater activity, production remained low. By the summer the mine was down to just 50 tutworkers, 5 boys and 40 tributers, which was the lowest total for several years.

Another slight diversion occurred at that time that served to take their minds off the sad state of the mine. Despite the agreement with North Roskear on the boundary at the Great Crosscourse, their miners had actually tunnelled right through it into Trevenson sett. They were 12 feet into EWC property. On behalf of the Bassets, James Lanyon wrote in his report, "Sort it out!" Capt. Vivian did so, and Crofty was compensated.

By October 1853 it was clear that the northern section of Trevenson was no longer viable. The adventurers put an advert into the Mining Journal for October 29 1853, which offered for sale all of the northern section's machinery.

By January 1854 the decision had been taken by the adventurers to divide the setts into two parts. The northern section, which had originally been Trevenson and Pool Mines, was to be known as North Wheal Crofty, and the southern sections, formerly Longclose, Dudnance and Penhellick Mines, would be called South Wheal Crofty. On January 27 1854, James Lanyon sent in his report to the

Bassets, giving his recommendations on how the setts should be spilt, and how they should be worked thereafter.

"East Wheal Crofty   January 27th 1854

Sir,

Having in the course of the last two days inspected the several lodes, levels etc in this Mine, I find that only two men are at present engaged on Tutwork and should the proposal be carried out of dividing the Setts, I would recommend the following objects for prosecution more particularly affecting the South part - Longclose, Dudnance and Penhellick.

Longclose

Resume sinking of the Engine Shaft, now about 6fm. below the 115....drive the 70 south to the crosscut ... Put men in levels east of Engine Shaft ... with view to finding Caunter Lode ... drive the 50 or 70 west towards Wheal Susan old Mine.

Dudnance

Drive the 16fm. level east on the north part with 4 men ... open a communication with the winze below the adit ... The 60fm. level in Tincroft is driven to the boundary, having opened some bunches of ore ground for a considerable distance ...

Penhellick

Drive the 110fm. level west from James's Shaft with 4 men. North of Robinson's Shaft is a large piece of unexplored ground, both in Dudnance & Penhellick. A well defined cross-course is seen at the Adit and that level is driven on at 30 or 40fm; this cross-course will no doubt be found at deeper levels and the 24 or 35 should be driven north on it with 2 or 4 men. In prosecuting these objects, a loss for some time at least must be incurred and the cost would not be less than £400 per month, and with the present probable returns the loss would be from £200 to £250 per month.

Trevenson

In this part there is no Tutwork at present, the ore ground on the 80 and 110 being set on Tribute, a very objectionable course and injurious to the future working of the Mine. Men should be put to sink the winze below the 80 on a south part of Reeve's Lode ... The 150fm. level is driven west to the cross-course and should now be driven north to the North Lode.

I remain Sir,
your obed't Serv't
(signed) James Lanyon" (Lanyon's Report to Bassets)

Thus, East Wheal Crofty came to an end. Since 1822 she had produced 102,000 tons of copper ore, over 40 tons of ton, and numerous small quantities of other minerals. Her copper had averaged nearly £5 10s per ton, and had realised in returns £554,162. For an outlay of £11,750, she paid dividends to the value of £79,860, during the years between 1830-54. At her peak, between 1834-44 Crofty sold £365,000 worth of copper ore, and during one period was averaging over £3,000 profit per month. In the late 1830s East Wheal Crofty had been the premier mine of the district, with over 1,000 workers, and some of the most modern machinery then in use. Her decline had been as rapid as her rise, and by the early 1850s it was apparent that she had no future working as she had done.

Chapter Four:
South Wheal Crofty

After the formal winding up of East Wheal Crofty, Capt. Joseph Vivian handed over the running of the new cost book Company, called South Wheal Crofty, to William Rutter. Capt. Rutter had been a mine-captain with EWC since 1836, and was a practical miner of great experience. The original sett of EWC was to be worked as North Wheal Crofty, and basically it was the old Trevenson Mine under yet another name.

The hard slog now began to make a success of these two separate ventures. In many ways the northern mine appeared to have an easier task. Their workings radiated out from one organisational centre at the western end of the sett. They had a continuous line of development along the route of the old Pool Adit, and their explorations north and west hinged on the central pumping shaft of the old Trevenson Mine. Communication, ventilation and drainage, were all more easily facilitated at North Wheal Crofty, than by her southern neighbour. She also has had the enormous advantage of the railway branch-line right into her centre of operations.

In depressing contrast was the situation at South Wheal Crofty. Here was a disjointed affair, with hardly any underground communication, virtually no mutual assistance with problems of ventilation, and only at the extreme western end of the workings, at Longclose, were there any practical and independent pumping arrangements. SWC dressing floors were also at Longclose, and she rented eight heads of stamps at Tolvaddon. The sole and most significant advantage that South Wheal Crofty has over her northern neighbour, was that she possessed the best copper ground. Penhellick Vean had not been worked as deep as the rest of the mine, and the estimated value of the unworked lodes in this sections was very great.

On July 6 1854, James Lanyon sent in his first report on the new mine to the Bassets.

"July 6th 1854.
South Wheal Crofty

Longclose
Engine Shaft now sinking is 7fm. below the 116, the lode is South of the Shaft which will probably intersect it in sinking 5 or 6fm. deeper.
6 men & 3 boys at £45

In this part of the mine there are 4 men on tribute at 10/- and 2 men 13s 4d in £.

Dudnance

16 driven East of cross-cut about 20 fm on the North Lode, 1 ft wide of no value.

2 men at £3 10s 0d

35 just commenced driven East of the cross-cut is about 12fm behind the 16, lode is disordered and poor.   2 men at £8

12 driving North, West of Robinson's Shaft to cut a North branch now within 6 or 7fm.   2 men at £2 10s 0d.

Penhellick

60 driven West from Tincroft boundary 5fm opening a little Ore ground, lode in the end 1ft wide worth £4 per fm.   4 men at £5 10s 0d.

100 driven West from James's Shaft 4fm., lode 1 ft wide worth £5 per fm.

4 men at £4

36 driving West from James's Shaft on a North branch disordered and poor; from the present direction of this end it will lead through a very extensive piece of unexplored ground in this part of the Sett.   2 men at £4 5s 0d.

Number of men on Tutwork   30
Number of men on Tribute   16
                            46

As the operations are so very recently begun little alteration could be expected as yet, but in Penhellick the 60 driving West is improved and also the 100, now about 12 or 15fm West of East Pool boundary. In East Pool the lode is divided, and it is probable that another part will be found North of James' Shaft. A cross-cut should be driven in that direction by 4 men at the 100 fm level a little East of the said shaft.

There is some Ore ground below the 100 - West from the boundary of East Pool; this should now be taken away, being almost the only available Ore ground at present in the Mine. In Longclose some search should be made after the Caunter Lode East of The Engine Shaft; some branches have been driven through but no Ore ground opened. The dams for preventing the water flowing from North Roskear are completed and found effectual, by which a great saving is effected in the expense of the water drainage. The mine at present is exceedingly poor, but the Tutwork should be prosecuted with all possible vigour.

(signed) James Lanyon" (Tehidy Mine Reports)

The tiny group of miners which South Wheal Crofty began with was increased the following year to 50. By March 1855 Longclose Engine Shaft was sunk to 126 fathoms below adit, and Copper-Tankard Lode was pursued at adit level. High hopes were entertained of finding good copper ground in that area. Some activity was reported in the Dudnance section, particularly on the 16fm level, near to Stainsby's Shaft. In Penhellick a cross-cut was driven north on the 80 from James's Shaft, to intersect a lode that had been located on the level beneath.

During 1856 the returns showed a healthy state at Penhellick, but near poverty at the western end of the mine.

August 1856 (2 months) Tons of Copper 97. Value £349 10s 8d

	£	s	d
Longclose	11	3	6
Penhellick	334	1	1
Dudnance	4	5	3
Total	249	10	8

October 1856 (2 months) Tons of Copper 109. Value £389 4s 5d

	£	s	d
Penhellick	387	7	3
Longclose	1	17	2
Total	389	4	5

December 1856 (2 months) Tons of Copper 149. Value £814 0s 0d

	£	s	d
Dudnance	8	0	0
Longclose	62	0	0
Penhellick	744	0	0
Tota	814	0	0

(Dues and Accounts Book T.M. 47D)

By 1857 the Thomas family had begun an association with South Crofty that was to last for the rest of the nineteenth century. Charles Thomas of Dolcoath, assisted by his sons, extended a paternal influence here. In one of his first reports, Charles Thomas recommends that South Crofty and East Pool co-operate in putting an engine at James's Shaft to pump Penhellick's flooded bottoms. James's was then only 30 yards from the boundary with East Pool, and all below the 110 level in that area was flooded. Thomas pointed out that South Crofty could not afford to do this alone, but assisted, she could. He showed that East Pool's western workings (on her Engine and Great lodes) would also benefit. South Crofty had at that time 33 men on tut, 5 boys and 29 tributers.

Undeterred by the poor results from Dudnance and Longclose, South Crofty adventurers seemed determined to continue the expensive search for copper in those sections. In Longclose throughout 1857-58 work continued on the Longclose Caunter, South Caunter, and Copper-Tankard Lodes. West of the Engine Shaft on the 125 and 115 levels, and on the 55 west of Mayne's Shaft, the Caunter lodes were followed. The Copper-Tankard Lode at the 70 was found to be characterised by mundic and quartz, but on the 24 level it had no value whatever. The Copper-Tankard 'New Shaft' was sinking once again, and was then at 32 fathoms.

Work was also going forward on what the reports called the 'North Lode'. By September 1858 four miners had driven east from Phillip's Shaft 25 fathoms, on the 16 level. In the rich Penhellick section however, they were still plagued by water. So desperate were the adventurers now that it was proposed to go ahead without East Pool co-operation and erect an engine at either James's or Bickford's. It was stated that the cost for running the mine was now £400, the returns £300, and the subsequent loss, £100 per month. Clearly, South Crofty needed the water out of its rich lower levels, in order to survive.

The situation did not improve during the following year, and by the Spring the cost of running South Crofty increased to £496 per month, the returns were £242 and the monthly loss rose to £254. The workforce underground dropped from 70 in September 1858 to 58 in March 1859 and the ground mined was poor. The October 1859 Mine Report concluded, once again, that deep in Penhellick lay the best prospects. The adventurers shied away from the expense of the new engine in Penhellick section by expressing the hope that the 132 level of East Pool, driving west, might eventually solve the drainage problems at Penhellick.

The 1860s began with expressions and plans that showed unrealistic optimism. In June 1860 it was suggested that Mayne's Shaft at Longclose be further deepened to exploit the South Caunter Lode. In Penhellick hopes were still being expressed to the effect that the salvation of the mine lay in the driving of the 132 level from East Pool. It was stated hopefully that they should hole through in eighteen months. The costs per month were then £414, and the results £334, which showed a loss of £80 - an improvement! There were only 9 tutworkers and 34 tributers.

By the beginning of 1861 the loss per month was further reduced to £50, but with costs at £309 and returns only £259, it was clear that work at South Wheal Crofty was gradually petering out. Only 26 men worked underground at that time and of these only 8 were on the 'company account'. The comments at the conclusion of the Report showed at last that the South Wheal Crofty adventurers had faced the amputation necessary for the survival of the mine, and it was recommended that the Longclose sett be given up. Now at last this little Cinderella mine could become a viable proposition. Despite the suggestion to give up Longclose sett being made in January 1861, it was March 1863 before it happened.

"At a special meeting of the adventurers in South Crofty Mine, held at the mine on Monday the 9th of March 1863, to consider and determine on a application from the agent of John Francis Basset esq. to surrender the sett of Longclose, the sett being applied for by another party."

J.F.Basset was of course not only the mineral-lord of Longclose, but also the principal adventurer of the mine. It was decided to comply with the request, and surrender the sett, with nearly five years of their lease of it remaining. The comment in the "Setts Book" says, "The above sett of South Wheal Crofty" was revoked the 28th March 1863, and granted to Elliot J. Squares". The Mining Journal, dated March 21 1863, makes this slightly unrealistic comment: "South Crofty. The Western part of this sett being the old Long Close Mine, near Tuckingmill, has recently been sold by the South Crofty adventurers for £1,100 to Mr. Joseph Elliot Squares, of Greshan House, London. The purchase includes two engines - a 36" pumping and a 22" winding, and other materials. I suppose the South Crofty adventurers have well considered the expediency of abandoning and selling this part of their sett; but, however this may be, I shall be very much surprised if Mr. Square's purchase does not command fully £5,000 profit within a month. It is to be called, I believe, Wheal Crofty". Subsequent editions of the Journal, which reported on the ore sold by these mines, show that Squares would have been fortunate to get his money back - never mind make a profit!

Whilst abandoning the western extremities of the mine, there was a move to increase and consolidate those workings centred on Bickford's Shaft. The Mining Journal of May 18th 1861, carried this report.

"The correspondence with the directors of Tincroft, relative to working within their boundary, was read, and the proposed terms explained, when it was resolved that "The offer of grounds at Tincroft", at a tribute of 9d.in the £1. on the terms proposed, be accepted; and that the purser be instructed to communicate the same to the secretary of the Tincroft directors, and to instruct the solicitors of this mine to see that the necessary agreement be prepared, with a plan of the ground, showing the boundaries of the two setts, according to the present arrangement; and that Capt. Rutter be requested to meet the agents of Tincroft to arrange the boundary line; and that the purser be requested to convene a special meeting of the adventurers, on the necessary documents being prepared; to confirm the same, and to determine the necessary engine to be erected at Palmer's Shaft".

Now that Crofty had acquired the piece of land with Palmer's Shaft on it, the adventurers authorised Capt. Rutter to purchase a suitable pumping engine and whim, either a new 40" engine, or a 60" second-hand one. Rutter took the engineer James Sims with him to inspect the 60" Trevoole Mine pumping engine. They thought it perfectly suitable for their needs and reported this to the adventurers. They also inspected a 22" whim engine that the Rosewarne and Hearland adventurers had for sale. They recommended that both be purchased with the various pieces of machinery that went with them.

The Trevoole engine was purchased for £1,360, and included in the sale were a 60" diameter cylinder engine, two boilers of 10 tons each (later found to be actually 21 tons together), balance-bob, capstan and rope, with the usual appurtenances to the engine-house.

The whim engine was bought for £330 and was described as being "almost new". The sale included the 22" cylinder winding engine, with fly-wheel and cage complete, and the 10 ton boiler. In the March 24 1862 accounts, the whim engine was paid for completely, and £235 was paid off the Trevoole pumping engine.

By March 1862 the whole of the whim was on the mine property, and was almost ready for use. The largest part of the pumping engine was also at Crofty awaiting erection. The first length of rod was also there ready to fit. Twenty-six men were employed in cutting down the shaft, widening and fixing it to the 100 level.

In the purser's report, E.H. Rodd comments on the improved prospects for South Wheal Crofty now that they had gained "the posession of Palmer's Shaft and the additional piece of ground".

By August 1862 the whim had been tested and was quite ready. The pumping engine was almost ready too, but due to unusually wet weather, the masons had been unable to work normally and the engine-house was behind schedule. In Palmers Shaft, work continued well, and the miners were then sinking below the 100 level to a depth of 5 fathoms. The 110 level was being driven under Palmers ready to rise and meet it. The balance owed on the 60" engine was paid in August 1862.

This was a great step by Crofty toward integral viability. She was for the first time becoming self-reliant so far as drawing her own water was concerned, and no longer forced to abandon the deeper workings every time some neighbours' pumps were stopped.

All the above arrangements, together with the surrender of Longclose, which followed in the Spring of 1863, made for a potentially succesful mine. But, these boundary changes were not the last word on the subject. During this period several of the neighbouring mines were looking at the position of their shafts, relative to the strike of their lodes and seeking to negotiate boundary changes.

Having conceded to Crofty the strip of land to the south of Penhellick Vean, Tincroft agents now sought a concession from Crofty. They wanted to work part of the extreme south-east corner of Penhellick Vean sett. They applied for this in June 1863, but after months of negotiation Crofty rejected the idea. This piece of ground straddled some of East Pool and Tincrofts richest lodes.

By the end of 1863 South Wheal Crofty had become a much smaller, but a considerably more compact and viable mine than at the beginning of the year.

She had sold the distant unprofitable section at Longclose, and had acquired a rich piece of ground immediately to the south of her new centre of operations. She had a sound 60" pumping engine at Palmer's and relatively new whim engine, and for the first time was no longer reliant upon the pumps of her neighbours. Bickfords, Palmers, James's and Robinsons Shafts were all either sunk on, or close to, rich proven lodes. Tin ground was being opened up, and the depths to which Croftys neighbours had stoped, was still virgin ground to Crofty.

Since taking over the management of the new mine in 1854 William Rutter had overseen its transformation. He had carefully searched the setts for new sources of mineral wealth, both copper and tin, and had kept development well ahead of production. He had seen the paucity of the Longclose sett, and despite its earlier wealth, had determined upon its abandonment for the good of the mine as a whole. Rutter had presided over the acquisition of Palmer's Shaft and its related sett, and had diligently searched for and acquired, with the help of the engineer James Sims, all of the machinery necessary for pumping, hoisting and treating the ore. With the loss of the Longclose sett and the dressing floors that went with it, he had organised the new plant at the western end of Dudnance. He reported on April 20 1863:

"We are glad to say that the western part of Dudnance, where our ore floors now are, will be the very place for erecting our Stamping power and dressing the tin, as there are plenty of levels for the fall of water and slime which will be available for the water-stamps below, and dressing the after slimes".

Rutter also organised the other necessary surface installations in 1863:

"The surface works, viz: Blacksmiths' and Carpenters' Shops, Timber House, Drying House, etc., are also completed". These were erected where the old stores and 'Samplehouse' were, these buildings being remnants of those built in 1863. Spalling sheds stood by the two principal shafts, so that the newly hoisted ore could be sorted, broken and loaded for carting to final treatment. In these sheds the hefty 'bal-maids' wielded their 'spalling-hammers', and broke the ore down to the size of a mans fist. Often men would smash the larger rocks with heavier sledge-hammers before the 'bal-maids' got to work on them.

Throughout the sett, on both the surface and underground, Rutter had turned South Wheal Crofty into a modern, well-run mine. He had been given £5,000 to spend on proving the necessary equipment and machinery, and he had used it to turn an apparently "no hoper" mine into a viable proposition.

On August 29 1863, Rodd, the purser, and Frederick Martin Williams of Goonvrea Esq, re-negotiated the lease of Dudnance sett on behalf of South Crofty Mine with the mineral-lord Thomas James Agar Robartes of Lanhydrock. In

November 1863 Rodd and Williams renewed the Penhellick Vean sett for a further 21 years.

The February 1863 Cost Book informs us that Crofty received the £1,100 for Longclose engines in the February, before the lease had actually been given up. At that time the monthly bill for coal was becoming a substantial item, and the new engine was already pumping below the 100 fathoms. William Colliver, assisted by nine men and a boy were sinking Palmer's below the 110 level, and at Evans' Shaft further exploration continued.

The Cost Books refer to Palmers' as Engine Shaft from this period onward. In November 1864, the Engine Shaft had been sunk to the 130 level, and Colliver and his men were sinking it below the 130, whilst the level was driven west. At Bickford's also the lode was being pursued westward on the 130, and at James's Shaft, the 120 was being driven in the same direction.

During the mid-1800s the authorities had begun to look closely at working conditions throughout industry. Mining was an area that caused some concern. Committees were set up with parliamentary powers of investigation. The results of these investigations were reports, and ultimately, new laws. The reports issued by these investigators, dated 1864, gave accounts of the testimony of South Wheal Crofty's manager, Capt. William Rutter:

"Never in any case is the 'club money' confined to visible hurt. The rule says it must be visible hurt, but we have always slipped it over as a matter of philanthropy, and we have relieved men when they have been home with severe colds, and so on, and have continued to do it all the way throughout. If a man has a broken leg, for example, we pay for persons watching him, and bandages and anything he wants. If he wants a bed or a mattress, or anything of that sort, we have always given it. We have many men home for years who have been fairly worn out in the mine, because miners do not live to be very old." (Parliamentary Papers 1864).

It was further testified, that at South Wheal Crofty Mine, if the 'club' was ever exhausted an extra call was made to the other miners for another 2d. in the pound for a limited time, "and they do it with great pleasure." Crofty, it was stated, often supported old and incapacitated miners until death. Capt. Rutter told the enquiry:

"I must have stood upon the hill, just where we cross North and South Crofty, many times, to look at the faces of the miners as they come up, and you will see very few old men. It has been sometimes complained of when men have a holiday. I have said you cannot err much in that. When I heard people complaining of a Whit-Monday or Whit-Tuesday, which are holidays with us, and that they do more harm than good, I have not thought so. With all their holidays they die off very early." (Parl. Papers 1864).

Testimony from miners during this investigation was also very revealing. It appears that conditions at North and South Crofty were reasonably good. One miner, a 47 year old, who had been mining since he was 16, suffered from miner's asthma, severe disorder of the digestive organs, had hepatic symptoms and diarrhoea. He had worked for 4 or 5 months in very bad air on the 64 level at East Wheal Crofty, but stated that throughout the mine the air was generally good.

A 33 year old miner, also suffering from asthma, testified that he had worked underground since he was 14, and that at Crofty the air was generally good. A 21 year old, suffering from mistral valvular disease, had worked at East Wheal Crofty and had experienced trouble whilst climbing the ladderway from 190 fathoms down. He blamed his condition on the long climb up from hot working places, and the walk often in the rain, to the changing-house 200 yards from the shaft. He had been "beating a borer" since he was 13 years old, working as a tutworker first for East and then North Wheal Crofty. (Reports to Commission on Conditions of all Mines in G.B. 1864).

The November 5 1864 Mining Journal reported a tragic accident at South Crofty, when Paul Uren, a 16 year old miner fell from a ladder to his death 70 fathoms below.

In his book *Mines of Cornwall*, (1865) Thomas Spargo gives this small pen picture of Crofty:

"South Wheal Crofty in the parish of Illogan, in 937 shares. Was severed from North Crofty a few years ago, and subsequently the western part of the sett has been sold, and is now being worked under the old name of Wheal Crofty. These three mines, together with East Seton, constituted the late "East Wheal Crofty" which gave large dividends. Of South Wheal Crofty the Purser is Mr E.H. Rodd, of Penzance; and the Manager is Captain William Rutter of Camborne. 120 men, 18 females, and 16 boys employed, total 154. The Lords are J.F. Basset, Esq., Mr. Tyringham and another. Dues 1/18th. Depth of adit, 32 fathoms. Depth under adit, 140 fathoms. Workings commenced in 1834, on which there has been a profit, but in 1864 a loss was sustained. The mine is drained by a 60-inch engine, and the ores and debris drawn to surface by a 24-inch winding engine. There is one water stamping mill lifting four heads. The position of this mine is such as to warrant results better than those of last year, and the prospects presented are highly favourable."

The Spring of 1865 found renewed activity in both the deeper parts of Penhellick, and also on the highest levels near to Evans' Shaft. By the Summer William Colliver had reached the 140 level with Palmer's Shaft, and was driving a cross-cut south of the Shaft. In July 1865 work was done on the engine, and Jeremiah

Williams was paid £8 10s 0d to "fix balance bob". In August Colliver put new pitwork into Engine Shaft down to the 140, and prepared to sink lower.

In October 1865 Colliver and his men began to sink Engine Shaft below the 140, opening up still further the area of unexplored ground that contained rich lodes on either side in East Pool and Tincroft. Men were driving on the lodes in her deeper levels and proving the ground to be rich.

Early in 1866 Capt. William Rutter died. Before a decision was made on his successor, the Committee asked Capt. John Daw of Redruth to inspect and make a report on the state of the mine. His report was dated April 4th 1866, and stated that he had been underground at South Crofty, "and have great pleasure in informing you that I have found the Mine much better than I anticipated".

The purser's report of May 28 1866 accepts this report, and says, "It does not appear to me to be necessary at the present time to appoint another Agent in the room of Capt. Rutter, as the Agents feel a confidence that they will be able to carry out the Agency of the Mine until at least the works are more extended."

Under the direction of Captains Francis Gilbert and Simon Toy, the shaft sinkers switched their efforts to Bickfords Shaft. In July William Colliver and his men began sinking Bickford's below the 130 level, leaving William Vivian to continue opening up the 140 east of Palmer's Shaft. The development of the 100, 120, 130, 140 and 150 levels continued to show good values, and the joint managers showed in their reports thay they had every confidence in their abilities to exploit economically the lodes being worked.

January 1867 found Captains Gilbert and Toy still without a manager over them, and out of appreciation for their efforts, their pay was raised to £9 9s 0d per month. William Colliver had by then reached the 140 level, with Bickford's Shaft, and was driving westward. John Trathen was driving the 130 west of Bickford's on the No.3 Lode, and also stoping it.

By the early summer Colliver was sinking Bickford's toward the 150, which he reached in August. Straight away preparations were made by him to go lower still, and by July 1868 he had reached the 160 level. The following month he was driving on the Penhellick Lode westward from the shaft. Bickfords was then "divided and cased" by Colliver, preparatory to further sinking.

November 1868 found Colliver and his pare heading for the 170 level at Bickfords. At this time James Rowe had begun the sinking of James's Shaft below the 130. The mines' development was still being kept well ahead of the stoping, and despite the small scale of the operations, everything was proceeding in a very orderly way.

11. Shaking tables in the Old Mill. The picture was taken in the 1920s. Crofty began to use these tables for dressing fine tin at the turn of the century. They remain the principal apparatus for concentrating tin at the mine's mill, now situated at Wheal Jane.

12. Round buddle for concentrating black tin. These buddles were introduced into tin dressing during the 19th century and were used until the 1950s. This buddle is convex, others were concave, but they both were based on the same principle of using water to wash away the lighter gangue material.

13. 16 cwt wagon being pushed across the bridge from the tramway to the Californian stamps. The photograph was taken just after the Great War. Note, the tracks of North Crofty branchline running beneath the bridge. Launders criss-cross the whole area carrying water for a multitude of purposes.

14. The beam of Fortescue 90" engine leaving Newton Moor to be hauled by traction engines to New Cooks Kitchen Shaft in 1922. The house that accomodated the engine was built entirely of mass concrete and was erected in a matter of five months.

In May 1869 the adventurers once again raised the monthly pay of Captains Toy and Gilbert in gratitude for their joint efforts. They now received £10 10s 0d per month each.

January 1870 saw Collivers's men pause in their continuous sinking operations at Bickford's between the 160 and 170 level, and drive off west, on Pryce's Lode, at the 160. A large area above the 160 level was now being opened up on the Penhellick, Pryce's, North and No. 3 lodes.

William Colliver and his men reached the 170 level in March 1870, and immediately began to drive east on Pryce's Lode. By mid-summer he was sinking below the 170, whilst other tutworkers opened up the level. At the end of 1870 James Rowe was employed driving a cross-cut south on the 170 level, from Bickford's Shaft. The 180 level had still not been reached at Bickford's when the year ended. According to Williams 'Mining Directory', there were in 1870, 210 people employed at South Wheal Crofty.

This period was another one of change and re-adjustment. The radical changes of 1854, when South Wheal Crofty was formed as an independant mine, and 1861-63, when Longclose was sold and Penhellick section reorganised, equipped and deepened, were as nothing compared with the fundamental changes that Crofty now faced. Although later than most local mines, Crofty now had to face the change to tin. This required new skills on the part of the management, the miners, and those responsible for ore dressing.

In 1868 Crofty still sold 3,170 tons of copper to only $4^1/_2$ tons of tin. The change-over was inevitable, as the depths to which her workings now extended meant that tin was to be found in greater abundance than copper. Because Crofty was not equipped for tin dressing, she now had to reorganise completely her milling arrangements. In 1871 Crofty still sold her tin 'in the stone' (unstamped) to those neighbouring mines that had already switched to tin production.

Crofty found that she was not up to the reorganisation necessary without outside help. Capt. Francis Gilbert, the senior agent since the death of Rutter in 1866, was himself now too ill to carry out underground inspections. Simon Toy carried the burden well, but with so much to be done in erecting new plant, negotiating new agreements, employing experts in tin dressing, and organising a modern, sophisticated stamps and dressing arrangement, he clearly needed help.

Early in 1871 the mine committee decided to recruit an agent to assist underground. A Capt. W. Martyn was employed, coming with very good references. Unfortunately, he was not what the committee had thought. The June 12 1871 Purser's Report said:

"I am sorry that I have to report that Captain W. Martyn our newly appointed agent, has absented himself from the Mine since Thursday week, and ... has not been heard of since ... It will be necessary ... that immediate assistance be given to the present agents; and they confidently recommend John Jory and William James, long employed on the Mine, and in every respect efficient and trustworthy, to be appointed to carry out the duties of assistant surface and underground agents respectively ... and that the appointment of Captain Martyn be rescinded by resolution of the cost book. E.H. Rodd, Purser."

The returns for the first three months of 1871 showed an almost equal revenue from tin and copper, but the tin was mostly sold unstamped and at a loss. Over 6 tons were sold stamped and dressed, and this fetched £70 10s. per ton (£431 12s 10d), but a much larger quantity was sold as ore, and this fetched £1,175 10s 9d). There was £1,586 9s. worth of copper sold, and with the costs at £3,394, there was a loss for the three months of £200.

After more than five years, work began again to continue the sinking of Palmer's Engine Shaft. By June 1871 Palmer's was divided and bed-planked to the 150 fathom level. Sinking commenced below the 150 level, with 6 men costing £50 per fathom. "The lode is 4 feet wide, producing stones of copper ore, and saving work for tin." The June 1871 Report concludes with the total numbers of miners given as, men on tutwork, 86; men on tribute, 36; average tribute paid 9s. Work had begun to erect new stamps, but these were still inadequate. New skiproad and tramway were also envisaged. The summer of 1871 was to be a very busy time at South Wheal Crofty.

The October 16 1871 Report stated that development had opened up 287 fathoms of valuable ground, and that "these operations have increased the value of the Mine about £35,000."

The Pursers Report of October 1871 commented on the deteriorating health of Capt. Gilbert, and said this:

"It has been deemed advisable from the inability through ill health of our respected Agent, Captain Francis Gilbert, to render practical help to the Mine, and from the general extension and development of the Mine, to call in the assistance of another agent as consultant agent. I need scarcely add that such assistance being solicited from our friend and neighbour Capt. Josiah Thomas and not objected to by him, has afforded general satisfaction."

The purser also commented that with the new stamping arrangements, Crofty could now return the tin on the mine, and not lose money by having to sell it 'in the stone'.

On November 13 1871, Capt. Thomas sent a report to the committee of South Crofty, on his visit to the surface and underground workings of the mine. He made some interesting observations on the so-called 'New Lode', which was proving so rich:

"The principal operations at present are on the South Lode which underlies north. This has been called the New Lode at the 100 and 110 fathom levels, but it is evidently the same lode that has been worked on at the deeper levels, Nos. 1, 2 and 3 lodes being merely droppers falling into it".

Capt. Thomas discussed the value of the various lodes and seemed to conclude that Crofty was well endowed, albeit on a small scale, with rich tin and copper lodes.

The Purser's Report for February 19 1872 tells of South Wheal Crofty passing a milestone in her development as a permanent tin Mine.

"Sir,
The balance against the Adventurers to-day in the Cost-Book is £4,852 8s., as against £653 16s 6d., at the last Account. This includes the purchase money of a good second-hand 40-inch Cylinder Engine, with Fly Wheel, Boiler, and other Machinery for the new Stamps now in course of erection and being laid out, and which may work from 80 to 100 heads. My tender for this, at £850 has been accepted by the Registrar of the Stannaries Court. The paramount importance of obtaining this Engine and Machinery at the present time, instead of incurring the additional expense and delay in the ordering a new Engine at the foundries, must be apparent, looking at the present position of the Mine, its opening into tin, and having already large and increasing reserves which are waiting to be returned, and which renders additional machinery absolutely necessary. The expense of laying out the Mine for a permament Tin Mine has been very great for the past four months, and is likely to continue for some time, and the returns of tin have not been adequate from the present Stamps to meet the expenditure ... I recommended a Call of £5 per Share to be made and allowed ...

I am,
Your obedient servant
EDWARD HEARLE RODD
Purser"

After 1871 Captain Francis Gilbert no longer signed the Reports, and it must be assumed that he had retired due to his continuing ill health. Surprisingly, Captain Simon Toy, who signed the Agent's Report, with Capt. Thomas and Capt. Jory, for February 19th 1872, does not sign the next Report dated May 20th 1872. There is no mention in either of these two Reports, by the purser or among the resolutions, of why Capt. Toy was no longer an Agent. His place was taken by Capt. James Johns, but there is no record in the Reports of his appointment or wage at that time.

The Agent's Report for May 20th 1872 refers to the progress made in developing above and below ground. It begins:

"Gentlemen,
Palmer's Engine Shaft, which is being sunk below the 150 fathom level, is producing a little tin.

We are driving west from the 160 cross-cut, north of Bickford's. The end is now about 2 fathoms short of Palmer's Shaft. As soon as the shaft is reached we shall commence to rise towards it, in order to hole it as soon as possible to the 160."
The Report concludes:

"Since the last Account we have done a large quantity of work, both underground and at surface. James's Shaft and Palmer's Engine Shaft have been prepared for drawing with wire ropes, which are now at work, and we expect Bickford's Shaft will also be completed in about a fortnight from this date. The new Engine House for the Steam Stamps will be finished in about a month, when we shall at once commence to fit the engine, stamps, axles, etc.

We have not yet settled the diallings of the encroachment on the Mine by East Pool, but hope we shall be able to settle the matter amicably.

Josiah Thomas
James Johns
John Jory."

This encroachment was related to the discovery in Penhellick Vean of the 'East Pool Lode' and was to be the cause of a rapid rise in the value of South Wheal Crofty shares. East Pool miners, following their rich lode westward, strayed into Crofty, and not only took ore for which Crofty would have to be properly compensated, but also established the exact location inside Crofty, of a lode that had already proved very rich in East Pool. South Wheal Crofty's shares rose from as low as £8 in 1871, to as high as £127 in 1872 on the strength of it. Eventually East Pool agreed to pay Crofty £2,012 compensation for the ore she had raised from inside Penhellick Vean Sett.

With everything going well inside the Mine, outside influences soon put a stop to Crofty's new confidence. The discovery of an abundance of cheaply produced tin in Tasmania meant that not only at South Crofty, but also throughout Cornish tin mines there was a slump. Crofty's shares which had so recently risen to £127, slumped to as low as £15 during the crisis of 1872-74.

Despite the tin price remaining disastrously low, South Wheal Crofty continued with her programme of modernisation. By August 1873 the manager was able to report that, "The whole of the Steam Stamps consisting of 84 heads is set to work, and with the exception of some extension of the dressing floor the Machinery it nearly completed."

Captain Thomas asserted that were it not for the low price of tin and copper, Crofty would have been making a very healthy profit. He reported that work continued in sinking Bickford's Shaft below the 180 level, and that there were high hopes for discovering still more rich lodes inside the existing setts. The returns for copper, tin and arsenic for April, May and June 1873 showed that the mine received £2,004 for copper, £3,176 for tin, and £385 for arsenic.

By the end of that year things had begun to look serious at Crofty. Although the returns looked healthy enough on paper, the plunging price of tin was beginning to bite. It was recommended to the adventurers that the assistant clerk, taken on at a salary of £2.2s in February 1872 be "dispensed with".

This was just one of the economies found necessary by the situation. The Purser's Report also stated: "It is proposed to suspend operations in such parts of the Mine as are purely speculative and at present unproductive." Josiah Thomas's report informed the adventurers that by February 1874 Bickford's was sunk to the 192 level, and he proposed that they cross-cut on that level to intersect the South lode. Despite the economies, Thomas felt that this development would reap both rich and early returns.

Thus Crofty soldiered on, and although it would have been unrealistic for her share-holders to expect early profits, those 'in' adventurers, with an interest in supplying the mine with materials or services, would find their outlay through the regular "calls", worthwhile. During that crisis in the mid-70s Crofty's copper returns held their own with tin, so that the abysmal tin price that prevailed was not so disastrous to Crofty as to those mines entirely dependant upon tin. As already noted, at Crofty arsenic was also returned in sufficient quantities to help defray the costs. The returns for the last quarter of 1874 show that the costs were £3,137; revenue from sales was, copper £758 (223 tons); arsenic, £451 (70 tons); tin £1,462 (30¾ tons); and the loss was £466. From December 1875 until August 1876, the returns from copper rose again well above that of tin. During this period the mine made a loss of £492 (December 1875 to August 1876, sales were Copper £5,268; Tin £3,778).

The Mine Inspector's Report for 1875 gives the production figures and also the number working at South Wheal Crofty. There were 304 tons, 11 cwt of arsenic; 1,810 tons, 13 cwt, 2 qts of copper; 173 tons, 9cwt, 3 qts of tin produced. Employed at Crofty: Men underground 89; Boys under 13 on the surface 4; Boys

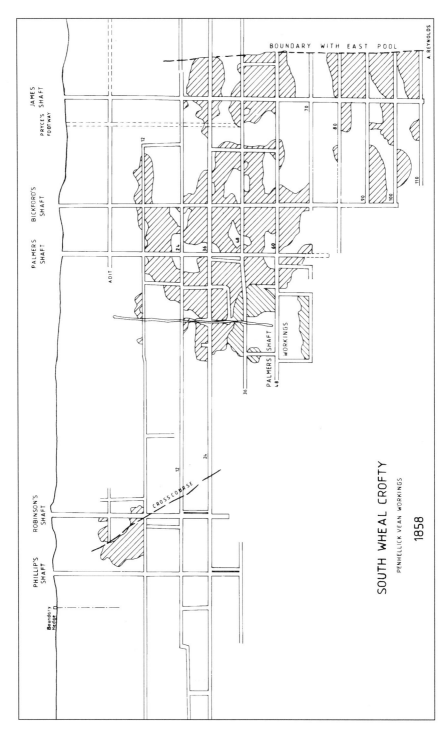

SOUTH WHEAL CROFTY

PENHELLICK VEAN WORKINGS

1858

between 13-18, 21; Females 13-18, 11; Females over 18,30; Males over 18, 47; Total 202.

In the early 1870s a Factory Act was passed that sought to prohibit children under the age of 14 from working in factories and mines. Josiah Thomas lost over 50 youngsters from Dolcoath, but fared better at Crofty, as the above figures show.

The February 17 1875 Report, shows that despite a loss of £550 on the previous quarter the agents were determined to continue development. They had "cut the plot at the 195, and sunk Bickford's Shaft 6 feet below that level, the shaft below the 180 having been also cased and divided." Thomas further reported that they were cross-cutting on the 195, with good prospects of intersecting the South Lode within a couple of fathoms. On the 160, 170 and the 180 levels tin ground was being opened up which contained "fine stones of tin."

The Purser's Report dated August 18 1875, refers to alterations being made to the pitwork in Palmer's Shaft, and to a new plunger lift fixed at Bickford's Shaft, at the 195 level. Rodd commented, that the alterations should save the mine 20 tons of coal per month in the pumping engine, and also enable the shaft sinkers to continue deepening Bickfords without interruption. A new wire rope had also recently been purchased.

On November 16 1875, Capt Thomas reported:

"The new Pitwork which we fixed in the Engine Shaft and in Bickford's Shaft, about three months since is working exceedingly well, and by the change we made, a saving has been effected of about 2S tons of coals per month. We have also been able to sink Bickford's Shaft without the hindrances we formerly had to content with from breakages etc.

Bickford's Shaft is being sunk by 8 men and 4 boys and is now 8 fathoms below the 195. The lode is worth for the length of the Shaft (12 feet) £30 per fathom. There is more lode standing to the South of the Shaft, and after sinking 2 months longer, we shall have reached the 205 fathom level."

Thomas also reported, that throughout the area being developed from the 160 downwards, tin was being discovered in encouraging quantities.

In November 1875 Edward Hearle Rodd gave up his position as purser, and was replaced by H.J. Lean. In his final report as purser, he speaks of taking back the Longclose Sett, and once again extending South Wheal Crofty's working area to the Red River. The surface area of Longclose was already back in Crofty's hands, and now she was taking back the lease to work Longclose Sett. There appears to be no evidence that Crofty worked Longclose immediately, or for some years after that, but she seems to have held the ground in reserve for the future.

A plan from that period, shows the stamps and mill at Longclose, after the re modernisation of the plant to cope with tin. The dressing floors occupied the area of the present Contractors Workshop. The Cornish stamps were in line on either side of the fly-wheel. The arsenic flues and stacks stretched alongside the old North Crofty Branch Line, in a southerly direction. The water gravitated by degrees through the various buddle arrangements, until it carried the tailings down into the Red River, to be further processed by the host of smaller tin stream works between Tuckingmill and the sea. The concentrate was taken by wheel-barrow to be calcined, having the arsenic removed, before being buddles, 'tossed' in small kieves, and then ready for 'ticketing', it was sold to be smelted.

A far-reaching development occurred in the mid-1870s when rock-drills were again experimented with. In the 1860s 'boring machines' had been introduced into Cornwall by F.B. Doering, but they had at that time proved unsuccessful. During 1876 Dolcoath tried a 'Barrow Rock Drill', on the 314 level. It was not able to cope with hard granite at first, but after some modifications it proved a great success. A different type was tried at Wheal Agar and this, too, was satisfactory. Crofty agents were also interested. In the February of 1876 the 205 level had been reached at Bickford's and it was in driving this level that the new 'boring machines' were to prove themselves at the mine.

With the price of tin still low, the management wisely decided to continue to supplement their production of tin with copper. Many local mines had gone over completely to tin decades before, but at Crofty many of the workings were still shallow and in good copper ground, hence both copper and arsenic could be sought to boost the returns. During 1876 copper ground as high as the 60 level was reopened for marginally economic reasons - even with tin down to between £40 - £50 per ton, it was worth far more than copper!

In June 1876 the Mine Committee met to appoint a replacement for Capt. James Johns who was leaving for a better post at Dolcoath. He was to rise there to a position of responsibility second only to Josiah Thomas. Indeed, when he was old, some twenty years later, and it was rumoured in Camborne that he was to retire, the panic among Dolcoath shareholders was greater than that which attended a similar rumour concerning Josiah Thomas. It was resolved to appoint Capt. W. Pascoe in Johns' place at a monthly salary of £9 9s. Because of the continuing crisis in tin prices, Sir R.R. Vyvyan agreed to reduce his dues to 1/60th, as Messrs Tyringham and Basset already had.

The returns for 1877 show that during that year SWC produced 229 tons of arsenic, 1,880 tons of copper and 136 tons 12cwt 12lb of tin. Clearly, the copper and arsenic were continuing to keep Crofty afloat.

In May 1877 two serious accidents happened at Crofty. The first concerned an aged tributer called Francis Tellum. He and two partners were working an underhand stope for copper at 12/- in the pound. During April they had earned £46 17s 5d, of which £28 2s 0d, was taken out for costs. They also earned £5 12s for tin raised. Split three ways this represented very high earnings at that time.

Tellum was a very experienced miner, who had spent most of his 73 years underground. When he took the pitch in the stope where he was killed, he was warned by the mine-captains that it was dangerous. They had said to him, "You must be careful, and take the risk of working there yourself." The inquest was told that the reason for these words was that two or three months earlier, there had been a 'run' of ground in the stope, and it was of such seriousness that the place was not not thought safe. The coroner made some interesting comments on the responsibility for Tellum's death:

"I think the agents of the mine were decidely to blame for allowing men to work as they did, because the place had never property been examined after the great 'run' or fall of ground. It is true that the walls near the floor of the chamber (stope) had been inspected, but the upper part which could not be reached without regular staging, was not looked at.

The agents evidently did not consider the place secure, for one of them told the deceased he must be careful, and take the risk of working there himself, also, the agents had said, (in evidence at the inquest), "We did not know whether it was safe or not."

The jury found that South Wheal Crofty's agents were to blame for allowing men to work in an unsafe place. the accident occurred on May 1 1877 in a stope that was 30 feet wide by 40 feet high, and the rocks that hit Francis Tellum were described as small.

Less that a fortnight later a second fatal accident happened at Crofty, when a 20 year old miner was killed. Henry Johns was working with his father and two other tributors in a stope, when he struck a drill into a socket left from a previous blast. There was a residue of dynamite left there and an explosion occurred which killed him. This was on May 12 1877.

The following month saw the arrival at Crofty of their first rock-drill machine. This was greeted with more interest among the mining fraternity in general than had the two fatalities. It was not every day that something as modern and revolutionary as a 'boring machine' was introduced into a small mine like South Wheal Crofty, whereas the loss of two good men was seen in the mining district as a daily occurence.

The machine that Crofty purchased was a 'Barrow Rock Drill', and it was the same model as the improved one that had been so successful at Dolcoath. It was patented by Hosking & Blackwell, of Barrow-in-Furnace, Lancashire, hence the name. This firm had Cornish origins and found a ready market for ther excellent drill in the Duchy. The drill was made of gunmetal and weighed about 120 lb. It was driven by air compressed to 50 lb per square inch. It proved considerably faster than hand-labour, and up to a quarter more economical. Between June and October 1877 the makers' agents, M. Loam & Son, operated the machine, but after that Crofty's own men took it over. The first men to use it were Richard Oats, William Oats and John Jeffrey, and starting in October 1877 they were each paid £5 per month as 'machine men'. The November 1877 Accounts show £65 paid to the Barrow Rock Drill Company.

1878 was another disastrous year for the mine. By October the adventurers had met to decide whether the mine should shut entirely. In the event it was resolved, "That the operations for the present be confined to the 205 fath. level, at a cost of about £200 per month, including all charges." The boring machine was to be used to continue development on the level and that was to be the sole work done underground. Capt. Josiah Thomas was asked to value all material assets on the mine, "against the person appointed by the Relinquished Shareholders." It was further resolved that East Pool be asked to help defray the cost of pumping through Palmer's which was essential in keeping that mine dry.

By February 1879 South Crofty had stopped even her pumps, despite a belated offer of £20 per month, from East Pool towards their continuation. With the two mines extensively holed through into each other above the 160 level, East Pool found herself in the position of Crofty 20 years before. Early in February it was decided that with the ruinous price of tin and the cost of staying open beyond the packets of the shareholders - 165 out of 888 shares having been relinquished - work would be confined to the area above the 160 level. Two 'pares' of tributers were given pitches working for copper, but the mine could afford no 'Company account' miners.

During March East Pool negotiated with Crofty to restart Palmer's engine. She upped her offer to £30 a month, and when this was refused sent the dispute to arbitration. The figure set was £35 and East Pool agreed to pay it for six months. Palmer's engine was restarted in May, and although it did not work to capacity, nevertheless it did keep the water at bay.

By August general mining was again in progress and cross-cuts had been driven well north of the area that had been mined for the previous twenty years. It was hoped to intersect a good lode that East Pool had driven in that direction. Unfortunately, although there was a chance that it would be found in South Wheal Crofty's sett, as it was a north dipper, it was estimated that it would dip into the abandoned North Wheal Crofty sett in a short distance. Caution dictated that the north sett be applied for before the lode was actually cut by Crofty, otherwide difficulties could be foreseen in obtaining it.

A report in the September 27 1879 Mining Journal indicated that South Wheal Crofty had been successful in gaining the sett of North Crofty, but there seems little other evidence to support this idea. Certainly by that time the lower levels were again in production, and a new Stephens drilling machine had been brought into use and was found successful. R. Stephens & Son, later known as Climax, continued to supply rock drills to South Crofty for 77 years, until they were taken over by Holman Bros.

In October 1879 East Pool accused Crofty of encroaching. The agents replied that it was impossible, as they had new maps of the mine bounds drawn up by Hendersons of Truro. At the outside it could only have been 8 or 9 feet, and as the lode in question was small and poor, they could not see what all the fuss was about. A measure of the sudden optimism that the Company felt, was reflected in the increase in salary that was given to the purser, manager and chief agent. The mood of optimism was as short-lived as it was sudden. Within a fortnight of the announcement of pay rises for its chief officers, the mine was cutting the overall management salary bill from £35 a month to £22. The price of tin once again had taken a disastrous turn for the worse.

The Mine Committee again decided that it would confine costs to £200 overall. £100 of this was to pay for the drive west on the 205 level by boring machine. The lode being discovered was 30 feet wide, and although the values were scattered in it, as it narrowed the tin became concentrated and very rich. The agents again felt the frustration that went with the job at South Crofty; whenever prospects looked particularly good underground at the mine, outside influences interfered with the promised profit!

By 1880 mining had been resumed, but returns from copper were beginning to dry up. From July through October 1880 only 15 tons of copper were sold, bringing in a mere £56 at an average price of £3 14s 6d per ton. The 23 tons 15 cwt of tin produced £1,063 10s 10d, and the arsenic sold raised £100. From then on arsenic became a more important product to Crofty than copper.

The November 12 1880 Agent's Report shows good tin ground being opening up on the 205 level, both east and west of the cross cut, on the 'Middle Lode'. This is the lode we now call 'Main Lode.' The 180 level was being driven on the North Lode and was averaging about £20 per fathom. Near to East Pool's boundary the lode was not so good, and so driving was suspended and a rise put up with Croftys new 'boring machine.' The value in this rise was £30 per fathom. Thomas also reported that since the last account, "we have cut down the Engine

Shaft, where necessary, and fixed a New Skip Road from surface to the bottom, which is now available for drawing stuff and for raising and lowering the men." Crofty was using skips for hoisting men, whilst many of the great mines continued with 'man engines'.

Sometime during the bleak years up to 1880, Capt. John Jory ceased to serve the mine and the overall responsibility of managing the mine on a day to day basis was left to Capt. William Pascoe. Josiah Thomas was still manager, but he had the mighty Dolcoath and other mines to worry about, and so for all practical purposes Pascoe was in charge.

During the February 4 1881 meeting, a letter was read from a Mr Provis, asking for a contribution to "the fund for opposing the renewal of the Dynamite Patent". It was agreed to send a contribution, as requested. The dynamite monopoly cost Cornish mines dear, the price being 2s per lb against only 1s per lb in Germany.

The January 6 1882 Report shows the mine benefitting greatly from having two rock-drilling machines on constant development. One of these was kept continuously at work on the 205 and the other on opening up the northern area on the 160 level. The Cost Book shows that the machines were operated by shifts of men, both day and night.

At the meeting of adventurers on January 6 1882, it was resolved, "That steps be taken for insuring the miners working in this mine, against accidents, under the Employers Liability Act." This was a big step forward in guaranteed protection for miners injured or killed whilst employed underground. It affected those employed on the surface also.

During 1882, a new mine-captain was appointed by South Crofty; he was Capt. J.M. Phillips. The Report of the agents for September 15 1882 shows that, despite good returns from most levels between the 160 and 205, the quarterly loss continued disturbingly high with the loss for June - August 1882 being £853.

A development that did speak well for the future was referred to at the end of the Agent's Report: "The new Engine and Air Compressor, which it was resolved to erect at the last meeting of the Adventurers, is being made as rapidly as possible, and is expected to be on the mine in about 3 weeks from this date. The foundations are already prepared for the reception of the Compressor, and it can be erected and set to work in a few days after arrival. It will be capable of driving four $3^{1}/_{2}$ inch Boring Machines."

The March 10 1883 Mining Journal informs us that in addition to the original 'Barrow' machine, Crofty then had a Stephens and a McCullock-Holman machine. The cost of the new compressor machine and pipes was £1,000. During that year South Penstruthal Adventurers paid Crofty for services rendered, and the implication is that, like New Cook's Kitchen, South Penstruthal Mine sent ore 'in the stone' to be stamped and dressed by Crofty. Another payment that appears regularly in the accounts of that period is the payment by South Crofty of £10 per month for water from Carn Brea Mine.

Much work was done during the spring and summer of 1884 to bring better ventilation to those parts of the North and Middle Lodes that were to be stoped. The May 22 1884 Report deals mostly with 'winds' being sunk, and 'rises' being pushed up for better air supply, and there is a general attitude prevalent to the effect that it was most undesirable that men should work in stopes without a good air supply.

The concluding paragraph of the Agent's Report of September 11 1884, says: "We have been considering the propriety of recommending the Adventurers to sink Palmer's Engine Shaft, so as to prove the value of the various lodes below the 205. We have now opened a great length on the Middle and North Lodes at the 160, 180, and 205 fathom levels, and, as part of the North Lode will probably effect a junction with the Middle Lode at about 15 fathoms below the 205, and as the lode at the 205 is very large and promising, we think it advisable to sink Palmer's Engine Shaft below the 160 as soon as possible. By energetic working this shaft can probably be sunk to the 205 in about 8 months."

At a meeting held on the 1 January 1885, it was reported that South Wheal Crofty had lost £1,453 18s 11d, for the 16 weeks ending November 1884, and that the "Balance against the Mine" stood at £5,437 12s 7d. The adventurers also heard that a communication had been received from the mineral-lords.

"A letter was received from Mr. Glanville on behalf of Mr. Tyringham, Mr. Basset, and Sir V. Vyvyan, stating that the terms on which they were prepared to grant a new lease for 21 years, were 1-24th Dues for Tin, and 1-20th for Copper, and they offered to remit all Dues for twelve months from the last meeting, provided the sinking of the Engine Shaft was continued."

It was also resolved:

"That the thanks of the Meeting be given to the Lords for giving up the Dues, but that considering the large outlay being made in developing the Mine, it is hoped that the Lords will consent to grant the New Lease on the terms as have been granted to the neighbouring Mine of Tincroft."

By the August 13 1885 meeting Palmer's Shaft was cut down, enlarged, and had skip road put in to the 205 level, and was already sunk 7 fathoms below the level. They were sinking at the rate of $3\frac{1}{2}$ fathoms per month (21 feet), and were expected to reach 220 level by the end of October. Due to the efforts at shaft sinking, only one stope was being worked in the whole mine, but much rich ground continued to be opened up. Very high hopes were entertained for the future prospects in depth on the Middle and North lodes, particularly when these made a junction.

Work continued to sink Palmer's Shaft during the autumn and winter of 1885, and by March 1886, having continued past the 220 fathom level, the 225 level was reached. With the results good on the deeper levels, and with the lodes appearing more regular and settled than higher up, the order was given to continue sinking Engine Shaft. By July 15 1887, Palmer's Engine Shaft was 245 fathoms below adit. A cross-cut had been driven south from Palmer's on the 245 and had intersected a rich lode after just 3 fathoms which was no less that 13 feet wide, and worth £40 per fathom. A special circular was sent to the adventurers when this lode was found. Drives on the lodes proved that, although it was somewhat disordered by 'red felspar', every confidence could be entertained of finding 'good tin deposits'. In neighbouring mines this red felspar had accompanied rich tin ground.

The November 4 1887 Agent's Report carried this information:

"The Engine Shaft is sunk 3 fathoms under the 245, which is deep enough below the level for the skip and also for the fork. We have fixed a new lift of pumps in this Shaft, from the 225 to the 245, for pumping the water, which had previously been done by an air winch. We are now fixing a new skip road which will be ready for drawing from the 245 fathoms level in the course of next week. We shall then be prepared for driving the 245 east and west on the course of the lode without interruption, and also for sinking the Shaft below the 245, when it is thought best to do so."

The June 1888 Report from the manager and the captains said that the 260 level was reached and that cross-cutting has started to prove the Middle Lode at that depth. The Report concludes, "We have spent several hundreds of pounds during the past four months in dead work - three Boring Machines having almost constantly been employed in sinking the Engine Shaft and driving cross-cuts in granite, without producing any tin." Now, they felt, they could use their men and equipment in producing tin.

By the autumn of 1888 Crofty was once again down to earth, with the newly opened up ends proving quite good, but not so valuable as expected. A more thorough search was to be made for the rich lode intersected in the Shaft between 245 and 260. With the values at the eastern end being disappointing, attention was turned toward the western drives. Meanwhile, the mine committee came under pressure from Mr Marriot, the Tehidy Agent to import coal through Portreath, owned by the Bassetts. The other 'in' adventurers resisted this.

Throughout 1889 the deeper levels were patiently explored for tin. On the 260 level good tin ground was located and although the values were not exceptional, there was a lot of it. On the 245 east of the cross-cut, the ground 'was very rich' for a while, but then moderated until by December, at a distance of 80 yards from the cross-cut, it was worth £25 per fathom. To the west of the cross-cut on the 245, the end was worth only £12 per fathom. On the 205, and 225 levels ground was being opened up valued at between £20 - £35 per fathom.

1890 saw an improvement in the values on the 260 level, and it was thought that, as the Middle Lode could not be found on that level, it had united with North Lode between the 205 and the 260. Values of £40 per fathom were found on the 260 level, and high hopes were held of finding rich deposits of tin in the eastern end of the mine where no exploration on the Middle and North Lodes had taken place below the 205. There was some disappointment when drives went under that had been good ground on the levels above, and was only moderate on the 245 and 260.

The fact that the 225 level had not been driven extensively continued to prove a problem. Rises and winzes had to be connected through 240 feet of ground, and stoping was rendered difficult by this. For many years it had been common at Crofty to drive in levels every ten fathoms, (60 feet) which made stoping with the tools then available quite simple. Safety was also a factor in keeping the stopes - (most of which were underhand stopes) - at a height that made examination easier, but after the 205 level had been passed, 20 fathom distances became normal.

During 1890-91 the ground explored on the 205, 225, 245 and 260 levels was proving good and the July 9 1891 Report speaks of consistently high values found. The pumping plant at Palmer's Engine Shaft, after thirty years use by South Crofty, was beginning to show signs of wear. A report by the Tincroft Mine engineers from that period shows the extent of the deterioration of Palmer's engine. They used the engine briefly to assist in unwatering Tincroft, East Pool and Crofty when they were threatened by rising water. The report said:

"There is not a single sound joint; steam is leaking wherever possible, and the boilers are on the point of 'busting.' The balance box at surface is heavily over-loaded and held together by means of iron rods and chains. The main bob is cracked and has had to be reinforced with K-posts. Otherwise everything is O.K., but there is a general sigh of relief as each stroke is completed."

Despite this condition, Palmer' continued to pump till 1908, when Robinson's Shaft was completed to the 205 level, and her engine took the load off Palmer' engine, which by then had completed 46 years with Crofty and an unknown time with Trevoole Mine.

When we estimate the service done by this old 60" engine, it is necessary to look at the difficulties it had to content with. Palmer's Shaft is so tortuous that in following the lodes down, it took no less that 15 changes of direction before reaching its final depth of 273 fathoms below adit. The rod negotiated the turns by means of 'fend-off' bobs, and it was estimated that a third of the horse-power was lost through friction in the shaft.

Clarence Paull, manager of South Crofty for about 20 years, gave a lecture in Falmouth on June 14 1933, in which he described Palmer's Shaft. "The Shaft is vertical for 90 fathoms then follows a south underlying lode to the 160 fathom level, here it turns completely over and follows a north dipping lode down to the 272 fathom level." He also mentioned that 'dolly wheels' were used to negotiate the main change of direction.

During the spring of 1892 little work was done on the Middle Lode at the deeper levels, as the machines were employed in driving the North Lode west on the 245 and 260 levels. The values were proving satisfactory there. Elsewhere development and stoping were continuing with quietly reassuring results.

The Agent's Report for June 9 1892, concludes:

"We have had a series of hindrances during the past four months, which have interfered with the working of the mine. The Shaft tackle having failed and the wire rope broken, the mine was idle for a week. We have had several tons at surface which were drawn up at too late a period to be returned and sold for this day's Meeting."

Captain John M. Phillips ceased to be an agent at South Wheal Crofty during that period and he was replaced by Captain Joseph Tamblyn, a miner of considerable skill and energy.

During the latter part of 1892 the Middle Lode on the 225 and the 245 levels was opened up for stoping. Drives were pushed out toward the western boundaries of the mine on these levels. There were still only 3 boring machines in use at Crofty at that time.

During the 1890s a new method of working the lodes was introduced at Crofty. Instead of stoping away the ground above and below the levels and replacing them with timber, crown and floor pillars were left, and the box hole and inter method was introduced. Mills or chutes were built into the box holes and the ore ran straight into wagons beneath. This increased the number of back stopes, and breast-stopes, and the records for that period show a marked increase in the miners working the back of the lode, whereas previously, the majority worked underhand. The new method was introduced piece-meal, and it was probably after 1910 that it became general throughout the mine.

15. *The 195 fm level pumping station. This came into operation in 1955, when Robinsons 80" stopped. The three Sultzer pumps at 340 fm level lifted the water to a reservoir at 195 level, from which the five Sultzer pumps, in the picture, lifted it to surface.*

16. *'Jimmer' Rowe back stoping with a Hydromax stoper during the Second World War. This machine was a very successful and popular stoper for over twenty years, despite it being a hand-rotating machine. Note, the miner has two carbide lamps, one on his hard hat and one on the wall.*

17. Hathorn Davy 3-throw pump on 140 fm level at Bickfords Shaft. Purchased from Tresavean Mine in 1929, it was installed in 1930 at Crofty.

18. New Cooks Kitchen 90" engine's beam, broken and hanging over the shaft. The pitmen are struggling to stop the beam plunging down through the shaft, where it would have done terrible damage. Bill Harvey, for many years pitboss at Cooks Shaft is standing at the top.

1893 opened with a costly boiler explosion at the stamp's engine, and production was interrupted. As 1893 progressed, attention was turned to the Middle Lode at the deeper levels. As exploration continued on this lode, particularly to the west of Palmer's on 245 level, tributers were set to work on the "bottom of the 245 level and the back of the 260" on the North Lode where a winze had been put down for proper ventilation. The Agents Report strongly recommended further sinking in order to prove these lodes at depth.

"With the object or proving the lode below the 260, we have been sinking under that level at two points to the East of Engine Shaft. The first sink is about 15 fathoms. The other sink, 40 fathoms further East, is down 4 feet, the lode being worth £30 per fathom. Seeing this valuable lode going down below the 260, we strongly recommend the immediate sinking of the Engine Shaft. The bottom of the present shaft is 4 fathoms to the North of the lode, but by cutting down a piece of ground to the South of the Shaft below the 245, we can without much difficulty, alter the underlie of the Shaft, and sink it on the course of the lode below the 260."

Examining the suggestion made there, concerning the alteration of Palmer's Shaft's underlie, it is not hard to appreciate the extent to which the energy of Palmer' Engine was squandered. No one can deny the ingenuity and skill of Crofty's shaftmen at that time in modifying the pitwork and devising methods (often unique) to carry the rod past these obstacles, but with so many changes of direction in Palmer's Shaft it is a wonder that any water at all came up from depths of over 1,500 feet.

Meanwhile, the price of tin, affected by the enormous production of cheap tin from the Straits, continued to drop. The average price had dropped from £62 for a ton of black tin in 1887, to £47 by 1893. The final paragraph of the Report for August 1893 shows the drastic reduction in revenue in a four month period. "During the past 16 weeks, we have sold $12^1/_2$ tons of tin more than in the previous 16 weeks, but the average price of tin for this Account is £5 2s 6d. per ton less, which makes a difference in our receipts of about £400".

South Wheal Crofty lost £1,168 during that 16 week period in the summer of 1893.

Despite the ominous news from abroad that cut the price of tin almost monthly, Crofty continued to open up the deeper levels and even sank the Engine Shaft to its final depth of 273 fathoms. Throughout the bleak financial winter of 1893-94 winzes were sunk, drives pushed out and new stoping ground prepared.

Tin production had increased well during this period, but continuing decline in price caused a loss over the four months before April of £1,933. Crofty could not continue to produce more tin for ever smaller returns indefinitely.

Throughout the latter part of 1894 and the early part of 1895 the ground between 260 and 272 was opened for stoping, particularly on the eastern side of Palmer's. By the autumn of 1895 tributers were set to work on good tin ground east of the shaft, but on the west side, although there were moderate values below the 260, little development had been carried out there. The north cross-cut on the 272 had not at that time reached the Middle Lode. Promising returns continued from the 225, 192 and 205, where on the Middle Lode west of Palmer's Shaft, values of £56 per fathom were encountered.

The October 24 1895 Agent's Report, makes mention of a development that eventually, eleven years later, was to transform South Wheal Crofty once again. "Pending the negotiations for the New Lease and the proposed conversion of the mine into a Limited Liability Co., with sufficient capital to sink a New Shaft and to work the mine on a large scale. We have not of late been spending so much in developing the mine as in ordinary circumstances would be advisable. The greater part of the tin ground is being worked on tribute, the average produce for the past few months being 60lb of Tin per ton of stuff.

Josiah Thomas Wm. Pascoe."

Before Crofty could get to grips with this far-reaching suggestion, another much more urgent problem had to be solved. In May 1895, Wheal Agar's pumps had stopped. The adventurers there had lost about £100,000, and with the price of tin dropping ruinously, they were unwilling or unable to keep their 90" engine going to help the neighbouring mines. East Pool was desperate, for the inflow from Agar could swamp her workings in a very short time. All of the other mines to the east of the Great Cross-course were interdependant for pumping. Carn Brea, Tincroft, Cook's Kitchen, New Cook's Kitchen, South Wheal Crofty and East Pool were all holed through into each other's workings, sometimes extensively, so that when Agar's engine stopped, all of their deeper workings would eventually flood.

East Pool Mine tried to negotiate with Agar, but without success. Eventually, after a short period of inactivity, the great 90" engine pumped again, with the adjacent mines making contributions toward the cost of running it. The Accounts for South Wheal Crofty from that period show that she made a "Contribution towards cost of working Wheal Agar Engine ... £45." (October 24 1895). However, the engine was again shut down by the winter, and this time there was little that could be done to avert disaster. With tin down as low as £36 per ton, and water pouring into Crofty from the flooded East Pool workings, the miners themselves stopped work. At East Pool work continued above the 50 fathom level, but all below was flooded and the water ran into Crofty through the innumerable holes above the 160 level. By December 1895 Palmer's engine had stopped pumping and no official mining took place at Crofty for nearly four years.

The tin price crisis, together with the local pumping crisis caused by Agar's 90" engine stopping, sent adventurers everywhere scurrying to arrange amalgamations. As well as mines like South Francis United and Wheal Basset coming together, most of the mines directly affected by the pumping crisis also sought to amalgamate for greater financial security. Cook's Kitchen, whose shares had become almost worthless, was taken over by Tincroft, which joined with Carn Brea to become "Carn Brea and Tincroft Mines Ltd." East Pool tried to unite with Wheal Agar, and South Wheal Crofty offered herself to East Pool. South Wheal Crofty took over the sett and machinery of New Cook's Kitchen, but found her advances to East Pool thwarted by a lack of willingness to compromise by both parties. Meanwhile, Wheal Agar was being coy about East Pool's proposed marriage, quibbling over the 90" engine 'bride price'.

By the beginning of February 1896, with the last of the miners gone from the now flooded levels, and with the offer to join with East Pool finally rejected, South Wheal Crofty was suspended. New Cook's Kitchen, virtually closed in 1894, now threw in the towel altogether and after a protracted period of negotiation with Crofty, her shareholders eventually accepted £650 plus an exchange of shares for the sett and machinery (It was actually 1899 before the deal was finally accepted and ratified by the adventurers of South Wheal Crofty.).

These negotiations by the mine owners, however, were not the prime concern of the miners themselves whose families were threatened with hunger. Their first concern was to get Agar's engine working again so that those mines that could still afford to operate at the abysmal price of tin then current, could do so. In the late winter of 1896, hundreds of miners from Crofty, East Pool, Tincroft, Carn Brea and Wheal Agar marched to the Fair Meadow at West End, Redruth, and protested at the apparent inactivity of those who they felt should be doing something to get the Agar pump working again. A week later another mass meeting was organised at Camborne and as a result of these two gatherings, a deputation was sent to the principal mineral-lord, Lord Robartes, to ask for his intervention so that the Agar engine might be brought back into action.

Meanwhile, Mr Straus, the Mining Division MP, was making strenuous efforts to effect its resumption. These concerted efforts did bring the engine once again into use, but, as before, only temporarily. When, in May 1896, water began to run through Crofty into North Tincroft, Agar's mineral lord, Mr Robartes intervened. By June both Wheal Agar's engine and East Pool's were hard at work again, lowering the water level throughout the adjacent mines. In the following January, with the help of Tincroft, Carn Brea and East Pool, Palmer's engine was again at work, albeit temporarily, in unwatering the workings of South Wheal Crofty.

As last the Wheal Agar adventurers were willing to negotiate the sale of their engine, and together with a 34" stamps engine, 24" whim, a double cylinder whim (12" and 22") and other equipment, the 90" pumping engine was acquired by East Pool, who negotiated an amalgamation with Agar, to be called "East Pool and Agar United." East Pool paid £4,000 for that one crucial piece of machinery. That particular crisis now seemed over!

With Crofty standing idle, it was time for the adventurers to take stock. After just over 40 years operating as South Wheal Crofty, the mine had made calls of £120,000, and only paid dividents of about £3,300, most of that being paid more than 25 years before. Clearly, if the suggestion to become a limited liability company was to be taken seriously, this situation would have to be remedied.

Under the old cost-book system, the 'in' adventurers, who usually held the majority of the shares, could profit well from the mine, even when it ran at a loss. The mineral-lords, who in Crofty's case held the biggest share, provided that their dues on ore raised, and water used, were more than the 'calls' asked for, could still profit from an apparently losing concern. The suppliers of timber, powder, fuses, candles, machinery etc., whilst only holding a small value in shares, and consequently only paying 'calls' of perhaps a few pounds a year, might easily make much more that that in profit through supplying this or that commodity to Crofty. This could not continue when Crofty became a limited company. There were obvious dangers in the step, in that the new share-holders would come from far and wide, and if the mine was profitless, shares would lose value, holders would sell, and the mine would close. With the local mineral-lords, merchants, ancillary craftsmen, and others all financially bound up and interested in the continued existence of Crofty, a loss, even over a long period, would not encourage them to close, unless it was very serious, as in the case of the situation in 1895. Under the cost-book system, however, all those interested parties were merely awaiting the revival of the tin price, so that they could resume operation. It would never be that simple, nor indeed would there every be that same incentive as a limited company, eventually controlled via the stock-exchange.

After 1896 the price of black-tin gradually began to creep up again, and by 1899 it had reached £69 (£127 per ton for metallic tin). By the summer of 1899 it was decided to resume working the mine immediately that the water was low enough to make it possible.

By September, Crofty had sold £55 10s 2d worth of tin; 7s 6d worth of copper; £5 19s 0d worth of arsenic; £3 2s 6d worth of wolfram and £2 15s 11d worth of sundries. This was raised with the co-operation of Tincroft Mine, from whose workings Crofty reopened operations. The Manager's Report for September 22 1899 was short, and described the first tentative moves before starting full scale working, which would follow the restarting of Palmer's pump.

"In accordance with the resolution of the last Adventurers Meeting, we at once commenced to drive a Cross-cut from Tincroft workings in the Western part of

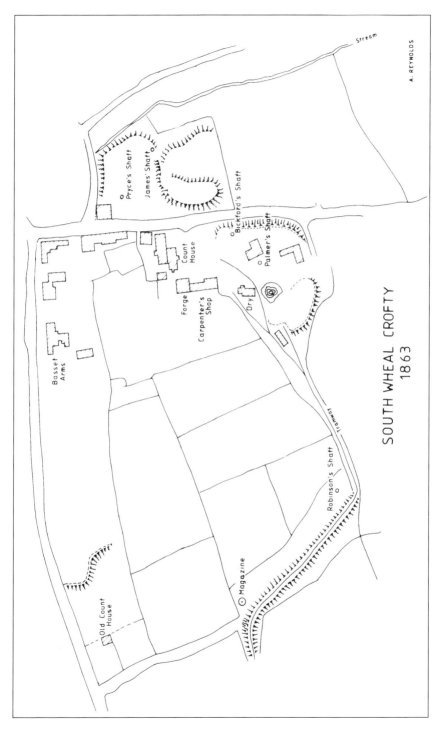

SOUTH WHEAL CROFTY
1863

A. REYNOLDS

the mine at the 140 fathoms level. We calculated that we might probably have about 25 fathoms to drive to intersect the lode in South Crofty, and met with it by driving 23 fathoms. We have since been opening East and West of Cross-cut on the course of the lode. The Eastern end is driven 5 fathoms and the Western end has reached the Cross-course, to the West of which the other lodes to the South have generally been much more productive. We shall continue driving West through the Cross-course and shall soon ascertain the value of the lode on the Western side thereof. Further operations can afterwards be decided on. Josiah Thomas."

The first period of renewed operation gave the mine a loss of £373 8s 2d., and necessitated a call on the 5,452 shares of 2/6 each. (November 17 1899). Carn Brea and Tincroft were paid £12 6s 6d. for "Drawing Tin-stuff" during the reopening of the 140 level workings, which preceded return to full production.

With the mine moving toward full resumption, a meeting of the adventurers was called to decide the future policies of South Wheal Crofty. Mr. Frank Harvey took the chair, and a large group of shareholders gathered into the Account House, Pool, to join the discussion. At this important meeting, which was held on November 17 1899, several far-reaching decisions were made that were to turn Crofty from the hand to mouth cost-book company it had been, into a 'permanent' mine.

For New Cook's Kitchen Mine, which Crofty had long since agreed to purchase, it was agreed to pay £650 so that the adventurers there could "discharge their liabilities" and that New Cook's shareholders should receive one Crofty share for each five they held in New Cook's. The New Cook's Kitchen Mine was to surrender, "if necessary," their lease to the lords of the mine.

With regard to the envisaged new company, it was decided to obtain the "surrenders ... of all existing Leases owned by the present Company and to obtain from the Lord a Lease or Leases of the new Sett on the following terms:-

AREA OF SETT. The land comprised within the following limits, namely, East Pool Mine on the East; Carn Brea and Tincroft Mines on the South; Dolcoath Mine on the West; and the Camborne to Redruth High Road on the North.

Length of Term. 60 years.

DUES. Tin - Black Tin at £50 and below   1/40th
                         £50 to £55   1/30th
                         £55 to £65   1/25th
                         £65 & beyond   1/20th
Copper and other Minerals   1/20th

ONE-HALF DUES. To be paid for the years 1900 to 1904 inclusive.

MINIMUM RENT. £50 per annum to merge in dues."

The South Crofty Mining Company was to try to obtain the new leases with the 'usual covenants', and hoped to pay the same rents for land occupied that they had done hitherto. The meeting agreed unanimously, to:

"Forthwith commence and as vigorously as they think fit to carry out the following operations, namely:

(i) Set the pumping engine to work, after making some necessary repairs to pitwork etc., and drain the Mine to the 245 fm. level, when some tin ground can be stoped from that level up to and above the 205.

(ii) Fix new set of launders and part of tram-road from Engine Shaft to the Steam Stamps. Repair Stamps, put in new Stamp Heads, etc., and (mostly new) dressing plant and calciners.

(iii) Drive the 140 West of Engine Shaft on Pryce's Lode towards the discovery recently made at the 160 North of Willoughbys Shaft in Tincroft close to South Crofty boundary, and rise over the 205 West of Engine Shaft, on the Main Lode where there is a fairly productive tin deposit worked by the Tributers several fathoms above the level. Overhaul and thoroughly repair the Air Compressor for working rock drills at the above and other necessary points.

(iv) Sink Robinson's Shaft (95 fms. West of Engine Shaft) which is already sunk vertically to a depth of 36fms below the Adit, and rise towards it from the deeper levels, so as to get it down as fast as possible for rapid and economical winding. This Shaft is in a good position for exploring both Pryce's and the Main lode to any required depth.

(v) Erect a new Winding Engine and Boilers on Robinson's Shaft, and possibly a new Air Compressor, if it should be found that the present Air Compressor is not of sufficient power to do the necessary development work."

Arrangements were made to protect the rights of the former adventurers of New Cook's and it was further decided to draw up a new set of rules and regulations for the running of the new company. Significantly also, the meeting resolved to obtain the services of "an Agent to devote his whole time to the interests of the Company." Clearly, despite the universal respect accorded Capt. Josiah Thomas, it was not felt satisfactory that he remain in charge of Crofty whilst too ill to run Dolcoath. Also there had been some disquiet over his apparent incompetent management of New Cook's Kitchen Mine.

The final proposal of the meeting was that there should be a call of £1 per share, and 10/- of it should be paid by December 16 1899, and the remainder by April 1 1900. With the total of over £5,000, it was hoped to implement all of the above recommendations.

Capt. Josiah Thomas's Report dated November 17 1899, shows the slow progress being made in actually opening up the mine for proper working. Work in the 140 level from Tincroft continued to open up promising lode, but was then suspended to concentrate on the overall preparation for full resumption. An examination of the Engines and pitwork had been carried out and it was found to be in 'fair condition.' Capt. Thomas thought a new cylinder for the air compressor would be needed, and he reckoned about £50 would cover it. A little work would be required on the pitwork in the Engine Shaft, but "the cost ... will not be great." He considered that there were good prospects in the western parts of the mine.

Early in 1900 Capt. John Penhall was appointed as agent by the adventurers. Although his name usually appeared below that of Josiah Thomas on the Reports, it seems that he was the real manager of South Wheal Crofty and he is thus described in local newspaper articles.

By May 1900 Palmer's Engine was overhauled and working. The Agents Report for May 8 1900 stated that the pitwork, pumping engine, adits, and machinery throughout the Mine were repaired and working effectively. Various other improvements had been made or were in hand, so that everything looked set fair for progress and profitability.

"We shall at once commence to fix the new lift of pumps, which are on the Mine, to fork the water which is at present about five fathoms below the 160 fms. level. The Winding engine has also been throrougly overhauled, and the drum moved further West so as to bring it in direct line with the shaft pulley. This has necessitated having a new wrought iron shaft for the drum, but the money for this is well spent, as we had formerly considerable trouble in winding stuff and lowering and raising men, owing to the wire rope not coiling regularly on the drum. The winding engine and skip road are now in good condition for working, and a new wire rope had been purchased and put on.

The Air Compressor has also been put in good working order, by being generally overhauled and a new steam cylinder fixed. This is now ready to be started, and after fixing the necessary air pipes we shall soon be able to commence driving the 140 West of Engine Shaft on Pryce's lode, on which we understand a fairly productive lode is now being opened up at North Tincroft in the 160 and 170 fm levels further West.

We shall now proceed as rapidly as possible with the forking of the water, so as to get down to the tin ground in the lower workings. When the 205 is reached we shall be able to raise tin immediately above that level, and when the 245 fms. level is reached the mine will be in full working order.

The principal surface work now remaining to be done is to put the steam stamps in order and to re-construct the dressing floor. The stamping engine is in good condition, and it will probably be advisable to erect some Frue Vanners for dressing instead of putting the old buddles in order.

As soon as possible we shall commence sinking Robinsons Shaft, the completion of which will be of great importance for the future of the mine.

Josiah Thomas
John Penhall."

In the August 30 1900 Agent's Report, progress was shown to have been steady but unspectacular. Underground, the Report said:

"The progress made in forking the mine has not been so rapid as we expected owing to the state of the shaft, which in many places was full of old timber and debris. Since the last meeting, however, the water had been drained from a little below the 160 to 6 feet below the 192 fms. level. Every effort will be made to fork the water to the 205 as rapidly as possible, and when that level is reached good tin ground will be available for working. We intend to drive the 192 West of Engine Shaft by rock drill, in order to communicate that level with the workings about the 205 for ventilation, when we shall be able to raise above that point in a productive tin lode."

By December 1900 the water in Engine Shaft was forked to within five fathoms of the 225. Mining was being resumed above the 192 level where good tin ground was opened up. On that level drilling machines were being used to drive on the lode with average results. On the higher levels some work continued Westwards and on the 140 tinstuff was mined averaging between £15 - £18 per fathom.

Thomas and Penhall reported that the 32 heads of stamps were working well as were the six new frue vanners, the new engines and other machinery. A new engine had been erected to drive the calciner and the dressing machinery at the burning house. They proposed that further money should be spent on extending the dressing floors, so that the residue from the vanners, which had the unfortunate characteristic of producing no 'middlings', could be more effectively treated.

On 4 May 1901, Mr Frank Harvey chaired a committee meeting which reported on the developments to date. New Cook's Kitchen Mine had finally been purchased together with their machinery and materials for the previously agreed £650, and the envisaged difficulties with regard to "Forfeited and Relinquished Shares," overcome. Harvey stated that the water was now pumped down to the 235 level, which although a little disappointing, nevertheless considering the debris in the shaft, and the frequent frustrating breakages of the pitwork, was really quite satisfactory. In the mill the 32 heads of stamps were being supplemented by a further 16, and two more frue vanners had been added to the six erected earlier. A new pulveriser had been put up in the burning house yard, and further work done on the calciner and the arsenic flues. Also, "slime pits, dipper wheel and dead frames have been made and are at work."

At Robinson's, a winding engine had been erected in readiness for sinking, and was being used at that time for work in connection with widening the shaft. Although the water was not yet forked to the 245 level, the point at which it had been projected to start general operations, nevertheless, "from various places at and above this level, Tin is being raised in increasing quantities, and when the 245 level is reached there is every reason to hope that at least 18 tons of tin per month will be at once produced."

On the 140 level, the drive on Pryce's Lode was headed for the area above the 160 and 170 levels in North Tincroft, where their neighbours had found this lode rich. Although the lode dipped south into Tincroft sett, there was an enormous amount of whole ground above the point at which the lode entered Tincroft.

The Report ended on a note of optimism, statinq that although the costs had been higher than anticipated, and forking the water had been slower than hoped, the future looked good, and with Robinson's Shaft sunk to the required depth, all would be well.

Statement of Accounts dated May 14 1901, shows the mine moving back to normal working, and by the next accounting, costs and returns were rising steadily. This, presented on August 30 1901, shows the wages bill up from £2,606 to £3,068 in the four month period between April and July, with tutworkers receiving £1,247 as opposed to £1,031 and tributers getting £76 against £32. Each department showed expansion and increase. The returns also improved healthily, with black tin production up from 35 tons 7cwt, to 45 tons 1 cwt., the average price improving from £67 18s 2d., to £70 13s 8d and the cash returns up from £2,402 to £5,184. There was a drop in the production of arsenic during this period.

The August accounts show the increased activity around Robinson's Shaft, with the whim, sinking operations and related plant costing £458 during that four month period. Over £1,200 was spent on adding to the existing stamps and dressing floors where an additional 16 heads were erected, together with another four new frue vanners. A new boiler cost Crofty £212, and was delivered to Robinson's Shaft.

The Agent's Report dated August 20 1901 stated:

"Robinson's Shaft is being cut down below the 12 fathom level. Operations have been delayed here by having to fork 6 fathoms of water which accumulated in the old workings."

The final four month period of 1901 showed wages again increasing as more miners and surface workers were employed. The wage bill was £4,422 and the merchants' bills came to only £2,576, which meant with 82 tons of black tin being sold for £5,476 things were looking up for the mine. The accounts show only £41 worth of arsenic being sold, but with new calcining equipment being installed, this would soon be increased. Elliot's Metal Co. bought nearly 12 tons of copper from Crofty for £35 19s 6d.

At 4 o'clock in the morning on Tuesday October 22 1901, at his summer house in Carbis Bay, Capt. Josiah Thomas died. For over thirty years he had dominated Cornish mining circles as no man before him had ever done. During his heyday he was undisputed 'King of Camborne', and his advice was sought the world over. At his word alone the incipient tin mining fields of North Dakota were abandoned, and no one was thought to know tin as he did. Since February 1895 he had been severely incapacitated by illness, but he had remained nominally manager of both Dolcoath and South Crofty. His son, Capt. R. Arthur Thomas took his place at both of these mines, but at Crofty, Capt. John Penhall continued at the helm. Like his father, Arthur Thomas was manager of Crofty in name only, keeping the position his father had taken at Crofty in 1871, that of 'consulting agent' to the mine.

Capt. Josiah Thomas was born in 1833 at Killivose, Camborne, the son of Charles Thomas who became manager of Dolcoath. At 15 years of age he went underground at Dolcoath to learn mining, and within a quarter of a century was made manager at the death of his father. He became manager of several mines, including Cook's Kitchen, New Cook's Kitchen, West Francis and other smaller concerns. In 1871 he was given the job of 'consulting agent' at South Wheal Crofty, and thereafter was described as 'Manager'. Under his agency many improvements were introduced at Crofty that were years ahead of Dolcoath. One feature of his reign that hardly endeared him to Crofty adventurers, unless they happened also to have been Dolcoath shareholders, was that of filching the best members of Crofty's management team for Dolcoath. in June 1876 he lured Capt. James Johns from Crofty to Dolcoath and Capt. Johns eventually became indispensable there. He rose to the position of chief underground agent at Dolcoath, and his knowledge of the mine was said to be invaluable (Mining

Journal February 23 1895) to such an extent that panic was caused at the time of Josiah Thomas's illness when the rumour went round Camborne that Capt. Johns was to retire due to advancing years. Another agent whom Josiah took from Crofty to Dolcoath was Capt. Joseph Tamblyn. He was described at the time of transfer as "one of the most energetic agents it is possible to find in Cornwall."

The miners of Camborne wanted to erect a statue of Josiah Thomas, but eventually they were satisfied by the building at the front of the old Camborne School of Mines which bears his name. Josiah Thomas may not have escaped criticism for his management of other mines, like New Cook's Kitchen and even Dolcoath herself, but as far as Crofty was concerned there were many benefits from his paternal interest, and under him South Wheal Crofty remained a small, well-run mine, usually with the best equipment that she could afford.

It was in a period of constant development and re-equipping that Capt. R. Arthur Thomas took over responsibility. Throughout October to December 1901 work progressed to open up the North Lode between the 205 and 215 levels, where the values varied between £14 and £25 per fathom. This development was concentrated on the eastern side of Palmer's. To the west, Middle (Main) and Pryce's lodes were being explored, with the latter opened up along the Tincroft boundary on the 140 level. The Agent's Report for that period, dated January 9 1902 concluded thus:

"Robinson's Shaft is cut down and timbered 24 feet below the 24 fathom level.

Owing to a breakage, about 4 weeks ago, in the 60 balance bob, drawing had to be suspended, and the returns of tin were consequently reduced; the water however has again been forked to the 245 fathom level and drawing resumed.

Since the last meeting the 245 pole has been put to work and is working satisfactorily. The No 2 Calciner has been completed and is working well, and we hope to complete the further 12 heads of stamps during the next few weeks.

(signed)
R. Arthur Thomas
John Penhall."

During the early part of 1902 the 225 level was opened again for development, and a 'boring machine' was used to drive on the North Lode westward. Robinson's Shaft was cut down to the 36 level, making sinking imminent. In the mill 2 new frue vanners were in use, and the 12 heads of 'Improved Cornish Stamps' were working well. Difficulty was experienced in maintaining an adequate water supply for stamping and dressing. It was decided to overcome this problem by 'repeating the water', through recirculation. New pulverisers were to be acquired to deal with the 'roughs' which were becoming a problem with the steadily increased volume of tinstuff being stamped.

The Agent's Report dated December 2 1902, concluded with this information:

"Having in view the decision to place on Robinsons Shaft the 80-inch Pumping Engine at Tregurtha Downs Mine, purchased on such a favourable terms, and the fact that it would be futile to continue sinking Robinson's Shaft with such pumping appliances as were employed, this shaft, after having reached the depth of 38 feet under the 36-fathom level, is suspended until the Pumping Engine is erected and the pitwork fixed to properly deal with the water.

A new Pulverizer, to deal with the burnt leavings, together with classifying arrangements and buddles, have been fixed and put to work with highly satisfactory results.

(signed)
R. Arthur Thomas
John Penhall."

The year 1903 was a significant one for South Crofty, because it was then that all of the preparation and cash outlay began to bear fruit. By the end of March the price paid to Crofty for her black tin had risen to £85 2s 6d a ton, and her production for the first four months of 1903 was 120³/₄ tons, for which she was paid £9,728. Crofty made a profit for that period of £2,058 - more in 4 months that in the previous 30 years! Old boilers and engines were sold for £180, and £170 was paid off the £375 owed Tregurtha Downs Mine for the 80" engine.

In the March 23 1903 Agent's Report, it was stated that excavations for the foundations of the new engine-house were begun, and it was expected that the contractor would begin building within the fortnight. Most of the 80" engine was on the site at Robinson's, and was said to be in "good order."

At the mill two new 6-foot vanners were being added to the 14 already at work, and a new 'Acme' concentrating table was being built. A new pulveriser was also installed and working well. The samples from the mill showed an average value of 52 lbs of tin per ton (2.1%).

With the quantity of ore being raised still increasing, it was decided in July 1903 to expand further the dressing capacity of the mill by adding 3 more round frames, and another 'Acme' concentrating table. During the 4 month period ending July 17, 5,223 tons of ore were treated, yielding an average produce of 45 lbs per ton. There was a profit of £188 for that quarter. Crofty sold 105 tons of tin for £8,529.

By July the engine-house that was to accommodate Robinson's 80" engine was completed, and the boilers were in position and being built in. The capstan engine was erected and housed. In the shaft itself, difficulty was being experienced in forking the water, as there was a blockage in the South Roskear Adit. Pumping was suspended at Robinson's until the adit was cleared and repaired.

The November 17 1903 Agent's Report showed Robinson's engine almost ready. With Robinson's Engine nearing completion, the time was fast approaching when Crofty could begin in earnest the sinking of her first vertical shaft. The advantages of this would be enormous.

Engaged in the erection of Robinson's engine was Nicholas Trestrail, an engineer of considerable knowledge and skill. He had designed the 90" engine for Highburrow East Shaft at Carn Brea Mine, that eventually was re-erected at Taylor's Shaft, where it worked until 1954. He was employed by Wheal Jane, Carn Brea, South Francis, Dolcoath and may other mines over a period of thirty years before erecting Robinson's engine. Shortly after erecting Robinson's he designed an 80" engine for Phoenix Mine, and thereafter, just before the First World War, designed Martin's Engine at Goonburrow clay-works. Robinson's was to prove an engine worthy of his expertise.

Designed by Samuel Grose, this beautiful engine was built for Alfred Consols by Sandys, Vivian & Co. (Copperhouse Foundry), in 1854. When new, she cost £2,700, with another £700 being spent on a couple of 12 ton boilers. At Alfred she was known as Daveys Engine, and she was erected and working by June 1855.

Within nine years Alfred was closed and the engine sold to Wheal Abraham where she was called Pelly's Engine. She started pumping there in January 1865, and did a tremendous job unwatering the old workings before other engines also were started. She continued working there until 1875 when the mine closed.

The engine remained idle until 1881, when she was purchased by Tregurtha Downs Mine near to Marazion. Loam's re-erected her at Tregurtha Downs, having to replace the cylinder which had broken whilst working at Crenver & Abraham, with a new one from Harvey & Co. They also supplied a steam capstan and other appurtenances. The engine began work there in March 1883, being renamed St. Aubyn's Engine. According to the West Briton, hundreds had turned out to see the progress of the 38 ton bob, hoping apparently, for the sight of Relubbus Bridge going down under the great weight. No less than 45 horses were used to haul this dead weight from Wheal Abraham through Leedstown, Townshend, Relubbus and Goldsithney.

Harvey & Co. took over the ailing Tregurtha Downs Mine in 1855 for less than £2,000, and during this period of ownership the engine suffered an almost disastrous accident. In January 1889 a fire broke out in the engine-house, and despite the efforts of Marazion and Penzance fire-brigades, the engine-house was gutted and the engine looked finished. The first assessment was wrong however, and after replacing the more vulnerable parts of the engine and repairing the engine-house, the engine was able to re-start. The whole operation took little more than seven days. She pumped then until 1891, when for a short time she was idle, and after re-starting she continued until the spring of 1895. The universal Cornish tin slump closed Tregurtha Downs as it did Crofty, and at the time that the rising price of tin allowed Crofty to re-open, so Tregurtha Downs also re-opened. The engine was re-started in August 1899 but within three years the mine had to close, and this great engine was once again on the market.

Put up for sale in August 1902, she was examined by Crofty's engineers who recommended her purchase. By November 1902 South Wheal Crofty committee had agreed to the price of £375 for the engine, and the deal delighted the adventurers. The main beam was hauled by two traction engines from Marazion to Pool in May 1903, and the rest of the engine was brought by smaller conveyances. As we have seen, Trestrail had completed the erection of the engine by the end of November 1903.

The cost of sinking Robinsons, equipping it with new engine, capstan and whim was running at over £5,000 by the end of 1903.

During the opening months of 1904, North Lode was steadily opened up for stoping on the levels between 180 and 235. The values were better than hitherto. The Middle Lode was explored below the 170 level west of the Engine Shaft (Palmers). Robinsons Shaft was sunk 10 fathoms below the 36 level, which had been its depth for over 60 years. The Report for March 1 1904 says that the water at the 36 level had been drained and a connection affected with the old workings to the North of the Shaft. "Every endeavour will be made to sink this shaft as rapidly as possible to reach the 60-fathom level, when cross cuts should be driven to communicate with the old level to the south of the shaft, and intersect the lodes both north and south of the shaft." The Report also referred to good copper ground found in the shaft, and said: "There are sound ground for expecting that Copper may be found in paying quantities in the upper levels." During those four months the miners had driven, risen and sunk 67 fathoms and raised £5,233 tons of "tinstone", which, after crushing, had yielded an average produce of $39^3/_4$ lbs (1.75%) of black-tin per ton. The average price received by Crofty was £76 9s 4d. per ton. There had been a marked drop in revenue from arsenic during those months.

For the 16 weeks ending in February 6 1904 Crofty sustained a loss of £2,049 18s ld, but if this is placed alongside the cost during that period for Robinson's Shaft sinking of £2,154 7s 9d., we find that Crofty would have made a profit of £104 9s

8d. Up until that time the sinking and development of Robinson's section had cost £7,545 3s 4d.

In the summer of 1904, development on the North and Middle lodes continued well, and on the 140 level, east of Bickford's Shaft, a large area of rich ground was discovered that had considerable quantities of wolfram, tin and arsenical pyrite. By October 3, Robinson' Shaft was sunk 8 fathoms below the 70 level, and the contractors were sinking at the rate of 6 fathoms a month.

For the four month period ending October 1904, $87\frac{1}{2}$ fathoms had been driven, risen or sunk: 4,762 tons of tinstuff had been raised and crushed producing a yield of 39 lbs per ton (1.75%). The mine received an average of £70 18s 7d per ton of black tin sold, £3 18s per ton for the $7\frac{1}{4}$ tons of copper sold, and £149 for 34 tons of arsenic.

Capt. Joseph Richards signed that Report with Capt. Thomas, and he apparently took over the day to day running of Crofty whilst a replacement for Capt. John Penhall was sought. Penhall had accepted the position of manager at Carn Brea and Tincroft Mines in August. Capt. W.T. White had retired as manager there in August due to ill-health, and through the good offices of Frank Harvey, who happened to be chairman of Dolcoath, South Wheal Crofty and Carn Brea and Tincroft Mines, Capt. Penhall was offered the job. It was a loss Crofty could hardly afford, but at that time the larger mine must have appeared to have been a much better prospect for Penhall. Subsequent events proved that even without Penhall's able oversight Crofty prospered, and despite it, Carn Brea and Tincroft didn't! (Mining Journal September 3 1904).

By the beginning of 1905, Capt. James Thomas was in charge at Crofty. The February 23 Agent's Report tells us that Robinson's Shaft was sunk 90 fathoms below adit. On 170 level, a cross-cut was driven from the Middle Lode underneath Robinson's Shaft, so that when appropriate a raise could be put up to meet the shaft. Extremely good tin ground was being discovered in the area below Robinson's. The footage developed and ore raised had dropped during the winter of 1904-5, and the average yield was down to 38 lbs per ton. The price for Crofty's black tin had risen a little to £72 16s 3d, but arsenic production had once again dropped dramatically. Expenditure on Robinson's development was £965 3s 10; Tincroft compensated Crofty for an encroachment, £16 10s 10d, and the mine made a loss over the 16 weeks of £2,289 5s 9d.

On October 24 1905 a horrible accident occurred at the stamps. Joseph Spear, 50, a 'stamps watcher', got entangled in the fly-wheel of the stamps engine and fell into the fly-wheel pit, where he was crushed to death. This was the first of a series of fatal accidents at Crofty, which reflected the trend in Cornish mines from well below the average of fatal accidents in 1902 to more than twice the national average by 1908.

19. *Strike meeting outside the Count House at Station Road, Pool, in 1939. The dispute, frequently violent, was supported by most Crofty men, but not by many Cooks miners. Police were drafted in to cope with the trouble, which lasted until the Second World War broke out.*

20. *King George VI and Queen Elizabeth visiting the mine near to the beginning of the War. The miners were still wearing their 'rags', and there appear to have been few concessions to their royal visitors.*

21. *Trammers on 310 fm level station. The wheel operated the chute at the bottom of the ore pass. Until the mid-1960s the full 16 cwt wagons were hoisted up Robinsons Shaft to the crusher at surface. When this picture was taken, in the 1940s, almost all ore was hand-trammed.*

22. *Trammer pulling a 'Cousin Jack' chute on 310 fm level. This picture was taken in about 1943. He is barring the ore from the chute by levering up the mill boards. It was the usual method of pulling ore until the 1980s.*

Underground development continued apace with the Middle (Main) Lode showing values of up to 56lbs per ton. Most of the work on that lode was above the 205 level, with one underhand stope below the 205 producing 56lbs per ton on average, one back-stope above the level averaging 28lbs and three underhand stopes below the 170 level averaging 45lbs. All but one of these stopes were between Palmer's and Robinson's. On the North Lode there were three underhand stopes below the 205, one below the 215 and one back stope above the 235 level. All five lay to the east of Palmer's and averaged between them 31 lbs black tin to one ton of ore.

The December 30 1905 Agent's Report, concludes:

"Robinson's Shaft is sunk 69 fathoms under the 60-fathom level, and the rise against it had been put up 15 fathoms over the 170-fathom level. There only now remains about 13 fathoms to communicate these two points. (The apparent discrepancy between these figures, is because the 170 level is from Palmer's section, where the adit was 12 fathoms shallower than in Robinson's section.).

At the present bottom of the shaft, and in the south part of it, a lode has been intersected which produces some very rich stones of tin. Whilst on the very limited extent of the lode observable we can form no definite opinion as to which part of the lode this may be, as far as can be seen it would appear to be a continuation of that worked on the 160-fathom level south of the shaft, and containing, as it does, some rich stones of tin, cannot but be considered as a satisfactory indication. It is not thought, however, advisable to delay the sinking of the shaft and to now open out on it.

During the 16 weeks working we have driven, risen and sunk 81 fathoms 0 feet 10 inches, and for the same period 4,818 tons of tinstone have been crushed, yielding an average produce of 42$^{1}/_{4}$lbs of black tin per ton of stuff.

(signed)
R. Arthur Thomas
James Thomas"

The Accounts for the last 4 months of 1905 (presented January 11 1906), show a profit of £386, despite the expenditure at Robinson's during that period of £936. The wages bill came to £5,019 ls 10d, and the merchants' bills to £1,858 17s 2d. Other payments were, "Employers Liability insurance - 6 months premium ... £45." "Doctor's Fees to December 9 1905 £48 9s 6d." "Rents, Rates and Taxes ... £111 10s 10d." The average price Crofty received for tin sold was £80 12s ld and for 91 tons the mine was paid £7,349. Crofty received a further £73 10s for 25 tons of arsenic.

During the first half of 1906 the final preparations were made in converting South Wheal Crofty from an old-fashioned cost-book company into a modern limited liability company. It had taken over a decade from the first suggestion, in October 1895, to convert the mine into a limited company, until its fruition in July 1906.

Dated July 8 1906, the Certificate of Incorporation," reads:

"I herbeby certify that SOUTH CROFTY, LIMITED, is this day incorporated under the Companies Act, 1862 to 1900, and that the Company is Limited. Given under my hand at London this eighteenth day of July One Thousand Nine Hundred and six.

(signed)
H.I. Bartlett
Registrar of Joint Stock Companies."

From its creation in 1854, until its conversion in 1906 into South Crofty Ltd., South Wheal Crofty had produced 5,080 tons of black tin, 36,908 tons of 25% copper, 1,110 tons of pyrite, 3,250 tons of arsenic, and considerable quantities of iron ore, wolfram and other minerals. On the financial side, South Wheal Crofty had paid dividends over its 52 years, of £3,279 10s., all paid between 1868-70, and had 'called up' from its adventurers a total of £148,000.

Chapter Five:
South Crofty Limited

The new limited company began with a capital of £50,000 in £1 shares, 15,000 of which were issued to the adventurers in the old-cost book company as payment. The other 35,000 shares were sold for a total of £60,000, which gave the mine a healthy financial base for development. The last 10,000 of those shares went for £3 each, reflecting the confidence the new company engendered. The Company was formed by Francis Allen, solicitor, of Croydon Surrey; Harry Meyerstein, gentleman, Chevening, Kent; Atwood Berney, accountant, Croydon; L.B. Oldfield, solicitor, London; George C. Deacon, stockbroker, Hertfordshire.

The first act of the Company was to appoint a new manager to reorganise, the now rapidly developing and expanding mine. At a meeting at the Account House, on July 24 1906, the directors appointed Capt. C. Fred Thomas, formerly manager of the Prince of Wales Mine.

His immediate task was to lay out Robinson's section, centred on the rapidly sinking new shaft. Decisions had to be made on the levels at which stations were to be made, the dimensions of these stations, the nature of the connections with Bickford's and Palmers Shafts, the development to be centred on Robinson's Shaft, the exact situation for each ore-pass deemed necessary and arrangements for collecting wagons on the stations prior to hoisting. Preparations had to be made for new pitwork, balance-box stations, and other appurtenances, once Robinson's had reached the 205 level. Capt. Thomas had to organise the modernisation of the entire stamping and milling arrangements, together with proper servicing facilities appropriate to a modern mine. He also had to organise the sinking of another vertical shaft at the western end of the mine, to replace the crooked New Cook's Kitchen Engine Shaft and the tiny East Shaft. The report he gave to the directors at the end of his first years work showed his capacity for organisation.

On August 15 1906 Capt. Fred Thomas placed before the directors a 'preliminary report'. After stating that they had on the mine at the time of the company's incorporation, 7 tons of wolfram and tin, which assayed at 7.92 percent tungstic acid, for which they intended to obtain a magnetic separator, Thomas then made the following proposals:

"Robinson's Shaft. - Cage Winding, Double Deckers, New Winding Engine and Compressor to go to the North of the Shaft. Headgear sufficiently high to permit of stage crushing.

Palmer's Shaft - New Winding Engine.

Underground

Robinson's Shaft. - To start on new pit work below 36 fms. level. Plungers to be fixed at 100 fms. and 170 fms. Balance Box Stations at 60 fms. and 140 fms. Stations to be cut out at 160 fms. and 170 fms.

Palmer's Shaft. - attention to be paid to the 140 fms. level West of Palmer's Lode, and the possibility of effecting a communication with Robinson's Shaft. Water to rise to the 205 fms. level. Attention called to Intermediate South Lode at 140 fms. level near Bickford's Shaft."

The concluding paragraph of the preliminary report read:

"I am convinced that it will be advisable to secure the Palmer's Shaft as an auxillary for hoisting. There is a large tonnage of payable ore in the Eastern section that cannot for a long time be hoisted from Robinson's Shaft."

The First Annual Report and Balance Sheet, dated 30 June 1907, showed how effectively Fred Thomas had carried out the bulk of the modernisation, whilst still keeping production up.

Despite the large amounts of 'dead work' carried out during that year, involving stripping Robinson's Shaft, starting to sink New Cook's Kitchen Vertical Shaft, cutting out stations, regrading old levels and driving new cross-cuts, South Crofty still produced 117 tons 15 cwt of black tin, valued at £13,152, 37$^{1}/_{4}$ tons of wolfram which sold for £5,596 and 160$^{1}/_{4}$ tons of arsenic which brought £4,244. This income of £22,993 gave Crofty a first years profit of £1,014 8s 7d.

In November 1906 Crofty purchased a Climax Vixen rock drill for £213 from R. Stephens & Son. The Vixen was the predecessor of the famous Imperial rock drill, which was introduced two months later.

After giving the production figures, the Report continued:

"During most of this time only 32 heads of Cornish Stamps have been running. An agreement has been entered into with the Urban Electric Supply Co., Ltd., for the supply of energy for driving the new battery, rock brakers, magnetic separators etc, and this should prove an economical supply of power.

The footage for the year amounts to 2,686 feet and has produced such satisfactory results that the underground developments are now far ahead of the 40 stamp Californian Mill. The remaining 32 heads of Cornish Stamps are being taken out in order to make room for an additional 20 heads of Californian Stamps.

Owing to the large quantities of Wolfram occurring in the lodes, a second separator of double the capacity of the first one had been ordered and is now being erected. A large new Calciner has been completed, and this will be followed by the erection of two more to meet the Companies large arsenic output.

The ore proves highly complex, but considerable wolfram sales have already been made at an average price of £150 5s 6d. per ton, and further experiments are leading to a still better separation of the wolfram. The tin sold averaged £111 13s ld. per ton. A new vertical shaft has been commenced at New Cook's Kitchen, and has already, in sinking, passed through very favourably mineralised ground. The developments in the eastern section of the mine, despite the large amount of mineral recovered from that section in bygone years, have proved particularly promising, and large bodies of ore may be hoisted. Bickford's Shaft is being re-timbered with a view of bringing it once more into use.

The timbering and completing of the pit work and cage road in Robinson's Shaft and the regrading of many of the levels has been a long and expensive piece of work, but it is now satisfactorily completed, except that Robinson's Shaft remains to be carried down and equipped to the 205 level.

The Directors consider it a matter of satisfaction that they have been able to cover all the working expenses of the Company during the period of reorganisation.

It is proposed to apply the balance of profit, £1,014 8s 7d., by writing off the items. legal charges and formation expenses, amounting to £544 14s 3d., the balance being applied in redemption of Development Account.

The Hon. John Boscawen was elected a Director of the Company to fill a casual vacancy.

Mr Francis Allen and the Hon. John Boscawen retires from the Board in accordance with the Articles of Association, and offer themselves for re-election as Directors.

Messrs. A. Dangerfield & Co., Chartered Accountants, offer themselves for re-election as Auditors for the ensuing year.

At the close of the General Meeting, an Extraordinary General Meeting will be held to make a small alteration in the Articles of Association.

By Order of the Board.
(signed) Francis Allen
Harry Meyerstein Directors
T. Wallace Evans. Secretary."

Thus, was the first directors' report given to the shareholders at the end of the first year's work. The principal directors, including Allen and Meyerstein, together with the secretary, T. Wallace Evans, were involved in a speculative company called 'Cornish Consolidated Tin Mining Ltd'. This company also had interests in Botallack, Wheal Sisters, Phoenix (Caradon) and Clitters Mine. South Crofty was just one of their ventures, but it was, as it turned out, the only successful one. In connection with this larger venture, the company created 'Tuckingmill Laboratory,' which was run by an assayer called H.W. Hutchins. His son Frank eventually took over the job, and was still employed by South Crofty as an assayer for 2 or 3 days a week in 1980. Wallace Evans was secretary for over 45 years.

On November 20 1906, a tragic accident occurred at the Mine. Whilst descending Robinson's Shaft in a kibble, three shaftsmen stopped briefly at the 60 fathom level for a fresh supply of candles. Upon continuing their descent they noticed that the cross-head of the kibble had remained suspended. Suddenly it dropped on to the kibble from a height of between 6 and 7 fathoms, and this resulted in one of the men being knocked from the kibble to his death. Thomas Philp, who was 40 years old, was picked up at the 100 level. The inquest could not determine whether Philp had panicked and jumped from the side of the kibble, or, as it seemed more likely was knocked by the cross-head into the shaft.

During the early months of 1907 two more fatal accidents happened at Crofty. Both were to men working on the modernisation of the mine, and both happened where the previous accidents had. On March 12 1907, Ernest Clemens, a 22 year old miner, was crushed to death in Robinson's Shaft. He was cutting a place for a cistern at the 100 level, when it appears, he tried to jump on to the passing cage to travel to the surface. He was crushed between the cage and the shaft timbering. The Mine Inspector's Report says that, "It would appear to have been an insane idea." The other accident was at the stamps. On May 21 1907, whilst engaged in laying rails and helping to fix fencing for the new tram-way, Fred Adams, a 35 year old carpenter fell from the gantry that led from the stamps, and was killed. It was the third fatal accident at Crofty in six months.

In January 1907, Crofty acquired its first Climax 'Imperial' rock drill, made by R. Stephens & Son, of Dudnance, and paid £39 15s 7d. for it. The 'Imperial' was a 230lb bar-and-arm machine, which had the drill steel and piston-rod reciprocating together, and turned through rifle bar rotation. To suppress dust, water was sprayed on to the mouth of the hole being bored, after being sucked into the side of the machine from a bucket. It was a highly successful drill which was manufactured until 1914, and was the basic drill used for driving at Crofty until the end of the Great War. Its bore could be adapted to either 3" $3^1/_4$" or $3^1/_2$". Many of the barrels drilled by those old 'Imperials' can still be seen on the sides of the levels they drove. Although Stephens made lighter stoping models of the

'Imperial' they were not used at Crofty. The heavy 'Imperial' drifters survived at Crofty until the 1930s.

During 1907 explosives were purchased from Ammonal Explosives Ltd., National Explosives Co. Ltd., Nobel's Explosive Co., Ltd., and gunpowder from East Cornwall & Kennall Gunpowder Co.

Under a covenant with the Basset family, the Company had undertaken the sinking of the new vertical shaft at New Cook's Kitchen. By July 1907 the shaft had been sunk 110 feet. In charge of the sinking was C.Fred Thomas's brother, Jack Thomas, who was able to report not only good progress in the sinking, but also that the shaft had passed through valuable mineral ground at a very shallow level. The covenant stated that the shaft must be sunk within 5 years and by the end of 1907 it was down 212 feet. The tiny $3^{1}/_{2}$ feet diameter East Shaft was still in use.

The accounts for the second half of 1907 show that production remained high. Revenue from tin was £11,349, from Wolfram £2,002 and from arsenic £3,766, which gave a profit for the six months of £195 17s 3d. For a time during 1907 with costs at £1 per ton for ore crushed, a profit of 10s. per ton was maintained. Shaft sinking and other essential costly development work was to continue to swallow up large amounts of profit for some time, however. In December 1907, Fred Thomas was given a bonus of £100, which was two and half months salary; the shareholders were apparently pleased with the way he was handling things.

1908 was another year of expansion and modernisation. Robinson's Shaft was completed to the 205 level, Palmers ancient pump was stopped and sold for scrap, New Cook's Kitchen Vertical Shaft was secured and timbered, and at the mill the new Californian stamps were increased to 60 heads. Bickford's Shaft was ready for its new skip road to the 170 level; in Robinson's section the water was allowed to rise to the 205, in Palmer's to the 225 and the deeper levels were permitted to flood. It was intended to concentrate their efforts on the levels above the 225.

On February 4 1908 there was another death at the mine, and once again it was in Robinson's Shaft. John Nankervis was a 21 year old trammer, employed on the 175 level, in Robinson's Section. His fellow trammer had climbed into the top half of the double-decker cage by means of a loaded wagon. Nankervis endeavoured to follow him, and in doing so, put his foot on the 'knocking-line' lever, which was used for signalling the surface. The 'one bell' signal indicated that the whim-man should hoist the cage, and when Nankervis pressed down with his foot, the cage was immediately hoisted, with fatal results. The trammer did not have time to get into the cage, and was crushed against the timbering at the top of the station, before falling into the sump. The inquest decided that, "the manager's instructions were not definite with regard to men riding, and supervision in the matter was unsatisfactory." (Mine Inspector's Report 1908).

C. Fred Thomas, the Manager, was having difficulties with the Board of Directors by the spring of 1908, and, despite his obvious ability in laying out the modernisation of the mine, and, so far as the foregoing facts indicate, in superintending the work, the Board was not happy with him. It has been said of him, that he was better at theoretical planning than he was at the actual practical 'delivering of the goods'. The charge seems, in the light if the work carried out both on the surface and underground during his period as Manager, to have been quite unjust. Not only did he plan an enormous undertaking, but the mine maintained production, remained profitable, and laid open new ground for stoping on a scale not thought of before.

Things came to a head in July 1908, when it is said, the letters carrying his resignation and his dismissal passed in the post. He was replaced by his own brother-in-law, Josiah Paull, and it caused a family split that lasted for a generation.

Capt. Josiah Paull was 38 years old when he became Manager, and he had used his time to gain wide experience of mining. He had worked in mines in Africa, Canada and elsewhere in Cornwall, and he proved more than able to complete the work started by his brother-in-law. He was a widely respected man, and at Crofty he was always referred to as 'Cap'n Paull.' Men who remember him relate that he would spend the mornings underground, and then before changing, would visit every working place on the surface. He would walk through the 'Old Mill' adjusting the tables, and advising youngsters on the need to watch carefully for the variation in the 'tin line' on the tables. He was kind, generous, respected, and viewed with genuine affection by the miners. He was first and foremost a practical miner from a hard school, who knew and understood the miners, their problems and the conditions and difficulties of their work. He took over a successful mine, and he was to make it even more so.

By the time of his arrival there were 7 'boring machines' on the mine, and with the 14 men operating them, there were nearly 40 men on development, not counting those engaged in shaft sinking. The stopes at that time were entirely worked with hand labour, and on average each of the dozen or so stopes had 9 men working them. They usually worked with 3 men on each bench or step, one turning the drill, and the other two beating it with 5 or 7 lb hammers. There were exceptions however, as some of the tributors worked in groups of 2,3 or 4. There were over 200 miners underground, 250 on the surface and about three dozen working in the shafts. Some of these were widening Cook's East Shaft, the little 3½ foot wide shaft, which during 1908 was widened down to 370 feet from surface. This section was providing one third of all of Crofty's tinstuff by the end of 1908.

During 1908 there were 41,628 tons of ore crushed, which produced on average 23.80 lbs of black tin and 5.18 lbs of wolfram per ton. Crofty sold 442 tons of tin for £34,162, 96 tons of wolfram for £8,676 and 396 tons of arsenic for £3,287. The stamping and milling costs per ton were £1 0s 10½d. For the year 1908 the mine had a profit of £287 18s 4d.

In February 1909, one of Crofty's Climax Imperial hammer drill stopers, column mounted, drilled 34 holes in granite, averaging 37 inches deep in 7 hours. Despite the success of this 75lb stoper, the mine continued to use hand-labour in stopes, but used this machine for development, especially raising.

All of the preparation and expense of the previous few years began to reap results by 1909. In Cook's section work had been halted on the new vertical shaft and effort was concentrated on exploiting the rich finds in the higher levels from East Shaft. Good finds of both tin and wolfram in this section boosted Crofty's production, and it had the bonus of being close to the surface and near to the mill.

In Crofty section, the value of the mine was increased by the discovery on the 160 level, of a large body of tin ore, that not only was rich, but also 30 feet wide! It was decided to sink Robinson's Shaft below the 205 level to the 225, and then to the 245 level. The water in Palmer's was up to to the 225, and was to be lowered as Robinson's Shaft went down. Bickford's skip road was down to the 180 level by the end of 1909, and Robinson's was 11 fathoms below the 205 level. The Old East Shaft was sunk 40 feet below the number 6 level in Cook's section.

In November 1909, another fatality was reported at Crofty. In the June, a labourer called William Hocking was working in the 'old mill' when he struck his head on a launder. The launder was only four-and-a-half feet high, and it was necessary to duck low to go under it. Hocking, who was 47 years of age, hit his head quite hard on the wooden gutter, and as a result went off sick. He died on the 8 November 1909 as a direct result of the accident.

In 1909, 59,327 tons of tinstuff were crushed for the production of 696 tons of black tin which sold for £52,481. Crofty produced 142 tons of wolfram which brought £12,462, and 666 tons of arsenic, which was sold for £6,949, all of which resulted in a profit of £10,791. The Board of Directors, the Shareholders and Josiah Paull were all very happy!

Things continued to improve in 1910, with Robinson's Shaft sunk to the 225 level half way through the year, and down to 238 fathoms below adit by December. Development opened up good ground between the 130 and 205 levels at Robinson's, the 140 and 225 levels at Palmer's, the 130 and 180 levels at Bickford's, the 120 foot level at New Cook's section and down to the 80 fathom level in the older workings. On the surface full production was achieved with the 60 heads of Californian Stamps workings for 353¹/₂ days in 1910. Three-phase electricity supply was connected to the stamps, making them both more efficient and also more reliable. At New Cook's section, the arrival of a new 5-drill compressor boosted the air pressure for the machines driving the ends.

All of this resulted in profits of £12,831. There were 60,916 tons or ore crushed in 1910, which produced 630 tons of black tin, 126³/₄ tons of wolfram and 736 tons of arsenic. Revenue from these minerals amounted to £56,561 for the tin, £13,569 for the wolfram, and £7,644 for the arsenic.

1911 was another very successful year for Crofty, with profits reaching £31,981. With most of the 'dead work' costs completed, the mine was able to benefit from the enormous preparation of ground made during the previous years. The tin price rose, the output of arsenic went up dramatically, costs were kept down, and the shareholders were happy. Tin produced was 677³/₄ tons, which sold for £76,587; wolfram came to 148³/₄ tons and sold for £14,717; arsenic amounted to 1008 tons, which went for £9,517. Robinson's Shaft was sunk to below the 260 level, and development was carried on between the 130-245 levels at Crofty Section, and between the 20-110 at New Cook's section. Capt Paull pressed to be allowed to restart the sinking of Cook's vertical shaft, halted since 1907. The Board of Directors agreed. He began preparations to sink by having erected a new 70' high head gear. At the stamps it was decided to increase the number to 80 heads, but nothing was to come of the decision.

The assayer's report for 1911 showed an average yield per ton of 23.76 lb of black tin, 5.22 lb of wolfram and 35.36 lb of arsenic. The total tonnage crushed and treated was 63,882 tons.

During 1911 a boy called Martin Crothers started work at Crofty, and even in his upper '80s he was still able to recall the four years he spent working at the mine. He first began work at Carn Brea Mine when he was 14 years old. When that mine closed he went to Crofty, and waiting at the top of Robinson's Shaft for the day-shift to come up, he then approached any likely looking miner and asked, "Any chance of a job?" There were three 'tutworkers' who came out of the cage together, and one of these, Jack Mitchell, stopped and asked Martin whether he had worked underground before. Martin replied that he had worked 'Beating the borer' for 18 months at Carn Brea Mine. Mitchell agreed to take him on in this capacity, and Martin was delighted. He left home in Illogan Church Town early enough to walk to Crofty where the morning shift went underground from 7 o'clock onwards. His father, who worked at Dolcoath, went down an hour earlier. Martin said that there were only about two bikes in the whole of Illogan at that time, and most men either went by donkey and shay, or walked as Martin did. Large numbers of men converged on East Pool, Carn Brea, Tincroft and Crofty during that period, and some of the larger mines, like the temporarily closed Carn Brea, had stabling areas and small paddocks for the animals which numbered several hundred. Martin, in common with most other miners, wore hob-nailed boots, a hardened felt hat, rarely worn while actually working, and a coarse vest called a 'worker', which was carried underground and put on in the working place. The stopes where Martin was employed, beating the drill with a 5lb hammer, were always cool. He worked at first, in a stope above the 170 level, just east of Robinson's Shaft. At that time, apparently, the 160 station was not used, and men working there had to climb up from the 170 level. There were about 12 men in the stope above the 170, and they were engaged in underhand stoping. Jack Mitchell, Bill Eddy, and Henry Truan were the 'tutworkers', and the others were called the 'boys', regardless of age. Before they began, Martin said, they had a "bite, a smoke, and a drink," then carrying their newly sharpened drills they went into the stope to begin the shift. The 'pare' was split into groups of three, with one man holding and turning the drill, and throwing water into the hole with "a penny mustard tin" to damp it down, and the other two beating the drill with 5lb hammers. The three men would aim to drill two holes between 3 and 4 feet during the shift, at the end of which these would be blasted. Martin said that it was common knowledge that Crofty ground was much harder than that in any of the other local mines, and it was certainly harder than the granite he had drilled at Carn Brea. When the holes were deep enough they would be cleaned out with a 'swab stick' and water from the mustard tin. If, as was usual, they were to use dynamite, they would tamp it with a wooden stick, as now, but if it was a 'tutworker' who happened to prefer black powder, then they would use a copper tipped tamping rod. Some of the older miners still used black powder because, they claimed it "broke a wider area." When all of the holes in the stope were charged, the tools and gear would be removed, and the 3 long, 3' minute burner fuses would be lit, the miners shouted "Fire!" and the men scrambled down the benches and out of the stope to safety.

"We had to 'crimp' the detonators onto the fuse ourselves, either with a crimper, or, as some did, by using their teeth. We always did this just before charging up."

"A year or two later, we went to a new stope on 225 level. This was an underhand stope and Bill Eddy was in charge. There were 9 of us in that stope. The stope was open at the top, and we couldn't get anywhere near the back, so we went up to the 205 and removed a wooden door that covered a hole into the top of the stope. We dropped a chain ladder down but no one would go down, so after a bit, I said, "I'll go, if you tie a rope round me." They hung a pinch bar on a length o'rope, and then lowered it to me, and I barred all shift. I barred tons of the stuff down, more than we'ld do in quite a few days work. When measuring day came, Bill Eddy said to the surveyor, Victor Paull, the son of C.H. Paull, "Well Victor, we barred down tons extra an' it'll affect our contract!" Victor said, "You're right boy! I'll put some on the next fortnight or it'll alter your rate." And he did! Good man he was."

Martin remembers what he did and where he worked, but could not be too certain about the rest of the mine. "Bickford's and Palmer's shafts were used, but I always travelled down Rob's where we had a double-decker cage. One half of the cage was very low, an' we had to bend double to get into it. It was the tutmen who paid me. At Carn Brea when I was 14 I got 15s a fortnight, but at Crofty I was paid a man's rate, and got two gold sovereigns a fortnight worth two pounds then, which was a lot more than a man on the surface would get. The tutworker had to pay for his drills to be sharpened out of his contract, and also he paid for his mens candles, for his powder or dynamite, and for his picks to be sharpened too. The drills were taken back to the shaft at the end of a shift - each drill was marked - and picked up from there the next morning. The tutmen were paid so much to break and tram the dirt to the shaft. The wagons were half tonners!" Martin said that despite the cage being bigger on the top deck, they still got six men on each deck. He said that miners reckoned at that time that Crofty was a good mine to work at and that it was considered a safe mine, with fewer accidents underground than others. He knew of no bad accidents in his work area. He said that a normal 'pare' of men in a stope was anything from 9 up to 18, with most being nearer the lower number, and a few, mostly 'tributers', with less. The shift was 7 till 3 o'clock, and croust was 10.30 to 11 o'clock.

He remembered a man called Bennie Vial, who was, he thought, the timber boss at Crofty at that time, but later the mine captain. Benjamin Vial started at Crofty in June 1907, when he was 42 years old. He eventually became 'underground manager' and was a bit of a character. Jack Mitchell who lived at Broad Lane, and started work at Crofty when he was 32, in 1909, and Henry Truan, worked in a wide stope above the 170 level on the Middle Lode (Main Lode) east of Robinson's Shaft during the period that Martin worked for them. Crofty's records verify the location and personnel of Martin's account, together with many other details he remembered.

After the Great War, which he spent in the Navy (1915-19), he returned to Crofty for a short spell, and then, in common with many miners at that time, went to America. During the 12 years he spent there, he worked for 2 years at a copper mine in Michigan, 7 years at a zinc mine in New Jersey and a year at a coal mine in Pennsylvania. During the last war he worked at East Pool, and after it had closed down, he went for a while to Geevor.

During 1912 production was maintained at the same high level. 66,076 tons were crushed in that year, producing 627³/₄ tons of black tin, 130¹/₂ tons of wolfram, and 986³/₄ tons of arsenic. This was sold for £82,481, £11,147 and £9,886 respectively. The tin averaged 21.28 lb per ton, the wolfram 4.42 lb per ton and the arsenic 33.46 lb per ton. Costs at the mill and stamps were £1 2s 6d per ton. Crofty made a profit during 1912 of £25,201, which, considering the fact that both New Cook's Kitchen Vertical Shaft, and Robinson's Shaft were being sunk, was extremely good. New Cook's was down to 417 feet from the surface, and Robinson's was sunk 78 feet below the previous year's depth of 265 fathoms below adit. Development was carried out in Robinson's section on the 260 level and upward to the 140, on the 160-245 at Palmer's, between 150-180 at Bickford's and between the 17 and 100 levels at Cook's. In Robinson's section on the 245 level west of the shaft, on what was called the 'New Lode', very high values were found that averaged 70 lb per ton. On the 260 level Robinson's and Palmer's sections were joined during 1912.

In 1912 a Royal Commission investigated the high incidence of 'hook worm' among Cornish Miners. Although South Crofty had the best record locally, with only 11 percent of its miners affected, against Dolcoath's 69 percent, Basset's 51 percent, East Pool's 47 percent, and Tincroft's 25 percent, nevertheless, Crofty found it necessary to introduce new rules to improve the standard of hygiene. Toilet buckets were provided and it became a serious offence to foul the workings. Many believed, and indeed still do, that the disease spread so rapidly at that time due to the large numbers of miners returning from Africa, where the disease was general in the mines.

The 'Sample Books' for 1913 give many details that are of interest to us. Most of the stopes were 'back' stopes at that time, with exceptions being, as now, some of the narrow ones. The names of the tutworkers are the same as those that appear in the records 20,50 and 80 years earlier, and indeed, that appeared on the working place 'boards' in the 1980s. The names Roberts, Thomas, Opie, Penrose, Williams, Davies, Matthews, Saunders, Mitchell, Hocking, Hosking, Richards, Rowe, Rule and Gilbert are all repeated throughout Crofty's history, and members of those families are still employed here. The stope that Martin Crothers worked in as a lad, with Jack Mitchell and Henry Truan, is described as being above the 170, east of Robinson's Shaft, on the Middle Lode (Main Lode). It is shown as a very wide stope, with Truan working the north part, and Mitchell the south part. It is exactly where Martin rememberered it. The same group of tutworkers worked the stope between 1911-1918.

During 1913 the 290 level was reached at Robinson's Shaft and the level was opened northwards. By the end of that year the shaft was 25 feet below the level, and altogether it had been sunk 108 feet in 12 months. New Cook's Vertical Shaft was sunk a further 278 feet in 1913, and the little East Shaft was down another 54 feet. On the 205 level a drive west from Robinson's section had covered 1,160 feet, and needed only 380 feet of crosscut south to arrive at a point directly under New Cook's Vertical Shaft. Miners working from New Cook's old Engine Shaft had discovered Pryce's Lode on the 148 level 50 feet north of the line of the new vertical shaft. This discovery was to prove valuable.

In 1913 the firm that supplied Crofty with its rock drills, R Stephens & Son, changed its name to the trade name used by it for a decade, becoming 'Climax

Rock Drill & Engineering Co., Ltd.' Thereafter, Crofty spent an increasing amount annually on their rock drills. In 1913 £509 was being spent with them, but by 1916 the annual total had doubled to £1,042. In 1913 the 'water liner' was developed, whereby the water was carried through the machine and up the hollow centre of the drill steel. Unfortunately, dry drilling continued at Crofty as elsewhere, due to the simple fact that there was no water available in many working places, especially raises.

The machine developed at that time, and sold to Crofty and other mines from the following year, was the Climax 'Britannia,' which became as famous as the 'Imperial', which it gradually replaced. The 'Britannia' B1 and B2 models were made between 1914-28. They were small, simple and light machines, with a ratchet and rifle bar type rotation. The weight of the machine without bar-and-arm and cradle attachments, was only about 20lb. Although it was basically a 'hammerjack' machine, it could be modified to drive, raise or stope. It was a fine machine in its day, and was remembered by many of the older miners still at Crofty in the late 1970s

Production rose in 1913 to 69,366 tons of tinstuff crushed. There were 633 tons of black tin, which sold for £78,441, 117 tons of wolfram, which sold for £11,008 and 744 tons of arsenic, which returned £10,634; all of this brought in a profit for the year of £18,886. The average yield was 20.45 lb of black tin to the ton, 3.78 lb of wolfram, 24.03 lb of arsenic, and the costs per ton at the stamps and mill were £1 2s 3d. Crofty received an average of £125 per ton for her black tin.

The fateful year of 1914 dawned bright for Crofty, but the high production figures brought no great profits and it was a year that ended as dismally for the mine as for the rest of society. The ore crushed that year was 69,842 tons, the highest so far, but at the end of the year with the tin price down to an average of £91 12s 1d., the profits were only £2,653, this notwithstanding the fact that crushing and dressing costs were down to only £1 0s 8d per ton. Crofty sold 644 tons of tin, 113 tons of wolfram, and 706 tons of arsenic, for £58,567, £9,390, and £10,599 respectively. The average yield per ton of ore crushed was 20.66 lb of black tin, 3.63 lb of wolfram, and 22.67 lb of arsenic. There was also a small production of copper that year, and with other sundry minerals it fetched £1,097.

In 1914 the 310 level was reached at Robinson's and the 190 at New Cook's vertical shaft. A drive on the 205 from Robinson's section westward was extended a further 211 feet in 1914, making a total of 1,355 feet into Cook's section. A crossscut south from this drive was under the vertical shaft, only 40 feet above. East of Robinson's, on the 290 level, a crosscut was driven under Palmer's Shaft, which was down to 273 fathoms below adit. At the deeper levels Pryce's, Middle and North lodes were all developed, but on 310 the Agents reported that Middle Lode had not been found yet. As the lode was met at the northern edge of the 310 fathoms station, it must have meant that no north crosscut had yet been driven.

By the end of 1914 Crofty had begun to lose men to the Forces, and, in common with other local mines, the loss of experienced men meant lower production.

In 1915 the quantity of tinstuff raised, the price of tin, and the profits all rose. There were 70,790 tons crushed, which produced 627$\frac{1}{4}$ tons of black tin, 97$\frac{1}{2}$ tons of wolfram and 660 tons of arsenic. The total returns were £82,860, which included £311 for copper ore sold. The average price Crofty received for her black tin was £94 2s 4d; the average yield per ton crushed, was 20.10 lb of tin, 3.09 lb of wolfram and 20.88 lb of arsenic. Costs per ton crushed were £1 0s 11$\frac{1}{2}$d. The mine made a profit in 1915 of £5,672.

During 1915 New Cook's Kitchen Vertical Shaft was sunk a further 198 feet to 112 feet below the 205 station. Robinson's Shaft was sunk to the sump below the 310 station, and was to remain at that depth for over 20 years. With the 205 connected between Cook's and Crofty sections the improvement to ventilation was very marked. All of the western workings were considerably cooler, and raises throughout the intervening ground proved most beneficial. Robinson's became the down-draught shaft, and New Cook's Vertical Shaft, the up-draught shaft. This was to remain so until 1976. In New Cook's section Pryces's Lode was intersected about 80 feet from the new shaft, and was very rich. In Crofty section, the old workings around Palmer's Shaft were being connected to those that emanated from Robinson's.

Late in 1915 one of the most important finds in the history of Cornish Mining was made on Crofty's door-step. In East Pool, the enormously valuable Roger's Lode was discovered. Such was the amazing richness of Rogers' Lode, that South Crofty immediately made plans to acquire the sett of the closed North Wheal Crofty Mine, that lay along the supposed strike of this great lode. Plans were also made to drive north on the 180 and 225 levels to intersect Rogers'.

With the Great War sucking so many miners into the Forces, all of the local mines were feeling the pinch. Despite the fact that Crofty men were exempt from war service due to the munitions industry's need for wolfram, which this mine and East Pool provided, Crofty still lost more and more ill-afforded men. The annual report moaned, "Labour is very scarce".

From a financial standpoint Crofty did somewhat better in 1916. She crushed 70,706 tons of ore, for the production of 607 tons of tin, 95 tons of wolfram and 783 tons of arsenic. The price of black tin rose £10 to £104 8s 1d, and returned £63,708. The price of wolfram went up sharply, so that with 2$\frac{1}{2}$ tons less than the previous year, Crofty received £4,686 more, with a total of £14,772. Arsenic also increased in value, so that the 783 tons sold for £24,391. Costs per ton crushed went up to £1 1s 11¹/₂d, and the yield dropped to 18.97 lb per ton of black tin and 2.95 lb of wolfram. The yield per ton of arsenic rose to 24.46 lb. South Crofty's profits trebled to £16,703.

During 1916 the 205 and 225 levels were opened up in New Cook's section. Pryce's, Intermediate, South and Middle lodes were all explored, and, although the values were disappointing, and where they were good, they tended to be bunchy, because they were close to Cook's New Shaft it was economical to work them. In Crofty section the great drive was on to locate Rogers' Lode inside Crofty's expanded sett. East Pool had discovered the lode on the 240 level, and it was not only rich, but as it was opened up it was found to be very wide also. As each story came out of East Pool, Crofty's shareholders licked their lips with renewed anticipation. On the 180 and 225 levels, double tram-roads were put in, in preparation for large tonnages being trammed. These wide, expensive cross-cuts went forward toward the estimated points of intersection. By the end of 1916 the 180 cross-cut had only 16 fathoms to go, and the 225 cross-cut 30 fathoms. During that year mention is made of the use at Crofty of a 'diamond drill' for exploratory work.

In 1917 the price paid to Crofty for her black tin went up to an average of £120 13s 7d. Black tin sold returned £84,438 for 610 tons; wolfram was £14,724 for 87³/₄ tons; arsenic was £40,388 for 828 tons. The total returns were £139,550, which was a rise over the previous year of £37,000. The yield per ton crushed was 19.51 lb of black tin, 2.81 lb of wolfram, and 26.48 lb of arsenic, and the costs per ton were £1 5s 7d. Arsenic and wolfram together realised a total of 18s 9d a ton, against 21s a ton for tin.

So far as the search for Rogers' Lode was concerned, Crofty drew a blank! The great lode petered out before it entered Crofty's sett, and the wide double tram-roads on the 180 and 225 levels were wasted. By 1917 the labour shortage was acute. Experienced miners were hard to find, and all of the neighbouring mines were after them also.

1918 saw the price of tin go through the roof, with the average price paid to Crofty being £196 16s 8d. per ton of black tin. The 67,588 tons crushed produced 581 tons of black tin, which sold for £113,042. Wolfram totalled 71³/₄ tons which returned £12,521, and arsenic was 562 tons, which brought in £69,300. The yields per ton crushed were 19.26 lb of tin, 2.38 lb of wolfram and 18.63 lb of arsenic, with the costs per ton of £1 14s 10¹/₂d. The profit for 1918 was £67,554. When the Great War ended in 1918 the mine employed 464 men, with 249 underground and 215 on the surface.

The search had continued during 1918 for any sign of Rogers' Lode but there was none! Work continued throughout the length of the mine to exploit the lodes

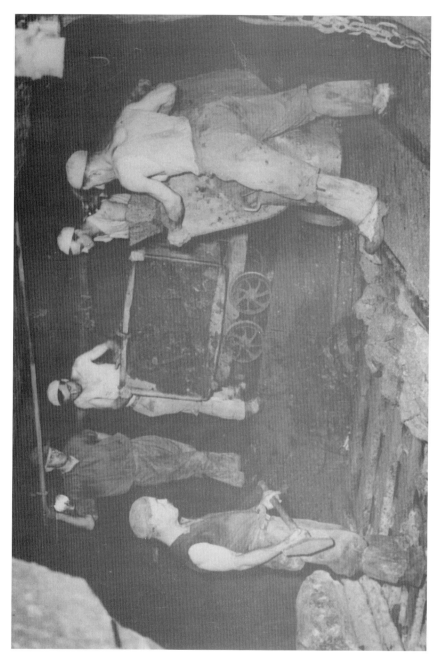

23. *Trammers tipping 16 cwt wagons into 290 fm level grizzly in about 1943. Tom Lawrence is breaking the rocks and the man holding the carbide lamp was the shiftboss, George Lampshire. A 14 lb sledge hammer remains the most efficient tool available for the job.*

24. Group of miners in the cage at Robinsons Shaft, awaiting to descend. Robinsons Shaft was equipped with cages from early in the century, whereas New Cooks Kitchen Shaft used skips for man travelling until the War.

25. *Diesel loco hauling one ton wagons to the mill in about the year 1960. The 16 cwt underground wagons were hoisted up Robinsons Shaft, tipped into the crusher hopper, and then the ore was taken to the mill for crushing and dressing.*

26. *Bridge over gunnis at 240 fm level East Pool. This bridge was built in 1978 to replace an earlier one erected there by East Pool Mine 80 years before. The photograph was taken from 260 fm level, South Crofty.*

opened up by the development of the previous few years. Crofty was still uncomfortably short of skilled men, and development could not be properly maintained. The 'diamond drill' bored 2,700 feet that year, compensating slightly for the lack of skilled developers. In the mill 13 new James' Concentrating Tables were installed to replace the older type. Castle-an-Dinas Wolfram Mine, on Goss Moor, was brought in 1918, but did not remain open for long, due to the price of wolfram dropping.

In 1919, with the miners returning from the War in large numbers, and war-time restrictions ended, Cornish mining should have had a boost, but alas it did not. The price of tin dropped by over a quarter, the price of wolfram by more than a half and arsenic fell over 60%. Ore crushed rose slightly to 68,056 tons, which produced 545³/₄ tons of black tin, 59 tons of wolfram and 631³/₄ tons of arsenic. The revenue from this amounted to £77,723 for the tin, £5,119 for the wolfram and only £30,521 for the arsenic. The yield per ton crushed was 17.96 lb of tin, 1.94 lb of wolfram and 20.79 lb of arsenic. The average price of the tin was £140 2s 2d., and the cost of crushing was down to £1 10s. per ton. The profit was a miserable £299 for 1919.

In 1919, New Cook's Kitchen's Vertical Shaft was sunk to 35 feet below the 245 level. Near to the new shaft, Middle Lode, by then re-named Main Lode, and Intermediate Lode, were being extensively opened up for stoping. In Crofty section, on the 225 east of Robinson's, a lode called 'Kellow's Lode' was being developed, but its average value was only 10 lb per ton. Exploration continued with the new 'diamond drill', and the search for Rogers' Lode went on without success. Crofty acquired a new compressor and was able to increase her number of machines.

So far as labour relations were concerned 1919 was a bad year. Many returning miners, like Martin Crothers, who had been promised their old jobs back once the war was over, found that the jobs offered were not always to their liking. Experienced men from other mines often got back before Crofty's own miners, and had the best of the jobs. Martin Crothers was given a job on night-shift, repairing the 'knocker line' in Robinson's Shaft. He did not want night-shift, and he did not like being soaked in the shaft for the whole shift. After a week he quit Crofty and went to America. This case was typical of many at that time. There was also industrial trouble among the surface workers. Their average pay was about £2 per week and they considered this much too low, with the War having caused considerable inflation. The miners were on average 2s. or 3s. a week better off, and so that were not quite so discontented as the surface workers, but they also were far from happy.

Throughout Cornwall miners were showing their disillusion with pay, by organising themselves into Unions. At Crofty it was the T.G.W.U., and in

February and December 1919 the union members on the surface came out on strike.

The firm responded by cutting out the monthly 'tin bonus' that all the men had come to regard as part of their pay. There was violence and other intimidation over the failure of some men to join the Union, but through persuasion and coercion, almost all eventually did. This industrial unrest disturbed all of the nine or so remaining mines in Cornwall, but it quickly became generally appreciated that the causes of the problem lay outside of Cornwall, and the remedy was far beyond the ken of the local miners' bosses.

Production was also cut during 1919 by the need to alter the winding engine at Robinson's Shaft. The work took seven days, and during this time there was virtually no production at the mine.

An old miner related to me how he came to work at Crofty at about that time. William Nettle of St Day Road, Redruth, was born in July 1906, and after leaving school in 1920 went to work in a shop. His older brother, Alfie, suggested that he go to New Cook's Kitchen, where he himself was employed, and see the mine-captain for a job. Willie Nettle went to see Capt. John Thomas who was in charge of New Cooks Section, and Thomas said that he should approach a miner called 'Solly' Truan. 'Solly' was something of a character, and he was long remembered at Crofty. He was very short, tiny in fact, and had only one eye, having lost the other one in a mining accident. Willie Nettle remembered that 'Solly' always worked in stopes with 'hand labour', he never had anything to do with machines. Some years later Mr Nettle had the roof of his working place fall on him and he was nearly killed, spending many months in hospital.

The mine-captain, John Thomas, who lived in Dolcoath Road, Camborne, was a character of even wider fame than 'Solly' Truan. He was born in June 1861 and started at New Cook's Kitchen in March 1907 at the age of 45. He was a tyrant, who ruled Cook's section with a rod of iron, right up until he finished on the last day of December 1933. He had various nick-names, 'Timber Jack', 'Captain Boo', and 'Johnny Boo'. This last name was one by which everyone knew him, and every older miner at Crofty, and quite a few younger ones who have heard their fathers and grandfathers speak of him, can tell tales of 'Johnny Boo'. Jack Trounson related to me a story from the mid-1920s, when he worked at Crofty during his summer vacation from the School of Mines. Capt. Thomas had been into an inter (sub level) above a new box-hole where timbermen were erecting a 'mill'. As frequently happened, 'Johnny Boo' had one of his 'turns' or as another miner called it, one of his 'quarms', and pitched unconscious down through the box-hole and out of the unfinished chute. Two miners, brothers called Stan and Matt Lee of Park Road, Camborne, came along, and looked down at him lying on his back with hin goatee beard sticking up.

Matt. Lee: "What's wrong with un?"
Timberman: "'Ad one of 'is 'ttacks, s'pose."
Stan Lee: "I'd 'ope the ol' bugger d' die!"
Johnny Boo: "The old bugger ain't gonna die. You two are for the 'urdle tomorrow.'

Fred Sedgemore, who started at Crofty in 1926, recalled that 'Johnny Boo' had regular 'quarms' and he can remember seeing him several times being run along the level on a trolly. "The only thing he seemed worried about when he came to, was if the reflector in his carbide-lamp was alright." Harold May, who went to Crofty in 1931, remembers the redoubtable Captain standing with foot up on the carbide barrel at Cook's dry, and waiting for a late miner to finish putting his underground clothes on. Then 'Johnny Boo' would say to him, "Go home, and have a good sleep, and come early in the morning." Harold said, "Johnny Boo was a hard, stern man."

Harold May recalled words spoken between 'Johnny Boo' and the mine manager, Capt. Clarence V. Paull, who played for Cornwall at cricket and was also captain of Camborne. Clarence said to 'Johnny Boo' that he would not be down the mine the following day as he had to play for Cornwall. Capt. Thomas replied to the effect that Capt. Paull only ever went underground a couple of times a months, and then added, "It will take a lot of that to keep a bal going!" Needless to say, Clarence went underground the following day, and went to the cricket match afterwards.

'Johnny Boo' was a disciplinarian who maintained respect through merciless punishments. The 'hurdle' to which he consigned the Lee Brothers, was another name for the grizzly or hopper, where miners being punished would spend a week or more breaking rocks with a sledge-hammer. Sending a miner home when he was a few minutes late meant the loss of a day's pay, that could rarely be afforded in those days. Another punishment that Fred Sedgemore recalls, was putting offending machine-men to drill the bottom of the main drain that ran between New Cook's station and Robinson's, on the 290 level. At Cook's end the ditch was ten feet deep, and the miner on 'punishment shift' would be up to his knees in mud and up to his chest in water. Despite all that has been said, 'Johnny Boo' was a good miner, who ran his section efficiently. The levels were all clean and tidy, and mining done economically and as safely as possible. He was conscientious, hard-working and knowledgeable.

Another character from that period was a tributer called Goldsworthy. He was typical of the tributers of an earlier period, and was proud of his skill, and disdainful of the common herd. He would arrive in the dry in the early morning, resplendent in black bowler hat, and long white beard. He was working on the Intermediate Lode on the 205 from when the mine re-opened in 1923, and in an underhand stope below the 195 level at Cook's section during 1925-30, and like his exemplars, he still only mined with 'hand labour'. At that time there were only two stopes that were worked without machines.

In 1920 the Crofty setts were being worked on a large scale. There were 40 stopes being worked which were evenly split between New Cook's section and Crofty section (Robinson's, Palmer's and Bickford's). In Cook's section there were 17 back-stopes and three underhand; at Crofty section there were 8 back stopes and 10 underhand, with the other two being worked by tributers working the backs of the 225 east of Palmer's and the 50 level close to Bickford's. Crofty section was working the levels between l00 and 260; only development was carried out at the deeper levels, and 'Solly' Truan, the tributer at the 50 level, was working ground long since abandoned by the mine. New Cook's section was working stopes between the 100 and 225 levels. Until that year much production had taken place from the adit level and down to the 17 level at the old East Shaft.

Development footage increased in 1920 with 212 feet more driven than in the previous year. This was in part due to the return from the Services of many skilled 'machine miners'. At Robinson's the No. 1, No 2 and No 3 North lodes were all driven on at the 260 and 290 levels, and were proving generally rich. From that period, particularly December 1920, the lodes at Crofty were numbered as they are now, thus avoiding much of the confusion previously suffered by the outside enquirer.

A little shaft sinking went on below the 310 fathom station to deepen the sump there, and at New Cook's section, the new vertical shaft was down to 255 fathoms.

Financially, the mine was doing better than in 1919. Production was up, with 69,690 tons crushed for 589 tons of black tin, 38 tons of wolfram and 645³/₄ tons of arsenic. The price of tin had risen to an average of £179 14s 7d; the price of arsenic had risen by over a third, but the market value of wolfram, due to the large quantities stock-piled during the War, was down to a mere fraction of the war-time price. Revenue from tin was £102,060, from wolfram £1,900 and from arsenic £41,881. The yields per ton crushed were 18.8 lb of black tin, 1.22 lb of wolfram and 20.68 lb of arsenic. Costs at the mill were £1 15s 8¹/₂d per ton, and the profit for the year was £3,056.

1921 was one of the worst years Cornish Mining has known. So far as Camborne district was concerned it was quite disastrous, and for Crofty problems piled up all around. On February 12 1921, due to the abysmal price of tin, active mining stopped. The surface operation of stamps, mill and arsenic recovery plant, all closed in July, by which time, with the collapse of East Pool Engine Shaft and the stopping of its engine, together with the 90" at Agar, Crofty's 80" engine at

Robinson's was finding it hard to cope. Water was rushing in from Carn Brea and Tincroft also, as their workings had been abandoned too.

What was worse, so far as Crofty was concerned, with the possible exception of East Pool and Agar, none of the other neighbouring mines looked like re-starting when the crisis was over. By the end of 1921 South Crofty had purchased the 90" Fortescue Engine from the liquidator of Grenville Mine and planned to erect it at New Cook's Kitchen Vertical Shaft. Robinson's 80" was working at double speed and the whim at Robinsons was baling as fast as it could.

Another related problem that Crofty was faced with, was that of the miles of adits that surrounded the mine, and which, as Josiah Paull said, "were the concern of no one but ourselves." The abandoned and semi-abandoned mines on every side of Crofty, with very old shallow workings and networks of adit systems, all connected to each other and interdependent upon each other, were now the sole concern of Crofty. They were to cause continuing problems, and over seventy years later, they still remained a significant item on the maintenance bill.

There was a loss in 1921 of £17,835, which all things considered, was not surprising!

Nothing was done underground or at the mill during 1922. The Company was planning on becoming a more independent mine, having come to terms with the fact that most of the adjacent mines would never fully operate again. East Pool, although re-organising to continue work when her own crisis was past, declined to assist Crofty over pumping. Crofty actually made a profit in 1922, of £784. She sold black tin to the value of £3,969, and arsenic to the value of £11,258, which, with other sundry sales, amounted to returns of £15,302. This revenue mostly financed the purchase and erecting of the Fortescue Engine at New Cook's Vertical Shaft, and the increased fuel costs of pumping and baling at Robinson's. The following Report from Josiah Paull to the Directors shows what was done that year.

March 10th 1923

"Gentlemen,
I beg to send you the following Report on the operations of the past year together with the position of the Mine to date.

No ore was mined during the year.

The operations of the past year were practically confined to installing the new pumping plant at New Cooks and in dealing with the influx of water from East Pool and Agar Mines. Briefly described, the pumping plant consists of a 90 inch Cornish Pumping Engine steamed by 3 Lancashire type boilers on the Surface and 4 sets of 20 inch diameter Cornish pit or pump work which have been fixed in the new vertical shaft at intervals of from 250 to 300 feet, or to a total depth of 1,165 feet from Surface. The plant is capable of pumping up to 900 gallons of water per minute. Excavating for the foundations of the engine and engine house was commenced on January 5th (1922), and the foundations and building, all of which consist of reinforced concrete, the building being 60 feet high, were completed ready for installing the engine on June 5th, or five months from the commencement of the work.

We were severely handicapped in putting in the pump work underground owing to having to handle the East Pool water while the work was in progress. The full inflow of this water commenced on April 5th, and from that date until November 1st we had to cope with this water as best we could by baling with our winding engines and by working our Cornish Pumping Engine at Robinson's Shaft at double its normal speed. We were unable to keep the water to the full depth required for the new plant, but managed to do so sufficiently to get in the third plunger set of this plant which is 909 feet below surface, and the new plant commenced operating to this depth on November 1st. Between November 1st and January 23rd of this year (1923), we were able to lower the water and complete the 4th pumping set to the required depth of 1,165 feet. By means of two bore holes through the water on the other side of our boundary, into which 4 inch pipes are cemented, we are able to get this water under valve control. The Tincroft and East Pool and Agar workings thus becoming one large reservoir from which the new pumping plant is fed. From January 23rd to date we have succeeded in unwatering our own workings a further 205 feet or to a depth of 93 feet below the 205 fathom level at Robinson's Shaft.

I anticipate, if no unforseen accident occurs, that we shall have the mine sufficiently unwatered by early in April to commence practically full mining operations, and by the end of the same month to be crushing very nearly our normal quantities of ore. So far, we have not found any serious damage to the underground workings through their being inundated, except for slime settlement, the levels and timber being practically as we left them a year ago.

As regards plant, the mill, concentrating machinery, ore furnaces and arsenic condensing flues, which have all been idle since July, 1921, have been or are being thoroughly overhauled, in anticipation of resuming milling and ore treatment operations.

In conclusion, I may say the period covered by this Report has been a difficult one for all concerned and has entailed a considerable capital expenditure, but I believe all that has been done was fully justified and that the future prosperity of South Crofty is again assured.

I beg to remain, Gentlemen

Yours faithfully

JOSIAH PAULL

Manager"

The Directors' Report, dated April 19 1923, for the year ending on December 31 1922, refers to the loan that the company obtained under the Trade Facilities Act. It was the first such loan obtained by a Cornish mine. The Report had this to say:

"The programme outlined in last year's Report, namely, borrowing £30,000 from our Bankers under guarantee of His Majesty's Treasury, and the installation of the large Pumping Plant, was duly carried out ... under the agreement with the Treasury no dividends can be paid until the £30,000 owing to the bank has been repaid."

Crofty received this loan in May 1922; during 1923 the capital of the company was increased by £30,000 by the selling of 120,000 new 5s shares, and by April 1924 the loan was repaid.

The early months of 1923 were occupied in unwatering the mine, which had been flooded to the 170 level. By May, both at the mill and underground, work had been resumed on a small scale. In June the mill was almost back to full capacity, and all but one of the stopes worked in Crofty section when the mine closed in February 1921, were being worked by June 1923. Several of the tutworkers were back in their old stopes. By the end of 1923 there were no less than 22 stopes being worked at New Cook's section, against only 16 in 1921. These workings places produced 41,999 tons of ore in the last ten months of that year, for 406 tons of black tin and 380¼ tons of arsenic. There was no wolfram sold, as the price was too low. The tin returned £51,586 and the arsenic £26,442. The average price received for the tin was £115 11s 8d. and for arsenic £63 1s 10d. The yield per ton was 21.66 lb of black tin and 20.82 lb of arsenic, which gave a return per ton crushed of £1 16s 0½d. Some of the revenue from tin and arsenic sold was from stocks left over from before the shut-down. The profit was £7,198.

Despite the problems during the first half of the year, there were 2,175 feet of development, much of which opened up rich tin ground. On 260 level No.1 North Lode was driven another 83 feet east, and although showing reasonable results at first, gradually petered out to only 13 lb per ton average. The No.2 North Lode, however, was very promising. On the 260 it was developed for a further 148 feet east and averaged 42 lb per ton. On 290 it was driven east of the main Robinson's cross-cut for a distance of 120 feet, and averaged 46 lb. The No.1 on 290 was proving even more valuable, averaging 48 lb to the ton on the drive west of the cross-cut. In New Cook's section the drive east on 175 level on the Main Lode gave an average of one per cent tin and one per cent arsenic. The North Branch of Main Lode on 205 level averaged 40 lb of tin and 36 lb of arsenic. The Main Lode on 245 level was "erratic ... and patchy. " Whilst driving the cross-cut north from New Cook's Vertical Shaft, a wide lode was discovered on 245 that was 15 feet across and averaged over its width 32lb of tin per ton. On the 205 level, T. Goldsworthy was working with a 'pare' of men using 'hand labour' to underhand stope part of the Intermediate Lode.

On the surface, with Cook's new pumping engine and other equipment taking so much room, it was necessary to remove part of the old 'dry', thus necessitating the building of a new one. A concrete block building was erected, with asbestos-cement roof, and a long boiler down the middle, for drying underground clothes. It measured 75 feet long by 24 feet wide and 12 feet high. That 'dry' was used until 1963, when the new dry at Robinson's was extended to accommodate Cook's men. It was later used by Cooks Rope Men, until being demolished to make way for the present modern dry and mine offices.

There was continuing concern about the state of the old abandoned mines, adjacent to Crofty, and also the unsafe condition of much of the adit net-work. East Pool had fully resumed work by the end of 1923, and even Tincroft was working on a limited scale just for arsenic.

In November 1923 Albert Gregor, a 31 year old Redruth rugby player, was killed in a stope between the 225 and 260 levels. A hole he was charging with an iron rod exploded and killed him instantly.

1924 was a good year for Crofty, with the average price paid for her tin going up over £36 to £151 18s 11d, and the profits rising to £30,019 19s 5d. The mine produced tin to the value of £106,803 and sold £95,131 worth during the year. The yield per ton crushed was 21.54 lb of tin, and 19.98 lb of arsenic. These two figures gave £1 17s 8½d, a ton crushed, and with costs of £1 7s 5d per ton, there was a profit of 10s 3½d. per ton of ore. Crofty produced 669 tons of black tin and bought 34 tons from smaller concerns, for a total of 703 tons. There was a production at the mine of 609 tons of arsenic and with the 43 tons purchased, there was a total of 652 tons. Although the price of wolfram was improving, it still was not high enough to sell. The stamps worked for a total of 350.4 days in 1924, and crushed 73,138 tons of ore. There were 60 heads of Californian Stamps in operation which were powered by three-phase electricity supply. These continued to work efficiently after 16 years use.

There were 4,447 feet of development during 1924, including the deepening of Cook's Shaft another 113 feet. No.2 North Lode was very rich on the 245,260 and 290 levels, and although it contained no arsenical pyrites, which accounted for the drop in the arsenic yield, it showed consistently high tin values. "Main and No.1 Lodes generally failed to reveal any appreciable quantity of ore," and the wide ore body discovered on the 245 level, 144 feet North of Main Lode proved disappointing upon further exploration. It averaged 15-18 feet wide but its value dropped from about 32 lb to 20 lb per ton. It was hoped that it might prove better on the lower levels.

The No.2 North Lode was proving Crofty's salvation at that time, with values between Palmer's and Robinson's on the 245 and 260 levels averaging between

65 lb and 88lb per ton, and most being in the mid-80s. On the 290 and 310 levels these high values were not maintained however, and in places on 310 some samples were as low as 14lb per ton. The Main Lode on 310 at Robinson's main cross-cut was poor on the east side and only moderate on the west. Cross-cuts were extended during 1924 on the 140 south of Robinson's, which went as far as the southern boundary without results, on the 245 north of Palmer's as far as No.2 North Lode and on 310 to No. 2 Lode. In Cook's section a cross-cut was driven northwards for a distance of 276 feet between the old workings and the new vertical shaft on the 80 level. In that section cross-cuts were extended from the new shaft northwards on the 205, 225 and 245 levels. The new shaft was down to 194 feet below the 245 level. All of the new development at Cook's was on the Main Lode, the Intermediate Lode and the so-called New Lode, discovered on 245 level.

There were about 30 stopes being worked in 1924, with two-thirds of them in New Cook's section between the 148 and 225 levels, and the others in Crofty section, with the stopes above the 260 being the deepest worked.

On Friday December 12 1924, there occurred the worst accident at Crofty this century. Seven men were working in New Cook's Vertical Shaft, extending the timber below the 245 level. As each new timber set was put in it was suspended on four chains, one in each corner. Suddenly, a large rock fell from the side, of the shaft onto the staging, causing one of the chains to break, tipping the staging and precipitating the seven men to the bottom of the shaft. The men were working 135 feet below 245 level, and fell over 50 feet into the sump. F.R.Daniel was killed instantly and Henry Pendray and W.J. Mitchell died soon afterwards. Three other men were seriously injured and one, amazingly, survived almost unhurt. At the inquest it was stated that the chain had been tested to 16½cwt, and that it should have held. The Mine Inspector said that either life-lines or safety-belts should have been worn by the men, and failure to do so had resulted in the tragedy.

By 1924 the use of stopers at Crofty was widespread. The Climax Light Weight (C.L.W.) 'hammerjack' stoper was introduced into stope and raise work, and could also be modified for driving. With cradle, shoe and all connections, the C.L.W. cost about £46. It had automatic rotation and frequently worked in raises and stopes where there was no water supply, so that the miners suffered the effects of dust. Hand labour was to persist among the older miners for some time, but by the end of the '20s it was all but a thing of the past.

There was a profit in 1925, after depreciation of plant and buildings, of £24,269 19s 1d. Black tin sales brought in £120,529, and arsenic returned £10,722. Crofty produced 766¾ tons of black tin, including 20 tons purchased, which was valued at £119,923, and 681 tons of arsenic, of which 178 tons was bought from smaller

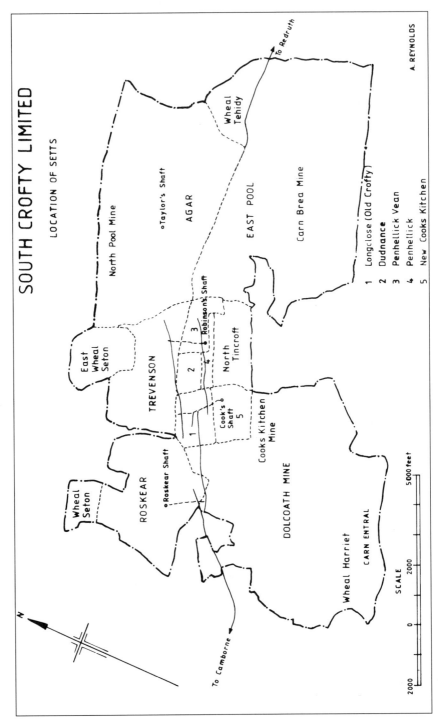

SOUTH CROFTY LIMITED

LOCATION OF SETTS

1 Longclose (Old Crofty)
2 Dudnance
3 Penhellick Vean
4 Penhellick
5 New Cooks Kitchen

A. REYNOLDS

To Redruth

Wheal Tehidy

North Pool Mine

AGAR

EAST POOL

Carn Brea Mine

o Taylor's Shaft

East Wheal Seton

TREVENSON

Robinson's Shaft

North Tincroft

Cook's Shaft

Cooks Kitchen Mine

Roskear Shaft

ROSKEAR

Wheal Seton

DOLCOATH MINE

CARN ENTRAL

Wheal Harriet

N

To Camborne

SCALE

2000   0   2000   5000 feet

concerns, and was valued at £12,648. The average yield of tin was 23.30 lb per ton, and arsenic yielded 15.26 lb per ton. With costs at the mine of £1 7s 4d per ton crushed, the profit per ton of ore was about 8s. The tin grade was an improvement but the arsenic showed a further drop, due to the large tonnage from No.2 Lode. The average price paid for Crofty's tin was £156 4s 5d., and for arsenic, £29 1s 3d.

The directors made the strange statement during 1925, that, due to the unsatisfactory rates that their insurers offered, the company had decided to carry its own insurance risk.

Development during 1925 brought good results, and with the higher levels beginning to dry up, the shareholders were encouraged to know that the deeper levels were sound. The No.2 Lode continued to prove rich on the 260 and 310 levels, but on the 290 there was some disappointment. At Cooks section on 245 the No. 1 Lode was averaging 18 feet in width, and looked good. The No. 3 North Lode on 290 had been intersected by the north cross-cut, and although only 2½ feet wide, over the width of a 5 feet drive it averaged 58 lb per ton. Main Lode, No.1, No.2, and No.3 North Lodes were being developed at the deeper levels, and the No.1 was being explored near to Palmers on the 225 level.

In Cook's section, where the vertical shaft was sunk a further 90 feet to the 290 level, arsenic and wolfram values were still high. With the price of wolfram increasing encouragingly the mine prepared to re-start selling it. Development continued as high as the 148 level in this section.

On the surface the work to replace the old rotting headgear at Robinson's Shaft was completed without loss of time at the mill, and only "a few hours in hoisting operations." Josiah Paull expressed himself delighted with the new steel headgear.

It is interesting to note, that with the tonnage crushed up on the previous year, and the development carried out increased from 4,447 feet to 5,407, the wage bill actually fell by 6 percent.

1926 was a very difficult year for Crofty, with the General Strike paralysing much of the country, and the price of coal soaring. Fortunately, the price of tin rose £15 per ton to £171 3s 5d. Arsenic continued to drop, and during 1926 it went to less than half the 1925 figure. The 60 heads of stamps operated for 349.85 days during 1926, and crushed 74,334 tons of ore for the production of 694¾ tons of tin, 296 tons of arsenic, and 10½ tons of wolfram, which was valued altogether at £124,507. The yield of black tin per ton crushed was 20.94 lb and 8.92 lb of arsenic. Costs per ton crushed were £1 8s 5d., which gave a profit of 4s 9d per ton of ore raised. South Crofty made a profit in 1926, after depreciation of plant etc., of £14,612 3s 11d.

There was a new record development figure, with 5,715 feet raised, sunk and driven, which was 308 feet more than 1925, itself a record year. Once again No.2 Lode carried the mine, although its values were not as good as hitherto. Capt. Josiah Paull referred in his Report to a newly discovered lode that had been explored:

"An interesting development point has been the rise mentioned as being put up 87 feet 3 inches above the 260 fathom level Robinsons section. This was started on a South dipping low grade lode which passes through and faults the No. 2 North Lode. Generally the No.2 has been poor above the plane of faulting with this South dipper, but we have been agreeably surprised in rising here, as for some 75 feet of rising on No. 2 North Lode above the faulting plane we have, as stated, had tin values averaging 76 lbs to the ton for a width of 4 feet."

This lode was often called Intermediate Lode, but it must not be confused with the lode of that name in Cook's section. On 290 in Crofty section the main cross-cut was driven further north and intersected No. 3 North Lode. It proved variable, with values erratic at first but improving above the level, with samples showing 48 lb and 56 lb per ton on both sides of the cross-cut. The No. 2 was in places poor, and in others up to to 48 lb per ton. On 310 level No. 2 Lode proved still reliable. Up on the 180 level, a 16 feet wide ore body was being worked which, although less than one-per cent of tin, and similar of arsenic, was worth stoping.

In Cook's section cross-cuts on the 225, 245 and 290 levels were driven northwards, but the ground opened up was unspectacular. Apart from the questionable value of the so-called Intermediate Lode at Robinson's 260 level, 1926 saw no new discoveries of ore that were likely to cause excitement to the shareholders.

The use of stopers further increased during the middle and late 1920s and by 1926 there were only a couple of stopes still worked by hand-labour. T. Goldsworthy and Tom Webster worked alone in a stope under the 195 level on New Cook's Intermediate Lode, taking it in turns to 'beat the borer'. Crofty at that time had a position called 'Machine Boss', and it was occupied at that period by Stephen Nichols. He was responsible for all of the machines and the work done by them. The 'underground manager' at that time was Bennie Viall, and he had risen from 'timber-boss' before the Great War, to mine-captain, and then, by the end of the '20s to what we now call 'underground manager'. The antagonism between him and 'Johnny Boo', was notorious, and things did not improve when Bennie rose to become his superior.

In 1927 H. J. Meyerstein died. He had been a director since the creation of South Crofty Ltd., and was highly thought of by his former colleagues. F.W. Franks, a prominent shareholder, took his place on the Board of Directors.

The market value of tin rose again during 1927, so that Croftys average return from its sale was £174 12s 6d per ton. The price of arsenic also went up slightly to £16 10s 4d per ton. Ore crushed amounted to 72,732 tons, the produce of 60 stamps working for 337.37 days. The yield per ton crushed was 24.87 lb of black tin and 8.20 lb of arsenic. Costs were £1 9s 6¾ per ton, which gave a profit of 10s 9d per ton of ore raised. Although there was a drop in ore crushed of 1,600 tons, the tin recovered went up to 807¾ tons, which was the highest total since the Companys inception in 1906. There was no wolfram sold in 1927.

The smaller tonnage milled was due to two stopes becoming unpayable, that for several years had provided the mine with a large quantity of low-grade ore. The lost dirt was partly made up by the increasing high grade ore from No. 2 North Lode. There was a total footage developed of 6,180 feet, which was an increase over the previous year of 465 feet. A big proportion of this was cross-cutting, with the 290 Robinsons cross-cut driven 1,101 feet from the shaft. 330 feet north of No. 3 a small north dipper was encountered, which assayed at 28 lb over one foot width. A further 65 feet, and the cross-cut intersected a 3 foot wide south dipper, which sampled at 48 lb per ton. This was later called No. 4 North Lode, and it was eventually to be as significant a find as was No.2. The main purpose of the cross-cut was to explore the Trevenson sett, so these lodes were not driven to any extent. On 310 level the north cross-cut from Robinson's intersected two branches of No. 3 Lode, which are now called North and South Branches of No. 3, and were still being reclaimed over 50 years later. These two branches can still be clearly seen in the cross-cut, being about 10 feet apart, and remaining almost parallel for a considerably distance. The old stopes of Wilson, Harradine and Giles lie along the northern branch of No. 3 Lode. The lode, despite being very narrow and petering out as it goes eastwards, possessed very good values.

In Cook's section the 290 cross-cut was driven 365 feet north of the station, and cut Main Lode and what was thought to be a disordered part of No. 2 Lode. Most of the development in this section was on the 225 level, where the North Lode was explored thoroughly. A miner called Judd and his mate, Fred Sedgemore, who had started underground that year, were using an old 'merry widow' stoper to put up a rise between 225 and 205 level, on the North Lode. Fred told the author that they emerged at the end of each shift, "looking as though they'd bin in a flour-mill for the day." The machine was a hand rotated 'Climax' stoper, and even had there been provision for water on it, there certainly would have been no water pipes into the rise. Fred Sedgemore worked at Crofty until the mid-1970s, and his son Jimmy followed him into the mine, in 1980 stoping the back of No.9 east, on 335 level.

The wide ore body on 180 Crofty section continued to be encouraging. Main Lode on 120 and 140 levels was average, No. 2 Lode was proving healthy wherever it was explored and No. 3 Lode was beginning to gain consistency.

There was an increase in stoping at Cook's and a tendency toward development at Crofty section in 1927. On 290 level there was good progress toward joining the two sections, and it was vital that they do so, as ventilation on the deeper levels was bad. The year ended with a profit of £35,383 10s 7d., the highest made since 1918

1928 saw the beginning of another serious slump in the fortunes of Cornish Mines. The statement made by Crofty's directors at the end of that year sums up the apprehension they felt at the outlook:

"The average price obtained for Tin for the year 1927 was £174 12s 6d. per ton, and for last year (1928) £141 15s 5d., the fall in the price per ton being £32 17s ld., which accounts for a reduction in receipts of nearly £26,000."

This price was disastrous, and with that of wolfram not sufficiently high to warrant its pursuit, and arsenic remaining steady but low, the mine looked unsafe. Despite these forbidding signs the tonnage increased to 74,039, development went up to a new record of 6,312 feet, and the yield per ton remained good at 24.07 lb for tin and 8.43 lb of arsenic. There were also $10^1/_2$ tons of wolfram produced, which was valued at £500. With costs at the mine of £1 7s $10^1/_2$d there was a profit of 4s ld per ton crushed. The company sold £112,167 worth of tin, £3,510 worth of wolfram and £3,035 worth of arsenic. There was a profit in 1928 of £13,968 16s 11d., which, in the circumstances, was quite good.

The drive to link Crofty and Cook's sections on the 290 level was completed in 1928, and the improvement in ventilation was immediate. The north cross-cut from Robinson's 290 was driven another 472 feet to 1,482 feet. Three small lodes were intersected by it, but no great exploration took place on them as they were considered too small to pursue at that distance from the shafts. Once again No. 2 North Lode continued to be the mainstay of the mine, with the newly discovered No. 4 and what proved to be No. 5 Lodes giving encouraging results. 310 cross-cut was advanced northward a further 123 feet without fresh discoveries. The low-grade ore body on 180 level was still being developed, and the 31 feet driven in 1928 averaged 14 feet wide and gave values of 18lb of tin and 22lb of arsenic. The management decided that preparations should be made to deepen New Cook's Vertical Shaft to the same depth as Robinson's. Although development continued between 120 and 310 levels at Crofty section, and 175 and 290 Cook's, stoping was confined to the levels above 290 in the former and the 245 in the latter.

During this period several miners lost their lives in separate accidents. A miner called Mann was killed by a blast whilst working with a tutworker called Vernon Kitchen, and another called Oates fell down a raise when he lost his hold on a stope chain, and was killed. A well-known Camborne rugby player called

William Care was stoping on 225 Cook's section, when he fell about 55 feet to his death. This happened on September 4 1929, and Care, an experienced miner, was 36 years old.

1929 saw Crofty's position deteriorate. The average price paid for her tin was down to £128 17s 10d., which was £13 down on the ruinous price of the year before. With the average yield per ton 23.54 lb of tin and 7.66 lb of arsenic, bringing a total per ton crushed £1 8s 0d., and costs at the mine of £1 6s 4d., Crofty actually scraped by with a profit of 1s 8d per ton of ore raised. "The tonnage sold was the same as for the previous year but the cash received was £10,486 less," reported the directors. The Company paid out £255 to join the International Tin Producers' Association in order to encourage the stabilisation of the tin price on the international market.

Despite these facts the financial base of the mine was sound and the shareholders were encouraged by the fact that wolfram looked like becoming profitable again. The 60 stamps worked for 349.37 days during 1929, and produced 795 tons of black tin, 258 tons of arsenic and 17 tons of wolfram. This was valued at £107,810, and with returns of £109,550, there was a profit in 1929 of £5,396 19s 11d. The expenditure details show £945 5s 10d for, "Silicosis Claims and Costs."

The Directors Report for 1929 made this statement: "Mr Josiah Paull, after acting for 21 years as the Company's Manager, has resigned his position but has been offered and has accepted a seat on the Board. His son, Mr Clarence V. Paull, has been appointed Manager, Mr Josiah Paull continuing to act in an advisory capacity."

Clarence Paull could not have taken over at a worse time. Having been reasonably successful during the 1920s when most Cornish mines had been either closed or grinding to a halt, Crofty was also beginning to feel the cold economic climate. Clarence was to be grateful for the continuing presence of his father during the next decade; indeed there are many former employees of Crofty who firmly believe that Josiah remained manager until the end of the 1930s, such was his active interest in the mine. Development continued apace, with yet another record being set when 6,770 feet were driven, sunk and raised. Once again, a large proportion or ore milled came from development ends on the deeper levels, which had the double benefit of opening up ground for the future, and producing ore for the present. There was little arsenic on the deeper levels and so the grade and quantity dropped as the tonnage from there increased.

The 310 cross-cut was extended a further 307 feet north of Robinson's, being by the end of 1929 just over 1,000 feet long. The No. 4 and No. 5 lodes were cut and proved stronger than on 290. The 180 ore body was proving narrower but richer than it had, with values of 20 lb of tin and 22 lb of arsenic over a width of 10 feet.

127

As in previous years the consistency with which the ends produced average values of one per cent was extraordinary. No less than 30 development points during 1929 averaged a fraction over or a fraction under one per cent. In Cook's section the tendency to work the lodes underhand had increased until by that year out of the 18 stopes worked, no less than 16 were underhand stopes. In 1920 in the same section the figures were almost exactly the opposite. Whilst driving east on No. 1 from Cook's section, 260, there was discovered a wide mineralised area marked by formations of stringers, This ore body was 25 feet wide and averaged 22 lb per ton.

In 1930 the price of tin dropped to near the 1914 figure. The average that Crofty received per ton for her black tin was £91 16s 9d., which was 4s 8d per ton more than 1914, when costs at the mine per ton crushed were only £1 0s 8d. With Crofty's 1930 costs per ton up to £1 3s 7½d the mine lost 2s 6d for each ton raised, of which, for the ten month period until the mine closed in October 1930, there were 60,273. There were 670 tons of tin produced, 239 tons of arsenic and no wolfram, although Castle an Dinas continued working for it.

The Directors' Report showed the progress made toward stabilising the tin price: "The production of Tin is now under the control of the International Quota Scheme regulated by a Committee representing the principal producing countries, viz: Malay, Bolivia, the Dutch Indies and Nigeria, and these countries have taken the necessary powers to control on an agreed basis the output of their respective countries. This Quota Scheme holds good for 2 years and should in due course result in a stabilisation of the price.

The Company continued to hold large cash resources.

The Company will recommence crushing when the price of Standard Tin reaches £140."

During 1930 the mine produced tin to the value of £59,557, and sold £62,961 worth, together with £6,443 worth of arsenic. The yield per ton crushed was 24.92 lb of tin, and 8.90 lb of arsenic.

There were 5,152 feet of development in 1930, with the No.4 and No.5 lodes being explored on 290 and 310 levels. The values sampled were very good on both of these lodes, and although ventilation was poor due to the great distance from the shafts, it was felt that once rises had been connected this problem would be remedied. The cross-cut north from Robinson' Shaft on 260, was extended with a view to intersecting the lodes proving so valuable on the levels below. On the 120 level south of Robinson's, a lode was developed that had good quantities of tin, 24 lb; wolfram, 36 lb; and also of mispickel and copper. Rising above the level, the tin content of the lode improved further. The previously wide ore body

27. Timbermen building stope rearing. They are working off a ladder to put in place planking to hold back the ore from the ladderway. The top man is using a 'dag', or small axe. G J Nicholas took the picture in 1956.

28. *Forest of timber in Slime Drive, No.4 Lode, 380 fm level. note, the height of the 'Cousin Jack' chutes, to allow the high-sided Granby wagons to pass beneath and be loaded. The rest of the timber comprises 'caps and legs' to support the back. The picture was taken by W J Watton in 1983.*

29. *Jeff Tonkin longhole drilling at the 410 Sub Level on Roskear 'B' Lode. The drillrig is a Tamrock L500 and the ANFO loader in the foreground is a Jet-Anol 300. Jeff is drilling almost vertical downholes. October 1993.*

30. Mark Kaczmarek shrinkage stoping Roskear 'B' Lode above the 420 fm level. He is using a SIG machine with telescopic leg. Shrinkage stoping has been used at Crofty since at least the 1890s. The miners work off the broken ore, which is pulled through chutes or draw points to give the miners room to work. February 1994.

on 180 gradually narrowed and became impoverished as it was explored westward. There was some cross-cutting on 225 level Cook's section for the purpose of improving ventilation. Clearly, with an improved price for her tin, Crofty could be making a very good profit, instead, in October 1930, all mining stopped, and no stoping took place until November 1931.

During the 1930 engineers installed at the 140 level station in Bickford's Shaft, a Hathorn Davey three-throw Ram Pump, which was electrically powered and capable of pumping 450 gallons per minute. The purpose of this pump was to cope with the water from East Pool and North Tincroft workings which poured into the mine in great quantities. With all pumping contingencies allowed for, the company could await the stabilisation of the tin price. Clarence Paull reported a loss of £14,063 10s 11d., for the year 1930.

On October 12 1931, crushing and milling were resumed at Crofty, and at the same time limited mining began again. £10,186 worth of tin was sold and £1,213 worth of arsenic in 1931, and Crofty sustained a loss of £22,328 16s 1d. The stamps worked for 46.76 days and crushed 9,306 tons of ore for the production of 113 tons of black tin and 71 tons of arsenic. The yield per ton was high, at 27.3 lb of tin, and 17.16 lb of arsenic. The latter high grade was attained by cleaning the arsenic flues during the shutdown. Maintenance was carried out on all surface plant while the mine was idle, so the closure was not entirely wasted. Another old problem reared its head at that time, that of the ancient network of adits that surrounded Crofty.

"PUMPING - As mentioned at the last Annual Meeting, owing to an almost complete chokage in the Dolcoath Deep Adit, the water in the abandoned mines on our Southern boundary rose far above its usual level. It actually broke into South Crofty, but by the rapid building of Dams the danger was quickly overcome.

During the last 12 months, the extra pressure of water has increased the percolation into South Crofty and considerably increased our pumping charges. The only means of relieving this pressure was to clear and renovate the Dolcoath Shallow Adit, parts of which have not been in use for 30 years.

We have been successful in clearing this adit from the outlet a distance of over 2,500 feet South, and have lowered the water 28 feet. We hope during the next few months to complete the repairing of this adit and by doing so permanently removing all future danger." (Clarence V. Paull, Manager).

By the end of 1931 there were 19 stopes in production, 10 in Cook's section, and 9 at Crofty, but although the tin price was high enough to justify operating, it had not reached the £150 per ton necessary for profitability.

During 1932 the mine ran to a severely curtailed schedule. There was only one shift a day underground, main development was cut back, and the stamps and mill worked part-time. 55,338 tons were crushed at the stamps, which only worked 252 days. The 644 tons of black tin was valued at a mere £55,579 and the 133 tons of arsenic at £3,542. The yield per ton averaged 26.09 lb of tin and 5.39 lb of arsenic. Costs at the mine were £1 2s 5½d per ton, which meant a loss of 1s 1d for every ton crushed. The mine lost £7,405 in 1932, and the Chairman blamed some of it on the new Silicosis Act, which, he said, cost Crofty £2,700 that year.

Most of what little development that did take place in 1932 was in preparing payable sections of lodes for stoping, by driving inters and putting up box holes. North-east of Palmer's on 245 level some exploratory work was done on No.2 North Lode, and the wide complex near to No.1 Lode on 260 north of Robinson's Shaft was also further developed. Values were 30 lb over a width of 12 feet. A raise was put up from 310 to 290 on No.5 Lode, and this improved the ventilation in that area.

The Dolcoath Shallow Adit was completely cleared in September 1932, and the water that caused Crofty such problems on the south and east was reduced by 30 feet. A couple of dams that had been built to keep the water back were removed so that the water could run into the adit. In July 1932 Crofty acquired the sett of North Tincroft Mine, so that ground to the west of Tyrie's Shaft could be worked.

On March 24 1932, Ralph Opie, a 51 year old miner, fell off the top of a skip to his death. He was travelling in New Cook's Shaft between the 245 and 205 levels.

1933 saw a steady improvement in the price of tin and in the prospects of South Crofty Mine. The average return per ton for the first six months was only £112 9s 9d., but the second half of the year saw the price rise to an average of £145 12s 6d. The slight loss recorded until June was more than covered by the profit of the latter half of the year. There was a profit in 1933 of £16,074 17s 5d.

The 60 stamps worked for only 249.88 days for the crushing of 56,597 tons of ore. There were 645 tons of black tin, 97 tons of arsenic and 5¾ tons of wolfram produced, at a yield per ton of 25.54 lb of tin, 3.87 lb of arsenic and 0.23 lb of wolfram. No wolfram was sold but £87,510 worth of tin and £2,914 worth of arsenic were disposed of. The costs per ton at the mine went down slightly to £1 3s 1½d, and with the value per ton up to £1 10s 7½d., there was a profit of 7s 6d per ton of ore raised.

The reason for the continued curtailment of production was that the International Tin Committee had set a quota for each tin producer, and although it was voluntarily entered into, Crofty honoured the agreement. There was no restriction of wolfram production however, and Crofty's wholly owned subsidiary of Castle an Dinas was in full production.

There were several changes on the board at the time. Henry Lovegrove had died in November 1932, and twelve months later F.W. Franks, who had replaced H.J. Meyerstein in 1928, died. It was proposed that T. Wallace Evans, who had been Company Secretary for 28 years, since the inception of South Crofty Ltd., should replace him.

Clarence Paull gave a lecture in June 1933, at the Greenbank Hotel, Falmouth, in which he dealt with the achievements of South Crofty since the Company's creation in 1906. The figures from 1907-33 show what had been done.

Development	-	16,300 fathoms (18$\frac{1}{2}$ miles).
Ore through mill	-	2,343,240 tons
Black Tin Sold	-	13,864 tons, returned £1,795,389
White Arsenic sold	-	12,504 tons, returned £397,167
Wolfram Sold	-	1,414 tons, returned £150,688
Capital Outlay	-	£117,000
Dividends Paid	-	£290,400

Despite the losses between 1930-31 and the severe cut-back directed by the International Tin Committee, the above figures demonstrated the sound financial base of the mine. The work force was smaller than it had been, and the wages paid to the men had not kept pace with inflation, so that even the skilled miners were often getting less than they had a decade earlier. Miners had gone from being the best paid workers in the district, to being among the lower paid, with factory workers and bus drivers frequently getting a higher rate of pay. Inevitably, it would lead to trouble. Crofty was able to benefit from more efficient machinery than hitherto, and although it made the job easier for the miner, it was the mine that gained financially. During the 1930s the Climax D.V. stopers, with their disc valves, gave way to the more efficient S.V. (sleeve valve) machines, like the 60 lb 'Hydramax' hand rotating stoper and although many miners were forced to use the old 'Merry Widow' (also known as the 'Widow Maker') machines of the early 1920s (and even earlier!), there was notably improvement in performance. Another innovation at that time was the introduction of a different method of blasting. As is often the case, its adoption was for mainly economic reasons. The explosive 'Burrowite' (made by the Burrowite Explosives Co,) was cheaper than other types, and although it was considerably less powerful than the explosive 'Victorite,' it was found that if 'Victorite' was used for the cut, the cheaper and less powerful 'Burrowite' could be used quite effectively for the rest of the round. It was a practice that saved Crofty a lot of money.

The most significant development of 1933 was the opening of the North Tincroft section. This was based on Tyrie's Shaft, which is an inclined shaft sunk on the

North Tincroft Lode, and which dips steeply towards Crofty's Dudnance sett. On its 194 level it is quite close to Crofty's boundary. Development was concentrated on the 110 level, where a short cross-cut was driven north, the 120 level, where a drive on the lode for 151 feet showed high arsenic values and moderate tin values, and the 130 level, where a drive westward went from reasonable values to nothing.

In Crofty section the development ends continued to show good results, particularly on No. 5 Lode, 310 levels. New Cooks Kitchen Vertical Shaft was sunk 40 feet in 1933, and there were problems with a small lode which went vertically with the new shaft. It only assayed at 4 lb per ton, but it produced 25 gallons of water a minute, which was most undesirable.

On 310 level a south cross-cut was begun to locate the South Lode and Pryce's Lode. There was an unexplored area above 310 level and below the old Tincroft workings that was 500 feet deep.

In 1934 the price of tin was kept stable, and an average of £151 14s was realised from its sale. During the first four months of the year almost £160 per ton was obtained. The prices of arsenic and wolfram were steady, so that Castle-an-Dinas and the North Tincroft section of Crofty covered themselves by their production of wolfram and arsenic reepectively. The stamps worked a restricted schedule again, crushing 60,277 tons in 251.517 days, for the production of 643 tons of tin and 124 tons of arsenic. The yield per ton was 23.90 lb of tin and 4.61 lb of arsenic, together valued at £1 12s 11½ per ton of ore. With costs at £1 5s 2¾d per ton, there was a profit of 7s 9d for every ton of ore raised.

Crofty sold £96,491 worth of mineral in 1934, and made a profit of £26,281 9s.

1934 saw a turnaround between South Crofty and one of its neighbours. In the late 19th century, Bartle's Foundry, of Dudnance Lane, had been prominent adventurers in the old Cost Book Company of South Wheal Crofty. In 1934 South Crofty purchased Bartle's Foundry, and expanded its plant and business considerably.

In Crofty section the north cross-cuts from Robinson's Shaft were extended on the 260 level and the 310. No. 1 North Lode on 310 level was driven east and west and proved good. The No. 5 Lode on 310 was averaging 44 lb per ton, although one section was disordered by a crosscourse.

In Cook's section the Intermediate Lode was being developed for its high arsenic content between the 175 and 195 levels. There was considerable exploration of the Main Lode and No. 1.

In the North Tincroft workings development was all but stopped, with a little exploration taking place to the west of Tyrie's Shaft on the 110 and 120 levels. Apart from the high arsenic values there were also good tin grades obtained.

The 315 level was reached by New Cook's Vertical Shaft in 1934, and by the end of the year the station was being cut out and preparations made for driving north. In the mill there was an addition to the plant of two units of the mineral separation type of flotation for the better recovery of wolfram.

The Director's Report for the year ending December 31 1935, contained this:

"The year under review has been an important one in the history of the Company by reason of the acquisition of the Dolcoath Mine, which is accessible from South Crofty New Cook's Shaft. The purchase of the property has been completed and the drive towards the Roskear Lodes of Dolcoath is being pushed on. The new capital issue in February last (1935) was heavily over-subscribed.

The average price of Tin realised for the year was £142 3s 4d. per ton, that of the preceeding year having been £151 14s 0d."

"Mr. Josiah Paull's Report re Dolcoath

We have purchased from H.M. Treasury the Dolcoath Mine and its assets, the latter comprising, in addition to various substantial buildings and a large quantity of valuable Mine Machinery and Plant, considerable areas of freehold land, the mineral rights of the Old Dolcoath property and the leases of the New Dolcoath Mine.

Both Old and New Dolcoath lie immediately West of our present South Crofty New Cook's Kitchen boundary, and the lodes worked by us extend throughout the area we are taking over for a length of 2,500 to 3,000 feet, and have been explored to a small extend only by the former owners, so that the acquisition of this further large area should, and we are confidence will, add enormously to our potential ore reserves and consequent life of the Mine as a whole, and should enable us to increase our output of Tin, Wolfram and Arsenic.

At a distance of 1,600 feet from our Western boundary the New Dolcoath Company sunk at great expense a vertical shaft 18 feet in diameter to a depth of 2,000 feet. This shaft is brick-lined throughout and it is our intention eventually to link up our workings with this shaft, as such linking up with our present Robinson's and New Cook's vertical shafts will provide excellent Natural Ventilation throughout the whole property, but our immediate intention is to extent our South Crofty levels Westwards into the new area, one such level being already practically on the boundary, and to explore and work the lodes by this means, and bring the ore to our New Cooks Vertical Shaft, the capacity of which, together with its large winding equipment, is capable of handling some thousands of tons of ore per month beyond what we are now able to supply the Shaft with. Our milling capacity also is sufficient for crushing and treating at least 2,000 tons per month more than we are doing at present, so that, beyond the purchase price, by developing the property in the way we propose, we do not contemplate any considerable Capital Expenditure will be necessary and the proceeds of the present issue should be ample for our requirements in these respects.

The New Dolcoath Company had already intersected two or three of our lodes, prior to closing down through insufficient Capital, and from the small amount of development and mining operations carried out by them sold some 170 tons of Tin, 20 tons of Wolfram and 370 tons of Arsenic, the aggregate value of which was £29,900, and their reports show the value per ton of ore in development drives as being quite equal to or in excess of our own at South Crofty."

"SOUTH CROFTY, LIMITED

6, Broad Street Place,
London, E.C. 2.
4th February, 1936.

Dear Sir (or Madam),
In July last you were informed that my Board had entered into a provisional agreement with the Treasury to acquire the Dolcoath Mine, which adjoins this companys property, and which will be accessible through our New Cook's Shaft. The formal agreement has now been signed and the sale was approved by the Court on the 29th January, 1936.

The reasons which actuated the Board in agreeing to the purchase from the Treasury are set out in the enclosed report from Mr. Josiah Paull, from which you will observe that this acquisition should add largely to the Company's ore reserves and become a valuable asset.

The purchase price is £22,000 payable in cash. In order to carry through the deal and to provide for the development in Dolcoath and for further sinking of shafts on our Crofty properties, without unduly depleting the cash resources of the company, it has been decided to offer to the shareholders pro rata, as rights, 78,000 unissued shares of 5s. each, i.e., one new share for every five old shares held on the 14th February 1936, with no fractions, at the price of 7s. 6d. per share, payable in full on application, which will provide £29,250. The share register will be closed on the 14th February 1936, and the rights must be taken up by the 28th February, 1936, when the list closes.

This will then make the total issued capital of £117,000.

Application and renunciation forms will be posted on the 18th February, 1936.

Your directors consider it unnecessary to have this issue underwritten. Should shareholders desire to apply for any excess rights in order to round off their holdings, they will be given an opportunity to do so. The directors reserve the right to take up the shares (if any) not applied for at the price of 7s.6d. per share.

The new shares will rank for dividend after the 31st March next. Application to the Stock Exchange for permission to deal in this issue will be applied for in due course.

By Order of the Board,
T. WALLACE EVANS
Secretary."

With her vastly expanded boundaries, South Crofty obviously appeared a good prospect to the investor. The mine had two vertical shafts, both situated close to the main lodes, it had modern plant, good grade ore, valuable supplementary minerals in wolfram and arsenic, and an enormous only partly explored area of ground to the west, north and south. The deepest level had been extensively developed but no stoping had taken place there until 1935.

The 60 stamps ran for 245.3 days and crushed 61,060 tons of ore. There was a recovery of 673 tons of black tin, 132 tons of arsenic, and $10^{1}/_{4}$ tons of wolfram, in 1935 at an average yield per ton of 24.69 lb or tin, 4.85 lb of arsenic. Costs per ton crushed and milled were £1 6s $9^{3}/_{4}$d, which gave a profit per ton raised of 5s 3d. Mineral recovered was valued at £98,905, and the amount sold was £93,462 worth of black tin, £1,915 worth of arsenic, and £983 worth of wolfram.

In 1935 South Crofty made a profit of £19,522 11s ld.

The manager reported that during 1935 the tin values at Cook's had improved so much that 30 tons of black tin extra had resulted. The installation of the wolfram recovery flotation plant was also a success, he said. The pitwork in New Cook's Shaft between 195 and 315 levels was completed, and Capt. Paull stated that after the raise to 290 level had improved the ventilation at 315, work commenced to finish the shaft to sump and put in an ore bin at that level.

The total development for the year was 6,200 feet. In Crofty (Robinson's) section, the 260 north cross-cut was driven 90 feet beyond No. 4 Lode, and on 310 level the south cross-cut was extended 283 feet toward Pryce's Lode. The results were very disappointing. The drives on No. 1 Lode, and on No. 5 Lode 310, were provinq very good. Stoping started on 310 in February 1935, when a miner call Artie Webster began to work just to the east of the cross-cut on No. 1.

Lode. It was 20 months before another stope was begun on 310, and then it was the No. 5 Lode that was worked.

In Cook's section the 315 north cross-cut was driven 365 feet to Main Lode, where drives on lode totalled 86 feet east and west. On 175 level the Intermediate Lode was further developed, and the 245 level was driven toward the boundary with Dolcoath. There was no development in North Tincroft in 1935, but a miner called Harris was stoping on both the 110 and 120 levels west of Tyrie's Shaft.

The tin price continued to fall, and the average received in 1936 was £133 15s 9d per ton. The stamps again only worked part time, and the total crushed was 61,235 tons for the production of 676 tons of black tin and 131 tons of arsenic. The tin was valued at £89,922 and the arsenic £1,258. The yield per ton was 24.75 lb of tin and 4.79 lb of arsenic. With costs per ton £1 7s 4d, the profit for each ton mined was 2s 5^1/2d. There was a slight improvement in the recovery rate of the tin, but with the price further depressed there was a decrease in the revenue of £6,054. There was a profit in 1936 of £7,319 9s 11d.

There were 6,400 feet of development in 1936, which resulted in some interesting discoveries. The faulted lower continuation of No.2 Lode, which had been examined for some time, was proving valuable, with samples of 44lb per ton taken at the 290. The 245 drive west toward the Dolcoath sett was driven through the Great Crosscourse, and a diamond drill was put to work 110 feet inside the Dolcoath property. An exploratory hole was drilled 304 feet north, striking killas at 250 feet. A wide 'complex' ore body was discovered by diamond drill, north of Main Lode in Cook's Kitchen on 290. On 290 in Crofty section, east of the cross-cut north of Palmer's Shaft, there was a drive on a 'wet' south underlying lode, which was dammed off in 1921. This lode is now called 'Wet Lode', and until the early 1980s it was still worked on 260, 290 and 310 levels. It carried less water in 1936 than it had when dammed off in 1921, and now it is no wetter than many other lodes.

There was a general increase in stoping during 1936 with 20 stopes being worked at Cook's and 17 at Crofty section. A second stope was started on 310 level, when a miner called Riches began stoping the No.5, east of the cross-cut. Preparations were made in 1936 for the sinking of Robinson's Shaft a further 150 feet, and work began to clear Dolcoath's Deep Adit to further reduce the water level in the adjacent mines.

On Thursday April 29 1937 there was a tragic accident at Crofty. A 16 year old miner from Druid's Lodge, called Richard Trengove, was assisting a 'machine man' called Joseph Rogers to pull an old iron peg from the side of the raise in an underhand stope. The stope was on No.1 Lode, below 290 level, just to the east of the main north cross-cut. The youngster was supporting his mate, who was leaning out over a one hundred foot drop, by holding on to his leather belt. The belt broke, but instead of Rogers falling down the raise, he managed to hang onto the peg, and Trengrove lost his balance and fell right though to 310 level. Below the underhand stope was one being worked by Artie Webster and another youngster, called Ronnie Opie, who was himself just 15 years old. The boy fell right through their stope, and sustained multiple injuries including a fractured skull. He died instantly. Richard Trengrove had worked at Crofty for seven months, and Joseph Rogers, who came from North Parade, Camborne, and was 26 years old, had worked at the mine for five years.

In 1937 Climax brought our a new streamlined 'Hammerjack' stoper. It was call the C.S.V. (Climax sleeve valve), and although it was much heavier than its predecessor (C.L.W.), at 50lb, it was considered a vastly superior machine. At that time the average air pressure had increased through more efficient compressors and superior pipe fitting techniques, from between 50-60 lb in the 1920s to 60-70 lb by the late 1930s. These new sleeve valve machines were designed to take advantage of the better air pressure. Crofty acquired C.S.Vs., and with the average air pressure at the ends of 70 lb per square inch, they ran efficiently.

1937 was another good year for Crofty, with the profits up, to £29,126 17s 7d. This was in part due to the fine increase in the tin price, which rose from £133 15s 9d., to £157 8s 7d. Sales amounted to £116,904 worth of tin, and £1,986 worth or arsenic. Wages leaped to £48,998, an increase of nearly 14 percent over twelve months, but with the footage driven in development rising to 7,500 feet an increase of 1,100 feet, the higher wage bill was more than accounted for.

Crofty produced 767 tons of black tin and $94^{3}/_{4}$ tons of arsenic from 62,349 tons of ore stamped. The tin grade went up to 27.57 lb per ton, and the arsenic dropped to 3.4 lb. With costs at the mine at £1 10s 3d per ton, there was a profit of 9s $5^{1}/_{2}$d per ton raised., The low grade and small tonnage of arsenic was due to stopping work in the North Tincroft section.

Robinson's Shaft was sunk to its new sump, 150 feet below the old 310 sump, and preparations were made to cut out the new 335 station. The No. 2 Lode on 315 was driven 655 feet, from 315 north cross-cut toward the Great Crosscourse, and averaged 40 lb per ton throughout. The 260 Robinson's cross-cut was extended 190 feet without results. A short cross-cut was driven between No. 1 Lode and Wet Lode on 310, and the intersected lode showed good values. On 310 level, No. 1, No. 2, Wet Lode, No.4, No. 5 and two small lodes north of No.5 were all developed. On 315 level, (Cook's), Main Lode, No.1, and No.2 lodes were driven.

On the surface there were changes to New Cook's headgear, necessitated by the state of the original. The timber one was removed and replaced by a steel one.

Engineers also installed a new 1,500 cubic foot Belliss and Morcom air compressor at Cook's Shaft.

On Friday 10 September 1937, there was a terrible accident at Crofty. Two miners died, three were made seriously ill, one of them also sustaining severe injuries, and another ten were in need of first-aid treatment. Stanley Bawden, of Condurrow Road, Beacon, had been putting up a raise from 290 level, assisted by Charles Smith of Carn Marth, a 19 year old miner with three years experience. At the inquest Bawden testified that he had gone up the ladder-way to check the working place at the beginning of the shift, and Smith had followed him. Bawden, the contractor had told Smith that all was well, and then went down again to fix on the water hose, whilst Smith went up into the raise. Bawden shouted to Smith but received no answer, and upon climbing back into the raise, he found his mate unconscious on the pile. Bawden dragged his mate back to the rearing but was unable to get him down unassisted. He went for help, and Richard Thomas Sedgemore and James Barnard arrived with other miners. Sedgemore and Barnard, who were relatives, immediately climbed up the ladderway, with disastrous consequences. Barnard was overcome by the gas that had affected Smith, and fell down the ladder-way unconscious. He was severely injured on the head and back. Sedgemore pushed on, and "lost his life in a gallant attempt to rescue Smith." (Inquest).

Bawden, who climbed up behind Sedgemore and Barnard, went up to Sedgemore, who was lying at the top of the rearing unconscious. Bawden spoke to him but got no reply, and feeling unwell from the gas, returned to the level. Capt. Tom Williams arrived with two shift-bosses called Nettle and Nichols, and they all made vain efforts to get up the raise to the unconscious men. Donald Downing of Lanner and C.H. Butler of Tregajorran made heroic attempts to rescue the miners, before succumbing to the fumes. Other miners had to be physically restrained from further attempts. After one and half hours C.V. Paull, the manager, decided it was safe to go up and retrieve the bodies, the carbon monoxide gas having been blown away by increased air pressure.

The description of the attempted rescue, by Capt. Paull, is graphic: "I cannot pay too high a tribute to the heroism displayed by all the men who assisted. Men were dropping all around as the gas reached them. The effect if it was almost instantaneous and I was also affected by it. Mr.A.Nettle and Mr.S.Nichols, shift-bosses, strove to get up the ladder through the waves of gas, and Nettle, rendered almost unconscious, fell onto the shoulders of Nichols, who by catching him probably saved his life. In spite of this, Nettle insisted on making another attempt to go to the help of C.H.Butler of Tregajorran, who had fought his way through the gas and up the ladder to the two deceased men. Up in the raise Butler worked like a Briton, lashing up Smith and Sedgemore in readiness for them to be lowered ...Wilfred Lawrence ... an ambulance man ... went up the ladder but was overcome. He recovered a little, and at once made another attempt. We positively had to remove him by force and take him to surface for attention, as the gas had made him almost blind." (West Briton September 13 1937).

It was felt that the prompt use of oxygen, administered by Supt. Jory of St. John's, saved other lives that would otherwise have been lost. Downing, Barnard, Archie Johnson of Redruth were all seriously ill from the gas, and in the case of James Barnard, from his fall, and all three were kept in the Redruth Miners' Hospital for some time.

James Barnard returned to Crofty, and in 1942 he had another serious accident whilst pulling a chute. He died some time afterwards, as a result of these two accidents. His nephew, Fred Sedgemore, brother to Richard Sedgemore, told me that he could still remember him tramming down 290 Cooks main drag toward the shaft, with his violently guttering candle stuck to the front of his wagon.

1938 was a year that looked good to the shareholders of South Crofty, but for those a little closer to the mine, there were ominous signs. The excellent nett profit of £22,300, despite the low tin price of £128 16s 7d, - a drop of £27 9s on the 1937 figure - gave the investors false optimism, which was no doubt boosted by the payment of a 25 percent dividend.

Whilst the shareholders were congratulating themselves, the miners had no reason to. In l919 the men found it hard to manage on weekly wages of between £2 1s 3d., and £2 5s 9d. Twenty years later, with prices considerably higher, many miners were taking home as little as £1 12s 6d. Many were so poor that they had to go the authorities for assistance to help feed their families and to provide footwear for work. Most miners' pride stopped them from seeking help, but they were very angry, as they saw the results of their hard, dangerous labour providing less for their families, while it provided more for the shareholders.

During 1938 there was a gradual increase in the number of stopes being worked. In Crofty section they rose from 13 at the beginning of the year, to 21 by the summer, with 310 level being worked increasingly. In New Cook's section there was a rise from 12 to 15 stopes during the year, with stoping taking place on all levels between 175-315.

At Robinson's Shaft the 335 station was completed and the Cornish pitwork lowered to the new sump. Preparations were made to drive the north cross-cut so that the lodes discovered on 310 might be proved. A raise was started from the 310 level on No. 2 Lode, that was to connect with a winze from below the 290 level. There were good values found there. The drive toward Dolcoath on the deeper levels continued. The new Wet Lode was driven eastwards on 310 level, and the tin content was above average.

Discontent over wages, that had simmered for some time, finally erupted in January 1939. The Transport and General Workers Union, which represented the miners and mill workers, asked for a minimum weekly wage of £2 5s. The Company refused the request and made it plain that they did not recognise the Union, nor have any intention of negotiating with it. The Manager referred to the Union as having, "persuaded some 40 per cent of our employees to withdraw their labour," and indicated that the strike was not the result if grass roots feeling, over a justifiable claim. Capt. Paull further bragged, that as "the mine is three years ahead of the mill," the strikers stood no chance, because the mine could "face a stoppage for two years."

It was not true, as Paull claimed, that 40 percent of the workforce was on strike; it was nearer 54 percent, with 234 men out of 435 having withdrawn their labour. The Manager sounded reassuring when he informed shareholders that "many new hands were employed", to replace those striking, but what he did not say, was that most of those on strike were underground workers, and the skilled 'machine miners' and their mates predominated. Only 3,036 feet of development took place in the whole of 1939, and most of the stopes were unworked during the first eight months of the year. Between January 9 and March 17, there were only two stopes worked in Crofty section, and although recruitment of new labour brought several more into production, it was August 20, with the end of the strike, that the rest were restarted. The position was different in Cook's section, where most miners continued work.

With so many workers, underground and at the mill, still working, and with the "mine three years ahead of the mill", it was apparent to the strikers that other methods would have to be used. Crofty sold its black tin to Williams Harvey of Bootle, Lancashire, and the Union decided to 'black' all shipments of it. This effectively stopped the movement of the ore through any British ports, and cut off the Companys' life-blood.

In April the Company sought to outwit the miners by hiring a fleet of lorries to take the accumulated tin to Gweek Quay, where they had arranged for a Dutch coaster to meet it. Many of the lorries were hired from Vincent's Garage, which was situated at the top of East Hill, Tuckingmill. The miners heard about the plan and tried to stop the shipment. A battle ensued between the police and the strikers, and heads were broken by truncheons, and windscreens by bricks. One of the trucks was overturned by the miners. The convoy eventually got away, and 28 lorries carrying 100 tons of tin made it to Gweek where it was loaded aboard the ship and taken away. The Company received £15,000 for the tin, but it was the last to be sold while the strike continued.

Some of the men who were on 'essential services,' or so-called safety work, like the shaftmen, were told by the management that they had to work, and the Union officials apparently acquieced. Harold May was employed in the shaft at that time, and although he had been on strike, Clarence Paull called at his home and informed him that he and his mate were expected to work, as they were classed as 'safety men'. The Manager picked Harold up at the beginning of his shaft, in his "posh, lovely Rover car". and carried him to the mine where they underwent bombardment from rocks and other missiles. The strikers formed pickets at the entrance to the Count House, at Station Road, Pool, the lane beside Old's Garage, and the Dudnance Lane entrance to New Cook's Shaft. Each of these groups would hurl whatever was to hand at the passing Rover, but, Harold recalls, only once did the windscreen get broken.

The strikers dynamited the engine pond at New Cook's mill, and the muddy water swept down into Tuckingmill, flooding many house's, some of them occupied by strikers.

As frustration mounted, the miners determined to damage New Cook's Shaft and headgear, to try to interrupt the steady production that continued. Unfortunately for them, the police got to hear about it and were ready with about 100 officers. The miners arrived and straight away mounted an attack on the police protecting the plant. A fierce battle broke out, with several policemen being thrown into the engine pond, and many miners being badly battered. Miners and police were injured due to the fighting occurring as a running battle through the rubbish and scrap-iron lying about the shafthead. Neither side really won the day, but both sides suffered many casualties, and some of the miners who were struck by truncheons felt the effects for a long time afterwards.

The stories and anecdotes that the miners recall about the strike would fill a book on their own, but among the funny ones that I have been told by those who were first hand witnesses to the events, is one by the former Personnel Manager of South Crofty, the late Ted Rowe. He had worked at Crofty in 1937, during his summer vacation from the School of Mines, and in July 1939, whilst back at the School, he was in Camborne one morning, when he observed C.V. Paull and another man from Crofty's staff talking to the manager of Tonkin's Cafe, which was opposite the room (in the present Berkeley Centre), where the strikers were scheduled to have a meeting at noon. He and his fellow student listened to the conversation and Clarence Paull was persuading the manager to let him use his upstairs room to observe the meeting and identify the 'ringleaders'. The cafe manager was reluctant, as he commented that his cafe would not be worth much if the miners happened to see Clarence through the window. However, Clarence's influence eventually overcame the objections, and armed with a couple of bottles to help pass the hour or two before noon, they went upstairs. The two students stayed to watch the fun, and apparently, long before the miners began to arrive for their noon meeting, they saw the cafe proprietor angrily ushering the two Crofty men out of his front door, as they sought to support each other. They still carried the bottles, now empty, and Ted Rowe told me that they had got noisier and noisier, until they were all but leaning out of the windows above the pavement. The cafe manager was terrified lest the miners arrive and see them, and so he threw them out.

The strike continued into the summer with sporadic fighting breaking out as the miners' frustration boiled over. There were battles at the Count House, battles at the entrances to the mine, and outbreaks of violence all around Pool. Sometimes it was caused by 'blacklegs' trying to get into work, sometimes by supplies going in, and sometimes due to miners invading the property to carry out sabotage. Many of the policemen genuinely sympathised with the strikers, but they had their job to do, and with full stomachs against men who had not eaten properly for months, there were sometimes completely one sided battles, with underfed miners throwing themselves over the Station Road gates, and being thrown bodily back again.

The stale-mate was eventually broken by the arrival of the War. The miners returned to work and the Company settled down to reap the rewards of wartime production and profit. Many good miners left Crofty during the strike, never to return. Some went into the Services and if they survived the conflict, and many did not, they sought work elsewhere. Othars had gone to Climax and Holmans and other local firms before the outbreak of war. At Climax in particular, there was a large group of former Crofty men working, during and just after the War.

It must not be assumed, however, that the strike was a straightforward dispute between men and managers. Crofty section, possibly influenced by outsiders (Welshmen), struck because of their pay and conditions. Cooks men were paid better and had better contracts. They were mostly against the outsiders and the strike.

The cause of the strike was resolved by the War, for ordinary underground labourers were earning far in excess of the minimum claim by the early 1940s. The Union had asked for 45s per week, and by 1943 the basic rate for an underground labourer was 66s per week, which was almost 50 percent higher than the original claim.

With partial output for 8 months and full workings for the remaining 4 months, 1939 broke no production records. The 60 stamps worked for 202.60 days and crushed 54,226 tons of ore, for the recovery of 616$\frac{1}{2}$ tons of black tin and 36 tons of arsenic, which was valued at £97,077 and £893 respectively.

The average yield per ton crushed was 25.47 lb of tin, and 1.52 lb of arsenic. The costs at the mine per ton crushed and milled were £1 11s 9d, which gave Crofty a profit of above 4s 4d for each ton of ore raised. The actual sale by the mine of tin and arsenic and other sundry products amounted to £91,876. The 1939 price for tin was £156 7s 6d. There was a profit in 1939 of £12,369 3s 11d.

Although development during 1939 was at a minimum, with less that half the previous years footage, there was some important work done. The 335 cross-cut north from Robinson's was driven 156 feet from the shaft, intersecting Main Lode and No. 1 North Lode. These lodes were indefinable and disordered by elvan, which made their identities and nature somewhat obscure. There was a limited amount of development on No. 1 and 2 lodes at the deeper levels in both sections, and the results were generally good. Due to the shortage of labour, little progress was made in the drive toward Dolcoath.

1940 was the first full year of war, and the Company had to adjust to an entirely changed set of circumstances. The price of tin would inevitably rise, but the problems encountered during the first world conflict would undoubtedly repeat themselves. There would be labour and commodity shortage, together with widespread wartime restrictions. However, if given a reliably high price for its tin, the Company would cope with the rest. The average price paid for Crofty's tin during 1940 was £170 14s., and with this healthy financial fact behind it, the mine looked set fair to weather any difficulties.

The stamps ran 249.5 days and crushed 68,840 tons of ore for the production of 770 black tin and 67 tons of arsenic. The tin was valued at £125,332, and the arsenic at £3,350. The average yield per ton crushed was 25.56 lb of tin, and 2.31 lb of arsenic. Costs at the mine were up, to £1 13s 9$^{1}/_{2}$d., and the profit per ton crushed was 5s 10$^{1}/_{2}$d. Crofty sold tin and arsenic to the value of £125,806, and made a profit for the year of £19,065 6s 2d. The wage bill rose 25 percent in 1940.

In his Report to the Directors, for 1940, C.V. Paull had this to say about difficulties encountered:

"Owing to present War conditions, we have been short of labour throughout the year. We have concentrated on keeping up our much needed production of Tin and Arsenic, but our main development had to be somewhat limited. We have purchased an Automatic Loader and should soon have in use an Electric Locomotive, which will enable us to continue the development into Dolcoath area". (April 26 1941.)

The Automatic Loader was a small, 4 cylinder, Eimco rocker shovel. Eimco sent a representative to instruct the miners in the rocker shovel's use, and Holmans and Geevor Mine sent men to watch it work. The Eimco was taken to the 315 level, Cook's section, where it was to be used mucking the drive into Dolcoath. Bert Rule was driving on the No.2 Lode into the Great Crosscourse, and Bert

Shortman was given lessons by the Eimco instructor, who used the mucker on Bert Rule's pile. After an hour the instructor had to go back to the surface as he could not stand the heat, there being no ventilation and precious little air in the end. Mr Shortman recalled how he took almost an hour to load each wagon with the Eimco, before finally getting the hang of it. The Eimco mucker had stood idle on the 315 level for six months before the instructor was sent to demonstrate it. It was used on the drive into the Dolcoath and Roskear workings, and for several years was the only one at Crofty. By the end of the 1940s there were a couple more larger machines, but it was the late 1950s before Eimcos were widely used, and even in the early 1960s it was not unusual for ore piles to be mucked by hand.

The electric locomotive, referred to by C.V. Paull in the April 1941 Report, arrived later that year, but it was 12 months before it went into use on the level. Once again it was the 315 level drive into Dolcoath that saw its first use at Crofty. By the end of the 1940s there were two more locos underground, but like the rocker shovels, it was many years before they became general at Crofty, and there was still some hand tramming until the early 1960s.

By 1940 the use of carbide lamps was becoming more widespread. The majority of miners still used their 'six candles a day issue', but many miners could afford to buy carbide lamps, and there was a tendency toward their general use. The practice of issuing carbide lamps began about 1950, but many miners still carried candles because of the resilience of the flame.

In 1940 there was 5,360 feet of development. The 335 north cross-cut was extended 368 feet and the No. 2 and No. 3 North Lodes were intersected with disappointing results. The Manager was optimistic about the prospects for No.4 and No.5 lodes on that level. On 310 extensive exploration took place on No.2, development at the deeper levels was mostly on No. 1, No.2, and Main Lode, New Cook's Kitchen Vertical Shaft was sunk to the 340 level, and by the end of 1940 the timbering of the shaft and the 340 station were completed.

On September 13 1940 there was a serious accident in Robinson's Shaft. N.K. Kitto and W.J. Curnow were travelling in the cage when the whim man overwound, causing the cage to strike the bottom with great force. Kitto, who was 42 years old and had rejoined Crofty's staff from HM Forces after the Great War in 1919, suffered very serious injuries to his spine and head. He recovered well, however, and eventually became Mine Manager. The other man was less fortunate. William Curnow, of Wheal Gerry, Camborne, was injured in such a way as to require long treatment in St Lawrences Hospital, Bodmin, where he died as a result of the accident in March 1942.

1941 was not an easy year for Crofty, with costs rising, skilled labour scarce and a reduced tonnage milled. There were 62,114 tons stamped, for the recovery of

31. Kevin Mutton mucking a draw point using an Atlas Copco LM56 loader on Roskear 'A' Lode at the 420 fm level. The air shovel is side-loading a Granby wagon in a train of four 3 tonne wagons, hauled by a 5.5 tonne Clayton loco. July 1991.

32. *David Eldred mucking the Second Sub Decline Shaft below the 470 fm level. He is driving an Eimco 625 loader, and the face at the bottom of the decline shaft can be seen on the right-hand side of the picture. Notice the wire mesh in the roof to protect the men below. The poor ground conditions were due to the shaft entering the Great Crosscourse. December 1989.*

33. Loading the conveyor below 470 fm level on the Second Sub Decline. The Eimco 625 is side-tipping into a chute which feeds the conveyor belt. David Abraham is on top of the hopper. December 1989.

34. *The First Sub Decline Shaft junction at the 380 fm level. This decline shaft was started in the summer of 1979 and had reached the 400 fm level early in 1980. Note the conveyor running down the right-hand side and the 22" 401b track down the left-hand side. May 1989.*

728 tons of black tin. The average yield per ton crushed was 26.26 lb, but with costs at the mine £1 18s 2d, which was up 4s 4d on 1940, even that improved yield was not enough to give a good profit. South Crofty made a profit of £13,122 3s 2d in 1941, which was nearly £6,000 down on the previous year. There was a continued rise in the wage bill, and from that year, Crofty had to make payments under the War Damage Act (1941) with the amount for 1941 being £410 7s 11d.

Underground activity continued, with the drive into Dolcoath on the 315 level being assisted by the new Eimco rocker shovel. The promised electric loco arrived on the mine, but it did little during 1941. The 335 north cross-cut from Robinson's Shaft was extended further, and the cross-cut from 340 Cook's station was begun.

By 1942 Crofty's tin had assumed greater importance that hitherto. The loss of the rich supplies of tin that had come from those parts of the East conquered by the Japanese, made Cornish tin highly valuable. Men were drafted in as 'Bevan boys' to work at the mine, replacing in numbers, if not in skill, the miners that had gone into the Forces. The records show that a large proportion of the underground workers during the War were from outside the district. Some stayed at the mine for many years after the War was over. During 1942 the long overdue use of the electric loco began. It was used in conjunction with the Eimco mucker on the drive into Dolcoath on 315 level.

Development was still slow due to the chronic shortage of 'machinemen', but the 310 (315) and 335 (340) levels were opened up further during the year. There was a total of 64,402 tons hoisted and milled in 1942, which produced 632³/₄ tons of black tin at an average yield of 22 lb per ton. The costs at the mine per ton crushed went up again to an average of £2 3s 7¹/₄d. The total tin sold amounted to £150,657, and arsenic sales totalled £4,376. Wages went up another 25 percent during 1942, and with other difficulties being experienced the gross profit of £11,432 16s 2d., was quite good. The Company paid out £209 under the War Damages Act.

On December 2 1942, James Barnard, who had been seriously injured trying to rescue a mate in 1937, was again severely injured. A rock rolled from a chute that he was pulling and crushed him between the wagon and the side of the drive. His shoulder and ribs were badly damaged, and he never recovered from the injuries. He was 50 years old and had worked at Crofty as a trammer for many years.

1943 continued in the same vein as the previous year, with tonnage up slightly to 67,331 tons treated, and 651 tons of black tin produced. The average yield per ton milled was 21.65 lb. There was a total of £170,703 worth of tin sold, and £2,546 worth of arsenic. Wages rose by 25 percent, the War Damage Act took £156, costs per ton crushed went up to £2 7s 6d. and the before tax profit was £10,048 10s 3d.

Skilled miners further diminished in 1943, but there was some development on the deeper levels. The drives into Roskear were continued, as was the exploration of 335 (Robinsons) and 340 (Cooks) levels.

On the 31 December 1943, Capt. Josiah Paull resigned his directorship due to ill-health and was replaced by his son Clarence Paull.

Costs spiralled in 1944 with wages rising to £103,725. Fortunately, the price of tin also went up, so that at the end of the year there wae a gross profit of £9,948. The ore crushed dropped to 62,712 tons, but with an increased yield of 25.40 lb per ton, there was a healthy produce of 711$^{1}/_{4}$ tons of black tin. Costs at the mine for tin crushed went up to £2 18s 3$^{1}/_{2}$d. There was £191,858 worth of black tin sold, and £4,233 worth of arsenic. The Company made payments under the War Damage Act of £103.

One of the men drafted into Crofty, Douglas Henry Couch of Liskeard, had a fatal accident. On January 26 1944, this 19 year old youth was walking alone along the 260 level, when he fell into a 'gunnies'. The boxhole into the 'gunnies' was fenced but Couch went through the fencing for some purpose and fell down through the open area onto rocks 100 feet below. He suffered multiple injuries, including a fractured skull, and died instantly.

On February 4 1945 Francis Allen died. He had been Chairman of South Crofty Ltd. since the beginning, and had played a great part in the expansion of the mine into a viable, modern firm. He was replaced as Chairman by Harry Rich, a director of Gopeng Consolidated Ltd., and Tronoh Mines.

During 1945 there were 59,193 tons of ore crushed, for the production of 586$^{1}/_{2}$ tons of black tin. There was an average yield of 22.19 lb of tin for each ton of ore. Costs at the mine amounted to £3 1s 4$^{1}/_{4}$d per ton crushed, an increase of 3s 0$^{3}/_{4}$d over the previous year. Wages were down slightly to £98,647, but the silicosis claims for the year leapt to £1,661, which was an increase of over £1,000 in twelve months. Tin sales returned £194,234, and arsenic brought in a further £3,580. Crofty made a profit in 1945 of £13,354 5s 7d.

With the end of the War Crofty faced new problems. In June 1945 East Pool closed down, throwing the entire weight of its water onto Crofty's pumps. By the end of 1945 there were 1$^{1}/_{2}$tons of extra water flowing into Crofty every minute. Crofty undertook the operation of Taylor's 90" engine, and with Robinson's and New Cook's engines running to full capacity, and the whim being used to bale, the mine was kept dry. In his first address as Chairman of the Company, Harry Rich spoke of the desperate need for more miners:

"The immediate need at South Crofty is for more qualified miners. In view of the fact as mentioned last year, that we are prepared to pay entirely satisfactory wages, depending on performance, it is difficult to understand why more younger men do not enter this industry, especially those with adventurous spirits. The management has been following up the opportunity of obtaining the assistance of Polish Miners, who are being sent to this country.....it is an essential condition of success at South Crofty that at the earliest date possible a sufficient additional number of skilled miners should be employed."

With the demise of East Pool Mine, Crofty purchased a considerable number of their Holman drilling machines, including several "Silver Bullets".

1946 found Crofty in dire straights. The need for miners was more desperate than ever, and with pumping charges so alarmingly high, it was becoming impractical to operate with so few workers. Harry Rich summed up the situation when he wrote, "With such colossal expenditure to keep the mine free from water it is tragic to find less than half the number of miners employed to justify such an outlay. Our Manager, Mr.C.V.Paull, has literally scoured the country for recruits, with meagre results." On the subject of the high pumping costs, Rich had this to say, "Our Manager has prepared a scheme for replacing the Cornish pumps with electric pumping plant at an estimated cost of £60 to £70,000. Such equipment should effect an annual saving of approximately £25,000 ... such an installation would cover an additional 400 galls. per minute of water beyond the maximum capacity of our present pumps."

The shortcomings of the Cornish pumps was underlined by the flooding of the mine in December 1946. With the three Cornish pumps going well above their economical speed, and with the whims baling also, the water was still hardly kept at bay in Robinson's section. Dams were built on several levels to keep the water from flooding the workings, but it was apparent that more efficient pumps were needed to cope with a repetition of the extraordinary conditions of that winter. Torrential rain, together with choked adits and a collapsed shaft in Tuckingmill Valley, combined to send an estimated 15,000 gallons a minute down Robinson's Shaft. Dolcoath New Deep Adit was blocked, the shallow adit could not cope, and with millions of gallons pouring into the old shaft from the overflowing Red River, there was a flurry of activity on the part of the masons to built yet more dams on the levels not yet flooded. On 290 station, according to Jack Trounson, the roar of the water going down the shaft was deafening.

With the two problems of labour and water it was hardly surprising that production dropped dramatically in 1946. Tonnage milled dropped to 40,361 and the black tin produced was down to 544 tons. The yield was 30.77 lb per ton. Costs at the mine for tons treated rose over a third to £4 8s 5d, and coal and electricity went up by nearly 20 percent to £47,594, which was £130 per day for power. Not surprisingly, the wage bill was down by almost £10,000. The silicosis claims cost jumped again to £2,381, but there were no payments under the War Damages Act. With £194,000 revenue from tin and arsenic, the mine made a profit of £12,759 12s 7d.

By 1947 the future looked bleak for the mine. There were only 32,310 tons crushed, for a recovery of 437¹/₂ tons of black tin. The average yield romained high at 30.33 lb per ton, but this was due to concentrating the stoping on the high value ground. Costs shot up again and averaged £5 12s 3d per ton crushed. The cost of power and labour condition to rise, and with the returns from tin and arsenic down to £188,500, there was a considerably reduced profit of £5,040 12s 9d. Claims under the Silicosis Act reached a peak in 1947 of £3,280.

Harry Rich complained again that year of the apparently insoluble problem of labour shortage, and pointed out to the shareholders that with sufficient skilled miners, the tin produced could 'easily have been 700 tons.' One again the pumps were a source of concern, with a strapping plate and main pumping rod breaking during the year, bringing, once again, grave problems. On the subject of new post-war financial conditions, Rich had this to say:

"Since the last Annual Meeting the Ministry of Supply have terminated the War Agreement paying our costs with a compensatory subsidy of £24 per ton of Metal Tin produced and no ceiling on price. In its place they have imposed a new Agreement in which the subsidy is extinguished with Metal Tin at £495 per ton and the ceiling on which costs are paid is £595 per ton. This means that no profit can be made by the Mine when the all-in cost is £495 per ton for Metal Tin. Moreover, as the last Austerity Budget takes a 25 percent levy on all dividends, followed by 9/- in the £ Income Tax on what remains, there is no inducement to shareholders to find the money for the new pumping equipment, as the Ministry would take the £79 per ton (£569-£495) profit if we keep our costs at £495 per ton all-in which is difficult owing to the depletion of reserves during the War, and the necessary additional costs involved in carrying out this development work."

The price of tin that year was fixed at £569, but with the crippling taxation of the Labour Government even that apparently healthy figure was not enough to keep Crofty safe from closure. As far as South Crofty's subsidiary companies were concerned, fortunes were mixed. Bartle's Foundry had severe problems that culminated in the resignation of its Managing Director, but the price of wolfram kept sufficiently high for Castle-an-Dinas to remain buoyant.

Underground development at Crofty was limited in 1947, as it had been for several years past. There were 1,740 feet driven, raised and sunk, with most of the new development being in the western parts of the mine. The 290 and 340 cross-cuts from Cook's Shaft had both intersected No. 4 North Lode, and the samples taken looked very hopeful. With this lode opened up it was foreseen that Crofty would have ore reserves of sufficient quantity to supply the mill with 5,000 tons of good grade ore each month. The management anticipated an eventual production of over 700 tons of black tin per annum, with a market value of over a quarter of a million pounds. Most of these newly opened up reserves were in Cook's section and the west of Great Crosscourse, in Dolcoath and Roskear.

Crofty began to take advantage at the time of the tremendously improved Holman machines, which delivered a more rapid but lighter blow on the drill. With carbide being used on the cutting edge of the drill to give it longer wear, machines were developed that struck with a lighter blow, as the carbide would not at that time stand the shattering effects of the much heavier blow delivered by the older machines. Improved air pressure also contributed to the efficiency of these new machines, the most famous of which was the Holman's Silver 3. South Crofty eventually purchased a great number of these fine machines, which although quite heavy at 50 lb, were very fast. The successor to the Silver 3, the slightly heavier Silver 303, later became the standard machine used at Crofty. Climax, however, was still to remain the principal supplier of rock drills to Crofty for some years.

The mineral-lords continued during that period to show consideration to the mine, by taking reduced dues.

1948 was a slightly better year for Crofty, with ore crushed up a little to 33,789 tons, and black tin recovered increased to 500 tons, which was a reflection of the improved grade of 33.16 lb per ton. Unfortunately, costs again rose to £5 17s 6d per ton milled. Wages were up £8,000 on the previous year, and power also cost another £8,000 more. With revenue from tin sales up to £201,809 there was a modest profit of £2,063 6s 7d. Concern was expressed over the financial condition of Bartle's Foundry, but it seems that the firm's sole redeeming feature of giving top priority to Crofty was sufficient to justify its continued support.

Once again the shareholders were groaning under the weight of taxation that the post-war Labour Government put upon them, but the Report of the Mineral Development Committee, gave them great encouragement. It stated that the continued existence of South Crofty was of vital national importance, and that ways must be found to guarantee it.

With skilled men still failing to come forward, development continued only at a very slow rate. No. 4 Lode at Cook's was driven east and west, and New Dolcoath lodes were explored with heartening results. 335 was opening up well and considerable quantities of ore being recovered from the higher levels. Production was still concentrated on stopes with higher values, as the high average yield for the year shows.

On September 21 1948, there was another fatal accident at Crofty. Norman Jones, a 47 year old shaftman from North Roskear Village, was inspecting pitwork in Robinson's Shaft when he fell through the shaft. He sustained serious injuries to his head and body, dying shortly afterwards. It was the first fatal accident for nearly five years.

In 1949 production rose to 39,808 tons raised and crushed, but with the average yield down to 27.99 lb per ton, the actual black tin recovered dropped to 497$\frac{1}{2}$ tons. Costs were held in check during the year, so that although the wage bill increased to £102,348, which was £8,000 more than the previous year, the cost per ton crushed and milled went down to £5 3s 6d., and the coal and electricity bills only rose slightly. The payments under the Silicosis Act went down to £511 in 1949. Sales of tin and arsenic returned £208,000 but despite this increase South Crofty sustained a loss of £702 19s 7d.

In November 1949, Capt. C.V. Paull, the Mine Manager, died. He had been Manager of South Crofty since 1929, when he had taken over from his father, Josiah Paull. Harry Rich, the Chairman of the Company, had this to say about his death. "After a short illness, our Colleague and General Manager passed away on Thursday 17th November, 1949, at the early age of 51. Coming so soon after the death of the esteemed father, on 11th February, 1947, it was doubly a severe blow to South Crofty." J.P.A.Harvey of Helston took Clarence Paull's place on the Board, and the directors also debated the position of Harry Rich, who was then 81 years of age. They decided to continue their support of him.

The new Manager was D.D. Belcham, who had previously managed East Pool for the last 10 years of its operation. He was well recommended, being qualified not only in mining but also in electrical and mechanical engineering.

The Board negotiated with the Ministry of Supply for a £50,000 loan to cover the cost of new electrical pumps, but despite the recommendations of the Ministry's officials, and the fact that the Company had ordered the pumps from the manufacturers, the Treasury refused to ratify the loan, and the mine was left disappointed and empty-handed. The annual cost of maintaining the old Cornish pumps and pitwork was rising rapidly, and the mine officials met with S.W.E.B. officials to discuss the use of 'off-peak' electricity, should electric pumps be installed. The need to replace the Cornish Beam Engines was now urgent.

Mr. Belcham, the new Manager, although only taking over the job at the end of the year, made out the Report to the Directors for 1949. There were 5,230 feet of development, with just over half being intermediate stope drives. Belcham said in this Report that there were over half a million tons of payable ore in Crofty's lodes, and that half of it was on No. 4 North Lode. He stated his intention to have the 340 level driven into Roskear so that a connection could be established with the 16 foot diameter bricked shaft there. The improvement to ventilation, he said, would be tremendous.

A five ton Austin lorry was purchased in 1949, together with two more Eimco muckers and a new scraper hauler.

At 1.45 p.m., March 31 1950, a 34 year old miner was crushed to death by a rock. Andrew Hart of Pengegon Coombe had finished drilling and was waiting for his mate, B.Rubisz, to bring the dynamite, when a rock fell from the back and killed him. The accident happened on No. 4 Lode 335 level, a short distance east of the cross-cut.

1950 was a year of mixed fortunes for the mine. Tonnage milled dropped to 37,716, and black tin to 478$\frac{1}{2}$, but the average yield was up slightly to 28.43 lb per ton, and with returns from mineral sold up nearly £60,000, there was a profit of £42,924 13s 11d. Apart from the £262,166 from tin and £1,185 from arsenic, there were also £819 from wolfram. Costs at the mine for each ton crushed were £5 15s 4d. The wage bill increased to £109,454, and the cost of power to £61,160.

The Cornish pumps coped well with the water right up until December 28 1950, when another disaster struck the mine. The 90" Cornish Beam Engine at New Cooks Kitchen Shaft, whilst with a full head of steam, broke its 48 ton main bob. The engineman escaped serious injury, but the engine suffered irreparable damage to the cylinder cover, cylinder bottom, spring beams and timber work. Once again Crofty was threatened with flood, and immediate work began to build dams on the 340 and 315 levels to stop the water flooding the workings. The Manager reported to the Directors:

"After careful consideration it was decided to install temporary electrically driven pumps with all possible speed … enquiries for these emergency pumps were made all over the country and eventually Messrs Sulzer Bros. located two sets of pumps which were adapted to suit the head against which they would be required to work, and at the same time enquiries were made for suitable motors and switchgear, transformers, cables and columns.

Two Beresford submersible pumps were obtained for lifting the bottom water to the Sulzer pumps which were installed at the 205fm. level.

After many efforts two shaft cables and the necessary rising mains were obtained, together with a temporary sub-station on surface to provide the power required for the pumps. Our thanks are due to the staff of the S.W.E.B. for the expeditious way in which the sub-station was completed".

This emergency plant was in operation by February 1951 and the bottoms dry by April 26th. Due to the highly corrosive nature of Croftys water, great difficulty was experienced with the metal pipes installed at that time. Rock lime was introduced into the water to counteract this affect, and special metal was also used. Permanent pumps were on order, and some anxiety was experienced due to delays caused by national shortages and restrictions.

It was about 1950 that Crofty began to use Diesel locos to draw the ore from Robinson's Shaft to the crushing and milling plant at Cooks side of the mine. Eventually, five locos were used, and continued in use until the late 1960s when all ore was hoisted at Cooks Shaft. The five locos came from S.J.Andrew and Son (Redruth), Campamax Oil, Ballast Pit (Ramsgate, Kent), Scottish Oils (Midlothian) and Macsalvors (Pool).

Footage developed in 1950 amounted to 4,907, with 1,692 feet being main development and the rest either raises or intermediate stope drives. The flooding of the deeper levels caused a delay in the 340 drive into Dolcoath, but on both 290 and 335/340 levels connections were made on No, 4 Lode, which improved ventilation on those levels. The continuing shortage of miners curtailed much needed development, and stoping was also again restricted.

To overcome the labour problems the idea was being explored of canvasing displaced persons, especially Poles, Spaniards and Italians. Enquiries were made to obtain Nissen Huts to accommodate any foreign workers recruited.

Holman's approached the Company with a view to taking over the works of Bartles Foundry, and as they gave an undertaking to give the same priority to Crofty that Bartle's had done; it was agreed. The deal went through in September 1951.

In January 1951 another misfortune befell Crofty. The Tinyard was virtually gutted by fire. The fire broke out in the south-west corner of the Tinyard, and despite the prompt action of the local fire brigade, there was very extensive damage. The insurance company paid the claim quickly and within four months the worst of the damage we repaired.

It is not surprising, that so far as production is concerned, 1951 was a bad year. With the water on the lower levels for the early part of the year, and the Tinyard out of action for nearly four months, the mine was in a parlous state. When the water was lowered there was a great deal of repair work to be done. Considering the difficulties, the management were well pleased with the effectiveness of the temporary electric pumps. Due to the corrosive nature of Crofty's water, Sulzer Bros, were having difficulty finding the best metal for the permanent pumping plant. Throughout 1951 Taylor's 90", Robinson's 80", and three electric pumps coped with Crofty's, East Pool's and Tincroft's water.

In 1951 there were 28,517 tons milled, for the production of 303^1/$_2$ tons of black tin and 5^1/$_2$ tons of wolfram, which together yielded an average of 24.29 lb per ton. The costs at the mine went up a staggering £2 6s 5d., to £8 1s 9d, per ton.

Wages dropped slightly, but the power bill, although remaining more or less the same at £61,000, was made up of double the amount of electricity, and considerably less for coal and coke, thus reflecting the changes in the pumping arrangements. The price of tin was very volatile in 1951, with the price going from £1,620 early in the year to £806 on August 3rd, and up again to £1,000 by August 27th. Crofty sold £222,120 worth of tin, £10,883 worth of wolfram, and £277 worth of arsenic. There was a profit in 1951 of £13,188 18s 2d.

The accounts show that some of the old round frames used in the mill were replaced by James Slime Tables, with beneficial results. Another 5-ton Austin truck was bought for general surface use.

Development in 1951 amounted to 4,694 feet. Half of this total was made up of intermediate stope drives, and 450 feet of it were extensions to cross-cuts. Work continued to explore Dolcoath and Roskear, and in Robinson's section there was some main development on 335 level. Work commenced to excavate the chamber to accommodate the new electric pumps on the 195 level at New Cook's Shaft.

Several Poles had been employed during the year, and they had proved very good workers, and got on well with the Cornishmen. Active negotiations continued throughout the year to recruit Italians, and arrangements were made to accommodate them. It was hoped to bring 50 over from Sicily as quickly as possible.

Harry Rich, the Chairman of South Crofty Ltd., died on May 15 1952. J.P.A. Harvey of Helston replaced Mr Rich as Chairman, and Sir Gilbertson Smith took the vacancy on the Board.

There was a marked increase in ore milled in 1952, when the tonnage totalled 44,182. Black tin produced rose to 475^1/$_4$ tons, and wolfram dropped to 3 tons. The average yield for tin and wolfram per ton crushed was 24.02 lb. Costs per ton also went down to £5 19s. With £303,641 worth of tin, £2,490 worth of arsenic and £4,621 worth of wolfram sold, the mine made a profit of £46,618 19s 10d. Wages went up £30,000 in 1952, but, as this was accounted for by the improving number of miners, which helped produce the high profit, the higher wage bill was a healthy sign.

The mine purchased another electric locomotive in 1952, which meant that at least three were in use underground. A second-hand boiler was added to Robinson's plant to make the beam engine more efficient.

With more skilled miners available development went up by 50 percent, to a total of 6,644 feet. There were 1,923 feet driven on the lode, 125 feet of raising, 836 feet of cross-cutting and 3,760 feet of intermediate stope drives. The permanent pump station at 195 level Cook's was almost completed by the end of 1952, and work began on the 340 pump station. On the surface there were extensive repairs to the arsenic flues, and although there was much still to be done by the end of the year, the mine did produce 63½ tons during the year, and returns for it were ten times higher than the year before.

Hostel accommodation for the newly recruited Italian workers was completed in 1952, and by the summer there were 20 installed. Another 19 were due to arrive early in 1953.

On January 12 1953, T. Wallace Evans, who had been Company Secretary for 47 years, died. He had, with Messrs. Meyerstein and Allen, formed the new South Crofty Limited Liability Company in 1906, and had been a Director since June 1934. Thomas Prior was elected to the Board and became Managing Director.

The tonnage milled went up to 52,140 in 1953, the production of black tin rose to 556 tons and wolfram to 3½ tons. Recovery of tin and wolfram per ton crushed averaged 24.04 lb. Costs remained steady at £5 18s 7d per ton. Despite the increased tonnage of tin and wolfram returns dropped by nearly £62,000, due to the Korean War ending, and the price paid for those two commodities slumping. The mine lost £56,586 5s 7d in 1953.

Once again the wage bill increased dramatically, with an extra £30,900 being paid out in 1953. This was partly accounted for by the steady stream of Italian and other foreign labour that arrived at the mine. By early 1953 there were nearly 40 Sicilians ensconced in the Nissen Hut accommodation at Dudnance Lane.

Thomas Prior's Report on the year 1953 showed steady progress maintained toward the mine becoming a viable operation. At present, he wrote, Robinson's and Cook's Shaft hoisted an almost equal amount of ore, but eventually it was planned to bring most of it up Cook's side. He pointed out that currently the two sections were connected on the 290, 310/315, and 335/340 levels, but that eventually it would be necessary to tram all dirt to Cooks for hoisting.

On the prospects from the various lodes, he said, "To the north of Main Lode, there are other lodes which do not outcrop to surface. Of these, No. 4 Lode, which is 875 feet north of the Main Lode, has proved of major importance in the three lower levels. At the bottom level, the 340 fm level, the oreshoot on No. 4 Lode is 2,625 feet long, averaging 5.6ft wide and carrying 31 lbs black tin per ton, by vanning assay".

154

The Report detailed the intersections with lodes made on the 290 north cross cut from Robinson's Shaft. At 945 feet No. 4 was cut, with good results; at 1,035 feet No. 5 was found, and 475 feet of payable ore had been opened up for stoping; at 1,225 feet No. 6 was intersected and although it was driven 200 feet, there was nothing of great value there; at 1,400 feet No. 7 lode was cut, and although this is probably Reeves Lode, which was so rich in copper at the higher levels, it only carried a small amount of tin; at 1,525 feet No. 8 Lode was discovered, and although it was only driven a short distance it had every appearance of being valuable; finally , at 1,603 feet, the No. 9 Lode was cut, and over a distance of 20 feet it proved between 8½ and 11 feet wide, and assayed at between 19 lb per ton on the west and 32 lb per ton on the east. The cross-cut was extended to a distance of 1,742 feet north of Robinson's Shaft. The end of the crosss-cut was near to the killas-granite contact, and Prior pointed out the importance of the 'entire zone of granite which lies within the first thousand feet of depth below the contact with the killas.' Further exploration in that region was suspended until the permanent electric pumps were in operation, as there was a fear of water.

The 340 drive toward Roskear Circular Shaft was 1,000 feet from the workings based on that shaft, and it was hoped to find other lodes west of Great Crosscourse, besides those worked by New Dolcoath.

Prior also reported on the state of pumping in 1953:

"The normal rate of pumping is from 800 to 900 gallons per minute, of which quantity two-thirds percolates from adjacent abandoned mines. The new pumps for Cook's Kitchen Shaft comprise three electric centrifugal pumps at the 340 fm level, and five similar pumps at the 195 fm level. It is intended to do most of the pumping at night, to get the advantage of 'off peak' rates for electric power. As soon as the new electric pumps are in commission the Cornish pumping engine at Robinson's Shaft will be stopped. This Cornish pump will be 100 years old in August of this year (1954). The Cornish pumping engine at Taylor's Shaft, East Pool, which is costing South Crofty Co. £15,000 per annum, cannot be stopped until a drive 300 feet long (which was started in April 1954) has been completed to convey East Pool water into South Crofty's underground storage 'pool' at the 1,000 ft level.

It is unlikely the new electric pumps will be in commission until late autumn, 1954. Once they are in full service, one of the greatest handicaps to the efficient working of the mine will have been overcome".

Vast improvements to the ventilation of the workings were made. Old Shafts were cleared, connection between the two sections were increased and electric fans were introduced to blow more air into the ends. On 340 level a fan was put in the drive into Roskear, and at Robinsons provision was made to put fans into the easternmost drives.

Finally, Prior had much to say on the present milling set up, and the need to enlarge and modernise it:

"The existing mill has a maximum capacity of 6,000 tons of ore crushed per month. Notwithstanding the fact that development drives often show stretches of ore assaying 30 lbs. black tin per ton, the experience of many past years shows that the average yield of the ore lies between 1 percent and 1.1 percent (22.4 and 26.4 lbs.) combined tin and wolfram recovered per ton crushed. This result is confirmed by the 2½ million tons or ore treated since 1906. Therefore, with the existing mill the maximum monthly recovery is 66 tons of black tin (i.e., 1.1 percent of 6,000 tons crushed). This quantity of black tin would be worth £26,400 with tin metal at £615 per ton.

When the electric pumps are in commission, it is estimated that the working costs of the mine and its development, with the mill treating 6,000 tons of ore per month, would be roughly £26,400 per month. Thus, with the existing mill capacity the Company could only make profits when tin metal was more than £615 per ton. In order to put the mine into a position to tide over periods of lower tin prices, the output of tin must be increased to help bear the heavy overheads of pumping and upkeep. The ore reserves are in a healthy position and could stand a greater monthly output. For several years past, shortage of underground machine men has been the limiting factor in the amount of work accomplished. Even when the dead work on the installation of the new electric pumps has been completed, it is not easy to foresee how the mine tonnage can be increased beyond 8,000 tons per month for some considerable time to come, though an output of 7,500 tons per month should be attainable comparatively soon.

By using the modern heavy-media separation process which rejects most of the unpayable material before it reaches the stamp-batteries of the mill, the present mill could be made capable of extracting the tin from upwards of 10,000 tons of mine ore per month, with only minor additions to the existing regrinding and slimes plant. Detailed consideration was given to this scheme, and tenders were obtained for the supply and erection of the plant needed.

It was found that it would involve a relatively hiqh capital outlay for ore bins, secondary crusher and conveyors to connect the H.M.S. plant with the existing mine layout, and that in running costs the principal economies of the H.M.S. plant would be attained when the throughout of the run-of-mine ore exceeded 7,500 tons per month. An opportunity arose to acquire at a satisfactory price a complete secondhand tin milling plant of 100 tons per day capacity, situated about eight miles by road from the South Crofty mine. This plan is in good condition and the whole of the buildings and machinery will be dismantled, transported and re-erected at South Crofty as an extension of our existing plant, thus providing the additional treatment capacity needed as and when increasing numbers of underground machinemen permit the tonnage milled to be increased.

Immediately the new Electric pumps at the 340 fm. level are satisfactorily at work, it is necessary to start sinking Cook's Kitchen Shaft 300 ft, so as to open up another two levels below the 340 fm horizon. This work is some years overdue, but has had to wait because of the lack of underground machine men. This cost of the shaft sinking will be met from the Mine Development Reserve Fund, which is shown on the Balance Sheet.

Other improvements to the equipment of the mine, which should be undertaken in order to make economies in present costs are a new electric winding engine for Cook's Kitchen Shaft, the electrification of the winding engine and steam driven compressors at Robinson's Shaft, and at some later date, the improvement of the rock-crushing arrangements prior to the stamps.

To sum up, the mine has satisfactory ore reserves and every likelihood of being able both to maintain and increase those reserves given the requisite number of underground machinemen; the mill is being expanded so as to allow the rate of tin production to increase in order to tide the Company over periods of low prices for metal; the other equipment on the property can be modernised at a cost which would show a very satisfactory return for the capital outlay. During the year there has been a small increase in the underground labour force but more machinemen are urgently required. It should be possible to obtain these additional machinemen, for to the best of my knowledge there is no industry in the county where a young man of good physique can make such high wages as by working a machine underground either in stoping or on development.

30th April 1954

T.Pryor
Managing Director."

In 1954 the tonnage hoisted and milled went up to 60,547, for the production of 590$\frac{1}{2}$ tons of black tin, 8$\frac{3}{4}$ tons of wolfram and 32$\frac{1}{2}$ tons of arsenic. The average yield of tin and wolfram per ton crushed was 22.17 lb. Crofty sold £278,000 worth of tin, £1,286 worth or arsenic and £8,258 worth of wolfram. Tin averaged £721 per ton, which was not enough to give the mine a profit, under the conditions that then existed. Crofty lost £25,883 in 1954. The wage bill was £170,867 and cost of power was £73,000, a rise of £10,000 on 1953.

There was 6,755 feet of development in 1954, with 2,470 feet driven on the lode, 236 feet or raises, 1,025 feet of cross-cutting and 3,025 feet of inters and boxholes. No exploration was possible on No. 9 Lode as there was still concern over the possibility of striking water, and the new pumps were not yet in commission. In Roskear on 340 level a new lode was cut that sampled at 66 lb per ton. On 335 the 'Complex' lode near to No. 2 was discovered and there were 'rich patched of tin above the level'. At Cook's on 315 level the No. 2 and No.3 lodes were proving good. No. 4 lode on 245 was being explored with good results, as was the No. 2A on that level.

Three of the new permanent electric pumps and their motors were installed on 195 station, together with the necessary 10-inch rising main. The first pump was working by May 24 1954. As a result, the expensive running of Taylor's pump was discontinued in September 1954. The 340 pump station was completed in 1954, with settling pits, and sump cut out, and two pumps and motors installed. By March 30 1955 one of the 340 pumps was working.

On the surface the Company erected new survey and engineering offices, and progress was maintained in the installation of the plant purchased from Mount Wellington Mine.

The mine was visited during 1954 by scientists from the Atomic Energy Commission, who searched the workings for uranium. They found quantities of it in No. 4 Lode, near to the killas-granite contact, but were quick to point out to the Company that there were no payable quantities, and no prospects of finding any at the mine.

It was decided in 1954 to move the Head Office of the Company from London to Pool, to save money, and from that time R.J. Thomas, the local secretary, was to become Company Secretary, in place of C.A. Heathcote; Thomas Prior became Chairman of the Board in place of J.P.A.Harvey, and the manager, D.D. Belcham was elected to the Board.

The year ended with a period of great expense for Crofty, as Robinson's pumping engine was still in use, and more and more electricity was being used to power the newly commissioned pumps. The last year or so of Robinson's 80" pump, had been attended with several breakages, mostly due to the engine's age, and the enormous burden placed on it during the last decade. On May 1955 this great engine finally stopped pumping.

Robinson's 80" engine was an engineering masterpiece. It had done an incredible amount of work over a period of 101 years, being used at Wheal Alfred between 1854-64, at Wheal Abraham between 1864-75, where it unwatered, at first alone, an enormous network of old workings, and then to Tregurtha Downs Mine, where it again was used to keep dry a very wet mine. South Crofty had purchased this fine Samuel Grose engine in 1902, for £375, only a fraction of its original price.

The company leased it to the Cornish Engine Preservation Society, which after becoming the Trevithick Society, passed the lease over to the National Trust. It can be visited by obtaining the key and permission, from South Crofty's Office.

Less than a month after the old 80" was stopped, the four electrical pumps on 195 Cook's and the two on 340 were all working efficiently. Crofty's water problems appeared over. Work could be commenced immediately on those drives near to the boundaries, where water was feared, and No. 9 Lode was one of the first to restart.

Apart from development on No.9 Lode, drives continued into Roskear, where miners were only 880 feet from Roskear workings on the 340 level. On 245 level the No. 2A Lode was showing values of 78 lb per ton over a width of nearly 4 feet, and other work progressed on No's 2,3 and 4 lodes. Development footage dropped 200 feet to 6,555 feet in 1955.

During 1955 negotiations to borrow £100,000 from Williams, Harvey & Co., Ltd., of Bootle, the tin smelters, and Tehidy Minerals, Crofty's principal mineral lords, were rewarded with agreement. The money was to be spent on the new mill plant, the H.M.S. plant, and on deepening New Cook's Kitchen Vertical Shaft, another 300 feet.

In 1955 there were 67,626 tons milled for the production of $711^{3}/_{4}$ tons of black tin (70 percent Sn), $2^{3}/_{4}$. tons of wolfram and 74 tons of arsenic. The average yield for tin and wolfram was 23.64 lb per ton. Costs at the mine were £4 14s 2d per ton crushed, and the wage and power bills went up nearly £20,000. The average price for Crofty's tin was £752, which returned £357,999, and together with £3,116 for arsenic and £2,061 for wolfram, the net returns were £363,176. There was a profit in 1955 of £37,736.

On March 23 1956, one of the Polish miners had a fatal accident. Stanislaw Szmal, who lived at Green Lane, Redruth, was working with Henry Kazmarek on the 290 level west of Cook's cross-cut, on No.4 Lode. Whilst engaged in barring down the back, he was struck by a rock, and his skull was fractured. It was the first fatal accident at Crofty to kill one of the foreign workers recruited by the Company.

The mill crushed and treated 71,105 tons of ore in 1956, and produced 729 tons of black tin, 7 tons of wolfram and $88^{3}/_{4}$ tons of arsenic. The tin and wolfram yield averaged 23.19 lb per ton raised, and the costs at the mine were £4 1s 3d. Tin sales amounted to £370,587, arsenic £3,576, and wolfram returned £6,035. There was a profit of £19,909. The average price paid for Crofty's tin was £760 a ton.

The new pumps at 195 and 340 level functioned well in their first full year of operation and kept the mine dry whilst holding the neighbouring mines' water at the 1,000 foot level. These eight permanent pumps were supplemented by a small submersible in Robinson's Shaft, and another in Mayne's Shaft, which provided the mill with extra water.

Development footage in 1956 amounted to 10,394 feet, and nearly half of this total was main development. The drive to improve the adit system link to Dolcoath New Deep Adit advanced 634 feet during the year. The diamond drill explored 1,907 feet of ground. The 340 level in Roskear was directly under the 1900 level of New Dolcoath Mine, and was finding payable lodes. The 310 cross-cut north of Robinson's Shaft was advanced 531 feet and cut No. 6 Lode, which averaged 48 lb per ton, No.7 Lode (Reeves Caunter Lode), which was almost barren, and No. 8 Lode which was disappointing.

A diamond drill hole encountered a wide lode formation 411 feet north of No. 9 on 290. It was 12 feet wide and averaged 61 lb of tin per ton. Throughout the deeper levels good tin ground was being discovered by driving or diamond drilling. No. 4 Lode was still proving the saviour of Crofty, with nearly half of the proven ore reserves to be found in it.

During 1956 a licence was taken out by the Company to work Wheal Agar sett, and East Seton sett, on the northern boundary, was leased in 1957.

No shaft sinking took place at Cook's Shaft, as there were insufficient experienced miners. It had been hoped to get this important project underway during 1956, but despite the healthy amount of development carried out by Crofty's increasing machinemen, none were found with sufficient skill in this particular job.

1957 was a bad year for the mine. Wages rose by over £11,000, power by over £6,000, and with the tonnage milled down to 70,633, and black tin to 725 tons, things looked shaky. The price for black tin dropped to £725, the costs per ton crushed rose to £5 3s 8d, wolfram production all but ceased, with only one ton produced, and arsenic was down to 53¼ tons. The average yield for tin and wolfram was 23.04 lb per ton. Crofty sold £352,818 worth of black tin (70% Sn), £1,959 worth of arsenic and £553 worth of wolfram. There was a loss of £22,003 in 1957.

Development was down to 9,678 feet, with 5,982 of that being main development. The drive to extend the adit system was advanced, as was the drive into Roskear. There were 973 feet of diamond drilling completed and a large area of ground to the north and west of the mine was explored. The north cross-cut on 310 level was pushed through the No. 9 Lode with quite good results. The cross-cut was driven further north to search for the ore bodies located by the diamond drill on the level above. Another electric fan was put to work in the 340 drive into Roskear, and it improved the air situation considerably.

35. *Jeff Gilbert, a surveyor, beside a 1.75 tonne Clayton loco in the 400 fm level charging bay. Note the manual hoist for changing over the batteries and fire extinguishers above the charging points. Crofty has some twenty 1.75 tonne and ten 5.5 tonne locos underground. May 1989.*

36 Peter Futcher operating the winder at 370 fm level at the top of the First Sub Decline Shaft. The winder is an M B Wild single drum machine, with 2,000 foot long 7/8" wire rope. It hoists from 400 and 420 fm levels. January 1993.

37. *Enormous gunnis on Great Lode near to Tolgus Tunnel at the 255 fm level in Wheal Agar. The gunnis is immediately below Crofty's 260 fm level. Treve Lawrence is in the foreground and Chris Price and John Eyre are furthest from the camera. The picture demonstrates the sheer scale of some of Crofty's workings. May 1990.*

38. *Pitwork in Barncoose Engine Shaft at the Adit Level. The author is standing on the northern side of the shaft. Note the Davy safety lamp used when the adits are inspected. Barncoose Adit, an essential part of Crofty's drainage system, was started in the 17th century and completed to South Carn Brea Mine before the end of the 18th century. June 1990.*

The re-organisation of the mill, and the installation of the new H.M.S. plant was well in hand, with a concerted effort being started in August 1957 during the annual holiday period. New cone-crusher, ore bin and conveyor belts were erected, and the modernisation of the whole plant was progressing well.

Early in 1957 N.K. Kitto, the Assistant Manager, was sent by the Company to Sweden to study the techniques used there for breaking and handling rock underground. He found that the Swedes were well ahead of most other countries in their methods. The Company hoped that Mr. Kitto would bring these improved techniques to Crofty.

Heavy capital expenditure continued in 1958, and the Chairman's Report stated that of the £49,597 spent, '£43,244 was on the Rod Mill, H.M.S. plant and other parts of the treatment plant.' In the short term this led to the loss recorded for that year of £51,575, but in the long term it spelt a healthy condition for the mine.

The tonnage milled went up to 75,596, the black tin produced increased to 741$^3/_4$ tons, the arsenic nearly doubled to 98$^1/_4$ tons, but there was no wolfram. The price of tin dropped to £717 per ton, but the amount returned was up to £366,674. The average yield of tin per ton was 21.98 lb, and the cost per ton crushed was £5, 0s 11d.

Development footage was 10,481, with 6,393 feet being main development and the rest sub-development. On the deeper levels the 3A and 3B lodes were opening up well, and No. 9 Lode on 290 and 310 was proving valuable. In 1956 a diamond drill had cut a 12 foot wide lode north of No. 9, but the main cross-cut on 290 failed to intersect it, and so a short diagonal cross-cut from No. 11 Lode was driven and this found No. 12 Lode. Both of these lodes produced samples of high value. No. 12 was 2,100 feet north of Robinson's Shaft.

The 335 main cross-cut intersected No's 6,7 and 8 lodes, but although No. 8 was hopeful, the former two were not. On 340 level the western drives holed through into New Dolcoath old stopes. There were 1,927 feet of diamond drilling in 1958, much of it exploring the Roskear and Dolcoath setts.

During 1958 Barncoose Adit was reconditioned, a headgear and hoist was erected at Whim-round to prepare for the extension to Dolcoath New Deep Adit, and 459 feet of new adit were driven. Old Cook's Kitchen Middle Engine Shaft was repaired as part of the new adit scheme with much work carried out on its collar. It was this shaft that was to be connected to the Dolcoath Adit system.

With the improved ventilation at the deeper levels in the western part of the mine, due to the connections to Roskear Circular Shaft at its 1900 and 2000 levels, and the imminent improvement to the water situation when the adit system was completed, the mine looked to be moving to a much sounder footing. The old pump column at Cook's was removed between the 245 and 340 levels, and preparation for sinking was well in hand.

On April 24 1958, D.D. Belcham resigned through ill health and N.K. Kitto became Acting Manager. A. Leonard Thomas became a director at the same time, and was appointed Managing Director. He also had close connections with Geevor Mine, and was a member of the Thomas family of Dolcoath. Mr Kitto was confirmed as Manager within a few months. In 1959 J.E. Denyer became Chairman of the Company, and was to preside over it during a period of great change and many improvements.

The amount hoisted and milled in 1959 went up to 92,530 tons, and the black tin produced increased to 892 tons, at an average yield of 21.59 lb per ton. Arsenic produced was 52 tons. Costs per ton dropped to £4 6s 4d. Wages and salaries increased by £10,000 to £213,433, but with the electric pumps removing the water economically, the new mill and H.M.S. working efficiently, and the price of Crofty's tin averaging £784 per ton, the mine made a healthy profit of £29,463. Returns from tin sold amounted to £465,483, and arsenic brought in another £1,875.

There was a total of 6,470 feet of main development, and 4,602 feet of box holes and inters. New Cook's Shaft was deepened from its sump a further 53 feet to the new 360 level, and work commenced to cut out the station. The diamond drill completed 1,595 feet of exploration in 1959, which was 330 feet less than the year before.

The No. 9 Lode was explored on 290,310 and 335 levels, and 43 percent of the distance driven was found to be payable. On 260 the north cross-cut was driven toward No. 9 Lode. On 335 the cross-cut was driven to 1,714 feet from the shaft and intersected what was then called No. 10 Lode. It is now usually called 'No. 9 Fault Lode.' The heat in No. 10 was unbearable and special measures were taken to cool the air being blown into the drive. A German team of technicians suffered badly from the heat and one of them was removed in an unconscious state. The effort of working in there was thoroughly exhausting, and it was reckoned enough just to stand still.

The drive on 310 level into North Tincroft found the expected junction of Pryce's and South Lodes, but although the ore body was wide, the expected high values did not immediately materialise. Further exploration was abandoned for a while. In 1959 the drive into Agar sett began from the 310 level, and by the end of the year miners had tunnelled 230 feet beyond Crofty's old boundary. The drive toward the new connection with Dolcoath New Deep Adit was advanced 625 feet.

162

In 1960 the production dropped slightly to 856 tons of black tin. Although the ore treated went up a little to 92,680 tons, the average yield per ton dropped to 20.7 lb, and this caused the smaller quantity of tin. With capital expenditure up 500 per cent, and all other costs also rising, there was a modest profit of £10,063. There was a slight fall in the actual costs per ton raised of 10d. per ton. Returns from tin were £436,811, but the amount received from the 25^1/$_2$ tons of arsenic produced was negligible.

On January 16 1960, J.H. Lucas of Beacon had a fatal accident. He was employed on 340 level in Cook's section, and whilst walking on the level he was struck by rock that fell from the side and roof of the level. He received multiple injuries from which he died a fortnight later. The mine-captain, Roy Thomas, and G. Contrino who was present, gave accounts of the accident to the inquest.

During 1960 Cook's Shaft was sunk to the 400 level's sump, and 380 station was excavated. New ore and waste passes were cut between 290 and 380, and preparations were made to bring the shaft into use as the main haulage shaft. The old steam whim at Cook's was to be electrified for greater efficiency and better economy. The boilers at Robinson's whim were changed from coal to oil for the same reason. A ventilation fan was installed at Roskear Shaft to improve further the flow of air through the western workings. The new plant at the mill was completed during the year.

In 1960 there was a general tightening up of the Mines and Quarries Regulations, with respect to explosives. New dynamite stations had to be built underground, and the handling of dynamite was subject to greater care. Special containers had to be made to carry it underground, and more attention had to be paid to security. The Joint Advisory Committee heard that the miners resented these changes, and the management conceded that some of the demands seemed excessive.

Complaints about the toilet facilities underground were also heard by the Committee, and promises were given to look into the possibility of installing Elsan units on the levels. Another cause of complaint at that time was the quality of the cheesas and fuses from I.C.I. The miners also reckoned that they should be provided with more eight foot capped fuses and less six foot ones. Electric cap-lamps were being experimented with, but there was considerable resistance to their use. The men working in the new shaft at Cook's were accused of causing deliberate damage to the lamps.

Development footage was 5,048, with just half of the footage on lode being payable. No. 3 Lode on 245, 260,290 and 335 levels was sporadic in value, but in Cook's Section No. 3A & 3B were very good, although 3C was poor. No. 6 Lode on the 260 north cross-cut was moderate, but what was disappointing, was the erratic nature of No. 9 Lode. Some 950 feet had been driven on No. 9 on the 260,

290, 310 and 335 levels, and only 700 feet had been payable. On 315 level No. 9 had been driven toward the western drive on 310 level, connecting before the end of the year, but only 97 feet had proved payable. Main Lode in Cook's section came in for re-exploration in 1960, and on 315 it proved good. Further examinations of the lode at 245 and 260 levels showed the existence of quantities of ore left behind, and this also was the case on No. 2 Lode on these levels.

A cross-cut was driven 244 feet south from No. 9 Lode on 310 level, into the old Agar workings. It eventually connected to the main drive into East Pool and Agar and provided better ventilation. More work was done to the adit system, with another 312 feet driven, the Old Cook's Kitchen Middle Engine Shaft being re-collared and concrete lined to a depth of 183 feet, and the water in Old Cook's Kitchen Mine, and the neighbouring Carn Brea Mine, being lowered 44 feet.

1961 was a good year for the mine. Ore treated was 92,990 tons, black tin produced was the same as the year before at 856 tons (70% Sn), arsenic was 44½ tons, the average yield per ton was 20.6 lb, and the price paid for each ton of Crofty's tin leaped to £895. With returns for the sale of black tin at £504,983, it was hardly surprising that the profits went up 380 percent, to £48,564.

There was a total of 5,368 feet of main development and 4,065 feet of sub-development (stope preparation), with 740 feet of diamond drilling. There had been none the year before. Drives on lode had only averaged 37 percent of payability, which was a considerable drop on the expected amount.

The development of No. 9 Lode continued to show erratic results, but a newly discovered lode on 260 called 'Elvan Lode,' was producing very valuable ore, with 200 out of 294 feet driven being payable. The '2nd South Dipper Lode.' which was just south of No. 1 Lode in Cook's section, was giving high values on over 500 of the 636 feet driven. It averaged 44 lb of tin per ton.

Work on the adits continued in 1961, with the drive toward Dolcoath's Valley Shaft pressing on through very bad ground. A diamond drill had been used to examine the nature of the killas that the tunnel was to go through. An old shaft in West Seton Mine was concreted and a connection made to the adit system.

On 380 level the skip loading bays were completed and working by August 1961. Work began on the environs of the station to prepare for its full use. The electric fan at the bottom of Roskear was reckoned by Mr. Kitto, the Manager, to have improved ventilation in the western workings by up to 50 per cent. The shaft was still partially blocked however, and the obstruction, which was estimated to be 1,000 feet from the surface, would have to be removed for the full benefit of the fan to be felt.

In the mill eight old Frue Vanners were replaced by James's Tables, and a ball mill was added to the regrinding plant. The changeover to oil at Robinson's Whim was complete by March 1961, the new Dry for Robinson's men was nearing completion by the end of the year, major repairs to Robinson's headgear were carried out, and, underground, the new Elsan toilets were found to be a success.

The controversial electric cap-lamps were withdrawn from use when the work on the shaft was finished. Members of the Joint Advisory Committee had constantly complained about the ill-use these lamps had received from the miners. At a meeting of the Advisory Committee on November 8 1961, with N.K. Kitto in the Chair, the issue of the cap-lamps was settled, albeit temporarily:

"It was reported that the Electric Cap Lamps had been withdrawn from normal use and would be put in order. In future they would only be used on special occasions. Mr. Stapleton reported only 18 lamps out of a total of 26 had been received back. Mr. Salmon asked if carbide could (again) be issued from the Dry at New Cook's Section. Mr. Symons said it could be."

It was over two years before moves were again made to introduce electric cap lamps.

In January 1962, and again in October, breakages to the skip runners in Cook's Shaft caused costly problems. Two weeks hoisting was lost in January, and four weeks in October due to these accidents. These mishaps contributed considerably to the low profit of only £539 in 1962.

There were 92,590 tons hoisted and treated in 1962, for the production of 822 tons of black tin (70% Sn), and 24$^1/_2$ tons of arsenic. The average yield per ton dropped to only 19.89 lb. Costs per ton crushed amounted to £4 16s 9d. The wage, salary and pension bill came to £257,000, and revenue from tin sold was £475,382.

Main development amounted to 7,257 feet, and stope preparation was 5,559 feet. Diamond drilling totalled 1,207 feet. A depressing 23.9 percent of the drives on lode were payable. The No. 2 Lode inside the Agar sett was very good and some of the values encountered on the north cross-cut from Cook's on 360 level were also high. By the end of the year the cross-cut was advanced 1,052 feet from the shaft, and had cut No. 1, 2, Pegmatite, and No. 4 lodes. Although it was difficult to assess the overall potential of the Pegmatite Lode, the samples taken assayed at high values, and the management viewed the results with controlled optimism. No. 4 Lode also showed some good results. The 380 station and the settling tanks were enlarged with connecting cross-cuts driven behind the shaft.

An improved connection was made in 1962 between the Dolcoath New Deep Adit system and the network of adits that had been repaired and enlarged around South Crofty. By the end of the year 8,000 feet of adits were completed and in good repair. The water in the surrounding old workings was lowered 35 feet as a result. At Roskear Shaft temporary headgear was erected to facilitate the clearance of the shaft that was partially blocked at 1,000 and 1,700 feet from the surface. Preparations were made to install a large exhaust fan at the shaft-head to draw the foul air up the shaft from the western workings. At Cooks Shaft the electrification of the whim was completed. By the end of 1962 the first part of the new Miners' Dry was completed, and Robinsons's men no longer had to use the 60 year old Dry.

On December 3 1962 a very serious accident happened to one of the Sicilian miners. He was blasting rock on a pile that he was mucking when the accident occurred. One of the 'pad' of dynamite had failed to explode in the normal time, and when the miner returned to check the pile, there was a delayed explosion, which destroyed the man's sight and caused serious injury to his face and arms.

Mr. N.K. Kitto indicated his desire to retire, and on May 1 1963 G.C. Pengilly became Manager of South Crofty Mine. N.R. Kitto had been at Crofty, apart from a short break during the Great War, for 50 years. He had returned to the mine from the Forces on January 7 1919, and had worked at the mine up until his retirement as Manager in April 1963. In 1940 he was severely insured in an accident, when Robinsons Whim was overwound, but although the other man involved died as a result, Mr Kitto survived to work at the mine for another 23 years. Mr. A. Leonard Thomas also indicated his wish to retire from the post of Managing Director, and he also quit at the end of April 1963.

1963 saw Crofty back on an even keel once again, and the profits jumped to £129,298 as 93,330 tons were treated for the production of 990 tons of black tin (70% Sn). No wolfram or arsenic was produced in 1963. The average tin yield per ton was higher than it had been, at 23.76 lb, and with the price paid for it rising to £939, the slump in profits was predictable. Costs per ton crushed rose slightly in 1963 to £4 18s 8d, and this was partly accounted for by the increase in the wage and pension bill. Returns from tin sold were £622,677. There was £5,590 paid out in dividends.

On 380 level a 24" x 36" jaw crusher was installed to crush the ore before hoisting. It was to work on until it was replaced by a smaller crusher in 1978. 380 station and environs were completed that year, and all was ready to start driving the north cross-cut. Ventilation was vastly improved in the western workings by the installation of the 90" exhaust fan at Roskear Shaft head.

Under Mr. Pengilly's direction the Mine Rescue Team was property organised and facilities provided for it. He also re-instituted the use of electric cap lamps. In

1963 a charging room was provided at New Cook's Shaft for the lamps. In that year the working week was reduced from six to five days for miners.

There were 5,817 feet of main development and 5,299 feet of sub-development in 1963, with 1,144 feet of diamond drilling. On No. 1 Lode 310, driving east in Robinson's section, the lode was 5 feet wide and averaged 44 lb, and in Cook's section on 360 the same lode west of the cross-cut averaged 137 lb, over the same width. On 360 the drive west on No. 2 averaged 44 lb over 5 feet, and the No. 4 drive east sampled at 66 lb per ton. Work was also carried out on the South Lode on 315 level, where the values were average. The footage driven on lode which was payable, rose to 62 percent.

Things continued to improve during 1964, and although there was a drop in the tonnage milled, to 88,410, the yield was up to an average of 25.18 lb, and the production of black tin was consequently also up, to 994 tons (70% Sn). The average price paid for the mine's tin increased to £1,229, a tremendous rise, and the profits, not surprisingly, also leaped to £267,755. The wage, salary and pension contributions went up £30,000, and the overall cost per ton crushed rose by 19s 2d., to £5 17s 10d. Crofty's tin sold for £828,489. Dividends amounting to £83,270 were paid.

Plans were in hand to replace the ancient steam whim at Robinson's Shaft with a new electric winder. The foundations were started in 1964. Large diesel locomotives and Granby wagons were purchased for the main 380 haulage-way. When it was completed it was intended to hoist all dirt from Cook's 380 station by connecting ore passes through all levels on both side of the mine. Using 380 main haulage-way, the new Hunslett diesels would carry all of Robinson's dirt from an air-chute at the bottom of Robinson's ore pass to Cook's crusher.

On the surface there was new timber impregnation plan installed, and a geotechnical laboratory started. A Training School for miners was also organised, with immediate benefits. The working hours for miners were further reduced from $42^{1}/_{2}$ to 41 hours a week.

There were 3,790 feet of diamond drilling in 1964, with extensive exploration from the surface of Carn Entral, which is part of the Dolcoath sett. The results were very good, and an apparently valuable lode was discovered.

There was a total main development footage of 6,739 feet, and stope preparation amounted to a further 4,589 feet. Drives on lode averaged 54 percent of payable ground which was high. Tincroft South Lode on 315 level averaged 88 lb per ton for the whole of the distance driven in 1964, and No. 1 Lode east of the cross-cut on 310 level also showed similarly high values. On 360 level No. 2 & No. 4 lodes

167

were encouraging, and on 380 level, west of No. 2 Lode, the samples were 31 lb over half the distance driven.

On the 380 north cross-cut, great difficulty was experienced due to the heat at the end. Men were overcome, and in May 1964 one was taken unconscious from the level, and as a result at least two men quit the mine. They returned some months later.

On August 4 1964, whilst working in Cook's Shaft, W.A. Martin was struck by a passing skip. He received head injuries which proved fatal.

In 1965 tin returns passed the million pound mark, with £1,016,019 worth of black tin sold. Wages rose nearly £50,000, capital expenditure stayed at over the £100,000 mark for the second year running and costs per ton crushed went up by 14s 3d to £6 12s 1d. With the average price for tin at £1,437 the profit made for 1965 was £376,140. £173,996 were paid out in dividends. Ore treated increased in 1965 to 88,760 tons, which produced 1,037 tons of black tin (70% Sn), at an average yield per ton crushed of 26.17 lb. There were also 23 tons of tin recovered from the old plant that was replaced, and so the actual total black tin produced was 1,060 tons.

In Cook's Shaft new runners were put in, and the old two ton steel skips were replaced by 2½ tons aluminium ones, which would increase the capacity of the shaft haulage from 40 to 50 tons per hour. A new 600 gallon a minute electric pump was installed at 340 pump station, and the mine's ability to cope with the neighbourhood's water was enhanced. The Tincroft 'pool' of water, which was held at about 1,000 feet, and supplied the 195 pumps with a reservoir to draw from, was to be drained. This was to enable the mine to develop the ground under the old North Tincroft Mine, and was also part of the scheme to work inside the flooded East Pool sett.

7,293 feet of main development was carried out on 1965, and 5,073 feet of stope preparation. There were 3,457 feet of diamond drilling underground, and 7,145 feet on the surface. The drives on the lode proved to be 51 percent on payable ground. The No. 3B Lode was proving of great interest to Crofty, and the Manager reported that, "There is a close relationship between this lode (3B) and the rich Rogers' Lode of East Pool." Despite its tendency to grow narrow as it goes eastward, it was to prove rich. The No. 9 Lode was still proving variable, but the 335 east drive in Robinson's section showed some good results and averaged 55 lb over a width of nearly five feet. Tincroft South Lode on 315 was also quite good, and the western drive on No. 3B in Cook's section was payable. On 360 level the No. 4 Lode was sampling at 62 lb per ton over a width of 4 feet, but less than half the ground driven was payable. On 380 the drive west on No. 2 Lode was good, with an average value of 57 lb over a width of nearly 5 feet, for three-quarters of the drive. The Great Crosscourse was proving a problem as No. 2 drive started to pierce it. The initial exploration of No. 4 Lode on 380 was disappointing.

During 1965 the working week was reduced to 40 hours, and the Company introduced an injury and sick pay scheme.

In order to work the wide 'Complex' ore bodies, new methods had to be introduced. Various techniques were tried to drill long holes so that large quantities of ore could be broken into the wide stoped out areas. One method which was tried was to set an ordinary 303 machine on a bar fixed across the stope, and drill 20 or 30 foot holes in a radial pattern. This was not as successful as the management would havs liked, and other methods were looked into. Atlas Copco Ltd., a Swedish firm, had developed a machine that Mr. Pengilly believed would answer the problem. The machine was the 'Simba' drilling machine, and Crofty ordered one from Sweden. It arrived at the mine and so did an instructor to demonstrate it. Unfortunately, he failed completely to teach Crofty's miners how to use it properly, and it was decided to send one of the mine's top machinemen to Sweden to be taught the machine's most effective use.

On November 28 1965, W.R. Opie, described in the official documents as 'Drillmaster' at South Crofty Mine, arrived at Arlanda Airport, Sweden, to begin his stay under the supervision of Atlas Copco. At the end of a fortnight he was thoroughly instructed in the 'Simba's' use. That original machine was used until the 1970s, long-hole drilling the 'pegmatite' area of the mine, between 315 and 360 levels, close to No. 3 Lode in Cook's section.

Ronnie Opie was eventually employed as a supervisor for the afternoon shift. He started at the mine when he was just 15 years old, after having worked with his father at Mount Wellington Nine. His father, Eddie Opie, was a shift-boss at Crofty until 1960; his grandfather worked at Crofty in the early years of this century, and his son, Roger, also worked at the mine. There have been members of the Opie family working at the mine since it was called East Wheal Crofty, 140 years ago.

1966 saw the price of tin fall to £1,259 per ton, the average yield go down to 22.7 lb per ton, and the profits decrease to £175,537. Ore treated went up to 96,120 tons and black tin produced was 984 tons (70% Sn), with a further 10 tons recovered from the old final concentration plant. There were also 40 tons of 'tinny wolfram concentrate' recovered. Costs per ton crushed and treated went up to £7 1s 4d. Capital expenditure dropped to £94,979, and the dividends paid fell to £98,971. Sales of tin amounted to £836,883, and there was a return on 'tinny wolfram' of £29,466. Wages, salaries and pension contributions cost the Company £427,252, a rise of £75,000 in twelve months.

Main development footage increased to 11,095 feet, and stope preparation footage was 5,712. There was no diamond drilling from the surface in 1966, but there was 3,836 feet underground. Of the footage driven and sampled on lode 48 percent was payable.

In Robinson's section No. 3 Lode on 290 and 310 was explored, with values of 61 lb in the former, and 53 lb on the latter level. No.5 Lode was wide and valuable on 360 level Robinson's section, and several other lodes were explored successfully there. In Cook's Section Tincroft South Lode and No. 3B were yielding good results. The 380 drive on No. 2 Lode was driven through the Great Crosscourse. It was attended with constant difficulty, and took considerable time to pierce. Once through to the Roskear side, development began on Roskear South Lode, which proved payable for the distance driven. On 360 level a cross-cut was driven south to pick up the Tincroft South and Pryce's Lodes.

It was hoped to see an improvement in 380 ventilation at Cook's section, when the raise being put up from 380 to 360 was completed. Conditions generally in the western workings were much improved since the various levels had been connected to Roskear Shaft.

Unwatering East Pool and Agar workings progressed well during 1966, with 20 million extra gallons per month being pumped. The water level in those flooded setts was lowered 280 feet. When the water in Taylor's section was down a further 300 feet, access to these workings would be possible. The Manager reported that, "The transfer sump, which is intended to replace the Pool or flooded lower levels of the North Tincroft Mine, is almost complete. It will then be possible to resume development eastwards on the Tincroft lodes in safety."

On 380 level there was good progress in the drive to create a main haulage-way between the sections. The Management instituted an investigation to improve shaft usage, so that when ore was hoisted exclusively through New Cook's Shaft the carrying of men and materials could be more efficiently handled. Out of date machinery was scrapped during 1966, and much of the capital spent was on replacing it with modern equipment.

Two new conveyors were installed to carry ore from Cook's Shaft to the mill, and a standby primary crusher was purchased. Mr Pengilly directed intensive research into the methods used at Crofty for the recovery of tin at the mill. Both the mine's own staff and outside experts were involved in this research. The electric hoist at Robinson's Shaft was almost complete by the end of 1966.

Industrial relations at the mine remained tranquil, and higher pay was negotiated, together with two extra holiday shifts per year. The Training School was extended to include new recruits, whilst continuing to improve the standard of machinemen. The change-over from carbide to electric lamps was completed but there were problems. The Accident Sub-Committee heard complaints from the Miners' representative that burns were caused due to acid leakage from the cap-lamp batteries. Better protective pads were promised.

On June 15 1967, Siamese Tin Syndicate Ltd. made an offer for the whole of the issued capital of South Crofty Ltd. Mr.J.E. Denyer, Crofty's Chairman since 1959, had been a director of Siamese Tin since 1958. South Crofty's shares were bought by exchanging 915,892 5s shares and £178,622 in cash. More than half the mine's shares were already in the control of St.Piran Ltd., a wholly owned subsidiary of Siamese Tin.

There were 103,380 tons treated for the production of 1,095 tons of tin concentrate. The average yield per ton was up slightly to 23.72 lb. Costs per ton hoisted and milled went from £7 1s 4d., to £7 3s 2d. Sales of tin and other sundry materials came to £938,231. The pre-tax profit for the whole group of Companies associated with Siamese Tin, came to £457,547, and that of South Crofty was £73,429 nett. Tin averaged £1,228 per ton.

There were 12,429 feet of development in 1967, together with 6,968 feet of diamond drilling, and Robinson's Shaft was sunk 35 feet. The drives on lode showed 43 percent of payability. Despite the drop in payability of the newly opened ground, the grade at the mill was up, and the tonnage treated was a record. Drives east on the Tincroft lodes were opening up very valuable ground, but before the year ended a temporary halt was called until the new transfer sump on 195 level was completed. The draining of East Pool Mine proceeded according to schedule, and it was hoped to complete it within a year.

The old steam whim at Robinson's Shaft was replaced by the new electric one, and the directors attended a ceremonial shutting down of the 60 year old engine. When Robinson's was sunk to the 380 level it was intended to use it for men and materials only, leaving Cook's to be exclusively used for hoisting, and a minimum of man riding. The new conveyors from Cook's to the mill were brought into use and when the main-haulage on 380 was complete, the mine could get the best economic use out of the jaw crusher and large hoisting capacity of Cook's Shaft. The workshops and changing rooms (drys) were to be concentrated at Robinson's.

The technical research into improving the recovery of tin, initiated in 1966 by Mr Pengilly, was having some success, but difficulties were experienced in getting staff of the right calibre.

1968 saw another increase in production and output. From a total milled of 110,760 tons there was a production of 1,148 tons of black tin concentrate, at an average yield per ton treated of 23.21 lb. Crofty sold tin and sundries to the value of £1,056,251, and shared in the overall profit of the group which was £458,792 before tax. Crofty's after tax profit was £94,449. The average price paid for tin metal in London was £1,323.

There were 14,165 feet of development, with nearly 50 percent of payability on the drives, and 8,832 feet of diamond drilling. The increase in payable lode developed was very encouraging, and the mine was opening up well at the deeper levels. Costs rose in 1968 to £7 6s 3d per ton hoisted and treated.

The deepening of Robinson's Shaft from the 335 level to the 380 level was almost completed, with 40 feet sunk during 1968. The 380 main haulage-way was being finished as were the ore passes, waste passes, and necessary work between levels throughout Robinson's section to enable materials to be taken to each level from the surface.

East Pool Mine was almost drained by the end of the year, but there was some hold up due to the nature of the granite near to the points where the entrance was to be made. Where the granite was weak and decomposed, support work had to be erected, and massive concrete dams were built with steel watertight doors. The drives on the Tincroft lodes were still delayed while the transfer sump on 195 was completed. They were resumed early in 1969.

Plans were explained to the shareholders of the Company's intended expansion, so that the milling capacity could be doubled. There were thought to be sufficient ore reserves in Roskear and Tincroft sections to justify this expansion, and with those being found in East Pool and Agar, not to mention the 360 and 380 reserves, the managers were confident that the expenditure of £650,000 between 1969 and 1971 was justified.

Siamese Tin Syndicate's Group Accounts for 1968 show that St.Piran owned 59.5 percent of Crofty's shares, and Siamese Tin the rest. Siamese Tin owned St Piran's equity entirely.

South Crofty Accident Sub-Committee discussed the use of ear-plugs and ear muffs for machinemen and mucker drivers. There was some resistance to their introduction, particularly from miners who had used the machines for many years without ear protection. One of the staff on the Committee asked whether, "It was the usual South Crofty reluctance to accept something new," and wondered how much of the objection "was genuine?" After some hesitation these innovations were accepted by the miners in general just as the introduction of reaming steels, to assist the breaking of the cut, was accepted after a period of resistance. Some of the older miners referred despairingly to the users of such new-fangled aids as 'mini-miners.'

In 1969 there were 105,270 tons treated, for the production of 1,119 tons of black tin concentrate (70% Sn). Yield per ton crushed was 23.81 lb, and the working costs rose to £8 10s per ton. The sales of tin concentrate, wolfram and sundry waste materials brought in £1,162,934, and the group's profits were £663,077 before tax. South Crofty made a net profit of £99,112. The average tin metal price during 1969 was £1,451.

During 1969 the programme to expand and improve the hoisting and milling capacity went ahead well. The three 500 ton coarse ore bins that were to supply the new H.M.S. with ore for treatment were almost finished by the end of the year, and the new 140 foot high headframe at Cook's Shaft was completed. The cost of the programme was in dire need of upward revision, and the 1969 estimate was increased to £1,000,000. By the end of the year, with preparation so well advanced, orders were given to the manufacturers for the new crushing and pre-concentrating plant, which was to help double the mill's capacity. The foundations for the larger hoist and headgear at Cook's Shaft were begun at the end of 1969.

Development footage was 13,394 feet, which was less than the previous year, and payability also fell to 38 percent of the drives on lode. There were 7,437 feet of diamond drilling exploration, with some good results. A vertical hole from 380 level located No. 4 Lode 350 feet below. The values were very good.

In December 1969 some exceptional values were encountered on the drives east in Tincroft which resulted in an abnormally high average yield at the mill. Several lodes were examined during the year that had indicated no great values, but were worth a closer look. Development was hampered by the expansion programme, which included the further deepening of both shafts. A total of 147 feet of shaft sinking took place toward the needed sump depth. This shaft sinking and necessary cross-cutting and station enlarging resulted in a greatly increased tonnage of waste being hoisted. Preparations to enter East Pool and start work on the boundary pillars were nearing final completion.

In 1970 the parent company became St. Piran Mining Company. "The Company was incorporated on June 9 1970 to acquire the share capital of Siamese Tin Syndicate Limited. In July 1970 the Company became a public company and the capital increased to 6,000,000 shares of 25p each of which 5,833,492 shares of 25p (subsequently converted into stock) were issued to the stockholders of Siamese Tin Syndicate Limited in exchange for their existing holdings." The directors remained the same as before, as did the secretary, registered office, bankers and auditors. The new parent company took the name of one of its subsidiary companies.

The mill treated nearly 10,000 tons less ore than the previous year, due to the major reorganisation taking place. There were 95,620 tons throughput, for the production of 1,128 tons of tin concentrate (70% Sn). The recovery rate was better than 1969 with an average of 25.88 lb per ton. Costs rose by 25 per cent to £10.52 per ton treated. Sales of tin, wolfram and other sundry materials came to £1,165,216. St Piran made a profit of £742,347 before tax, and South Crofty's net profit was £43,699. The average tin metal price in 1970 was £1,529.

The tonnages given from 1970 are metric tons (2,204.6 lbs - tonnes). The fall in Crofty's profits in 1970 was almost entirely due to the increased cost of both wages and supplies. Power, materials, miners and surface workers wages, staff salaries, all increased to an alarming extent as the inflation spiral began to affect Britain. The Company hoped to benefit from Government grants towards capital expenditure investments in development areas.

A highlight if 1970 was the visit to the mine of H.R.H. Prince Charles, who flew to the mine by helicopter, and went underground. He was shown a stope on the 335 level, and spent some time visiting the various working places.

Development footage amounted to £13,562 feet with payability of drives on lode up a little to 41.1 percent. There were 8,810 feet of diamond drilling. The final 40 feet of sinking took place at Robinson's Shaft, to carry it down to the sump.

Teething troubles were encountered in Cook's section, where the new hoist and 7 ton aluminium skips came into operation. All dirt was hoisted through Cook's Shaft from 1970 onward. East Pool was at last drained to the 1,800 feet level, giving opportunity to develop there. An enormous amount of work was carried out in the building of the new heavy media separation plant (H.M.S.), and the new mill. The former was months behind schedule, but the latter was progressing accordingly to plan.

In 1971 there were 113,750 tonnes treated for the production of 1,195 tonnes of black tin (70Sn.) The grade dropped to 10.50kgs. per metric tonne (23.1 lb per ton), but with the new H.M.S. and the new mill beginning to operate properly, after expensive and frustrating delays, the costs per tonne crushed were actually down to £9 11p. The mine sold £1,147,103 worth of tin, wolfram and sundries, and made a profit of £110,349. The Group of companies made a profit of £341,528, but South Crofty's problems had a serious effect on their profitability and this profit was less than half that of 1970. The average price of tin metal was down to £1,437.

Development increased dramatically in 1971, with a total of 17,374 feet. Unfortunately, payability went down to 35.4 percent of the drives on lode. The diamond drilling team explored 9,836 feet. There was a little shaft sinking to deepen Cooks sump below 400 level.

Good progress was made in the exploration of East Pool, with valuable lodes encountered and a considerable distance driven toward the Tolgus Tunnel Lode. Pumping continued to drain the levels below the 1,800 level. A large block of ground in the Dolcoath region was developed during 1971 with valuable ore discovered.

In 1972 there were 145,000 metric tonnes treated and 1,572 tonnes of black tin produced. The average yield per ton crushed was up to 10.84 kgs. (23.85 lb). Working costs per tonne rose a little to £9.79p. Tin and other minerals sold brought in £1,569,518, which produced a profit of £149,753. The average tin metal price in London was £1,506 per tonne, an increase over 1971 of £69.

The Manager, Mr.G.C. Pengilly, received the M.B.E. in 1972, and was made a director of St. Piran Mining Company. Toward the end of April, N.E.J. Ebsworth was made Underground Manager of South Crofty. Leonard Thomas, after a long association with the mine, retired when he reached the age limit for directors. J.E. Denyer also retired from the Board of St.Piran after many years service to its predecessor, Siamese Tin and also South Crofty Mine.

There was a total of 16,869 feet of development in 1972, and payability was 38.8 percent of footage developed on lode. The diamond drill examined 6,548 feet of ground. The new mill and H.M.S. had its first full year of operation and the tonnage throughout showed a marked increase. Underground, the results from development in the newly opened areas was mixed. Drives eastward from the 260 and 310 levels into East Pool were fruitful.

1973 saw several changes at the mine. At the beginning of June South Crofty purchased from the Official Receiver, the company called Camborne Mines Ltd., which operated Wheal Pendarves and Roscroggan milling plant. The capacity of Crofty's new plant meant that ore from Wheal Pendarves could be treated without any expansion. Pendarves' manager, J.P. Weeks, became 'acting general manager' of both mines, under Mr. Pengilly. Control of the parent company moved into the hands of a new groups of shareholders in 1973, led by Mr J.J. Raper, Mr. G.V. Shaen-Carter and Mr.P.A. Delme-Radcliffe. In June 1973 moves were made by Faber Merlin (Hong Kong) to acquire 16.2 per cent of the issued capital value of the group.

The figures for 1973 are for the fifteen months ending March 31 1974, as the financial year was adjusted to end each year on that date. In that period there were 162,831 tonnes hoisted and milled, and 1,255 tonnes of black tin produced. The average yield of tin metal was 7.70 kgs per tonne and payability was down to only 30 percent. Costs per tonne went up to £11.48p. Recovery yield was given for tin metal produced from Crofty's black tin from 1973 onward, as opposed to the figures for concentrate (70% Sn) sold.

Development amounted to 5,258 metres and diamond drilling to 1,397 metres. From that time on payments were made to miners on 'metres' not footage, and figures generally changes over to the metric system. The drive to open up East Pool and particularly the Tolgus Tunnel area, went on apace during 1973, and a large area of ground was explored. Tincroft and Dolcoath continued to give good results.

Early in 1974 the price of tin metal on the London Metal Market was up to £4,000, and although this figure dropped by October to around the £3,000 mark, with inflation rising the upward trend in tin's value was very welcome. There were 139,342 tonnes treated in the twelve months ending March 31 1975, and 1,038 tonnes of black tin concentrate recovered. The average yield of tin metal per tonne was 7.45 kgs, and the cost to treat each tonne raised was up to an extraordinary £16.09p. Development went down to 3,565 metres, diamond drilling exploration was up to 1,597 metres, and payability was back to 45 percent of drives on lode.

On November 31 1974, N.E.J. Ebsworth, who had risen from Underground Manager to General Manager, left the Company. Mr. Pengilly remained in overall change having been joined by H.R.M. Hodding, a director of St.Piran, in July. Mr. Pengilly resumed the day to day running of the mine. G.V. Shaen-Carter became Chairman of South Crofty in 1974, replacing P.O.H. Gadsden.

The March 1975 to March 1976 figures show a general increase, and although they include production from Wheal Pendarves Mine, they are still impressive. 205,371 tonnes were put though the mill, and 1,453 tonnes of tin metal were smelted from the mines' black tin. Recovery was up a little to 7.08 kgs of tin metal produced from each tonne raised. Costs at the mine per tonne treated were £17.30p.

There was a total of 2,588 metres developed in the year ending March 31 1976, which showed 46 percent of payability on lode. There were 1,919 metres of diamond drilling.

On November 25 1975 a miner was killed. William A. Trevena was working in a stope on 290 level, when he was buried under a rock weighing about four tonnes. With him in the stope were his mate, Colin Jeffery, and two samplers, John Hendra and Michael Merry. Jeffery was barring down, when a large rock, estimated at about 16 tonnes, suddenly dropped from the back of the stope. Upon falling, the rock split into four parts, one of which narrowly missed Hendra, and another buried Bill Trevena. It was some time before he could be released, and by then he had suffocated to death.

During 1975 work got underway to prepare for the Third Stream, which was to treat alluvial deposits from the Red River and old mine burrow dirt. Various

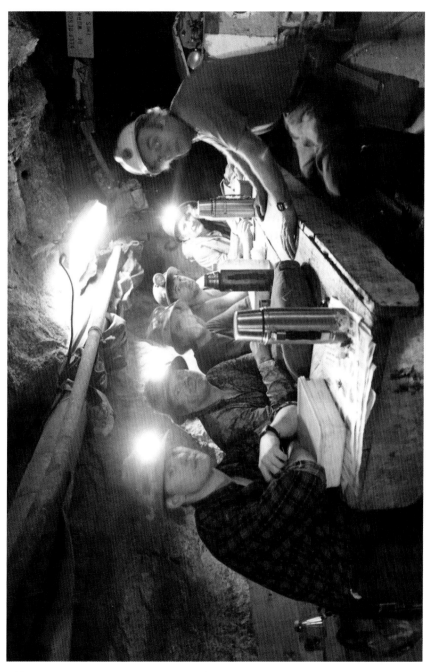

39. Crowst time on 380 fm level. The shiftboss, Raymond Thomas, is seated on the right, and the group of miners include trammers and machinemen. The crowst seat is on the junction of the north crosscut and No.2 Lode. December 1989.

40. *Ladderway to clean water bay above the 400 fm level pump station. Jeff Gilbert, surveyor, is seen climbing toward the bay in December 1989.*

41. New pump chamber at New Cooks Kitchen Shaft station, 400 fm level. This vast chamber was excavated in the late 1980s to house the pumps, which were to replace those on 195, 340 and 380 fm levels. The scheme was never completed as the government withdrew its financial support for the mine. The picture was taken in May 1989.

42. Development miners, Paul Gallie and Dave Cooke starting to drill an eight foot round in a draw point on Roskear 'D' Lode, at the 400 fm level. The machine is a SIG with telescopic leg. February 1992.

experiments were carried out at the time to improve the recovery at the mill, and the H.M.S. plant was also rearranged for greater efficiency.

In July 1975 there was a week long strike by the fitters. The mine was halted as the ore bins between Cook's and H.M.S. were all full, the production screen in H.M.S. was under repair, and the bins that fed the mill were empty.

The year ending March 31 1977 was one of further expansion. At the mill there was a total of 218,800 tonnes of ore from Pendarves and Crofty treated. Tin metal produced from the mines' concentrate was 1,545 tonnes, at an average of 7.06 kgs. per tonne. Working costs rose to £20.58p per tonne. South Crofty made a net profit of £802,063.

The Third Stream operation came into production in 1976, boosting the throughput at the mill. Another rod mill was purchased and installed at the north-east corner of the old mill, rendering the re-lining process far less costly to the Company.

At the end of 1976 New Cook's Kitchen Shaft became a down-draught shaft, and with Taylor's and Roskear shafts both updraught, ventilation was immediately improved. Underground, there was a total of 4,594 metres of development, which showed 38 percent of payability on lode, and 1,571 metres of diamond drilling. On 360 level Tincroft was further explored, and on 380 the south cross-cut from Cooks Shaft was advanced toward Tincroft South and Pryce's lodes. The north cross-cut from Robinson's was extended to No. 9 Lode, and promising values were found.

In July 1976 Col. P.C. Buchanan became Chairman of South Crofty, taking over from G.V. Shaen-Carter. G.C. Pengilly remained the Managing Director, and H.R.M. Hodding also kept his position.

Between March 1977 and March 1978 the mill throughput was 214,701 tonnes, from which were recovered and smelted 1,548 tonnes of tin metal, at an average yield of 7.21 kgs. per tonne. The cost at the mine to treat each tonne of ore raised soared to £27.98p. South Crofty made a net profit for that twelve month period of £1,232,920.

The total development amounted to 4,943 metres, with 31 percent of the drives payable. There were 1,477 metres of diamond drilling, and that from 380 level showed good values below the present mine. There was much activity to prepare for sinking the 'Jubilee Shaft,' but despite considerable expenditure including the installation of a jaw-crusher for waste rock at Cooks 360 station, the scheme was abandoned, when it was decided instead to sink a sub-incline shaft from 380 to 420 level. Some £150,000 had been wasted.

On 380 level the Tincroft South Lode was driven east and west, and stope preparation started on the west side. No.9 Lode was driven eastward in Robinsons section with variable results. Drives on No. 4 Lode on 380 also produced good values, as did drives into Dolcoath and East Pool on the higher levels.

The period between March 1978 and March 1979 showed another healthy increase in production. 236,300 tonnes of ore were treated and 1,605 tonnes of tin metal produced from the concentrate. Recovery amounted to 6.79 kgs. per tonne. Working costs per tonne treated were on average £29.56p. The pre-tax profit was £2,304,376.

4,943 metres were driven, raised and sunk during that period, and the percentage of payability was down to 28 percent. The diamond drillers bored 1,378 metres, exploring ground on all sides of the mine. On 380 level No. 1 Lode was driven westward from Cook's cross-cut and in Robinson's section the 3B Lode was driven east. On 360 level the drive below East Pool toward the valuable No. 6 Lode was well advanced. On 360, 335, 310 and 290 levels side-tyes were driven to bring into use drawpoints, so that the wide ore bodies in parts of No.4, No.9 and Pryce's lodes could be exploited. Beneath Tolgus Tunnel drives were advanced eastward to prove the rich lode discovered there by East Pool miners in 1920. A rich new lode, called Dolcoath South Lode, was discovered on 340 level.

The old jaw crusher on 380 level was replaced in August 1978 by a new Brown Lenox crusher. It was smaller than the one it replaced, but it was to cope well with the rock put through it. Preparations were made to begin the Sub Incline shaft from 380 level. Two new Sulzer Pumps were installed on 380 level, and necessary sump and chambers excavated. A large new engineering workshop was built close to the old mill at Cook's side of the mine, and the engineering staff was concentrated there.

September 22 1978 South Crofty acquired Tehidy Minerals Ltd., the mine's principal mineral-lords. This company owned 35,000 acres of mineral rights in Cornwall as well as Delabole Slate Quarries.

On January 1 1979 Mr. H.R.M. Hodding became Chairman of St. Piran's Board of Directors. On the 23rd of August Col.P.C.Buchanan resigned as Chairman of South Crofty, and was replaced by Mr Hodding. On the July 31 1979 Mr. G.C.Pengilly resigned as Managing Director of South Crofty, and after a short interregnum, Mr. Peter Goram was appointed General Manager. Mr. C.J. Dungey became Mine Manager under Mr. Goram. Mr. Dungey had previously been Manager of Wheal Pendarves.

On April 1 1979, F.J. Bessell, a pumpman, fell from the cage in Cook's Shaft, and was killed. The cause of this tragic accident remains a mystery.

During the summer of 1979 the members of the Transport and General Workers' Union were on strike for a period of four weeks over a pay claim. A compromise was eventually reached, which enabled the men to return to work.

By the summer of 1979 preparations were complete to start the Sub Incline shaft. Raises had been put up from the waste and ore passes and another to the top of the shaft. From 380 level, the top part of the shaft was raised, and the chamber excavated for the hoist and other plant. After stripping out the top part of the shaft to the required dimensions all was ready to start sinking. By Christmas 1979 the shaft was a considerable distance toward the 400 level, which was eventually reached in February 1980.

Chapter Six:
The Modern Mine

The year 1980 began a period of change at South Crofty Mine. After a decade and a half of expansion and relative affluence for the mine and the miners, management and ownership changes brought greater investment and new attitudes, leading to a harder and more inflexible approach to the mine and the men. In September 1980 Dr Paul Mihalop became Managing Director, with overall responsibility for South Crofty, Wheal Pendarves, Tehidy Minerals and Delabole Slate Quarries. Dr Mihalop was 37 years old, had learned his mining in Australia, and introduced a quite new management style. 'Call me Paul' is the line for which he is best remembered by the miners. Despite this seemingly relaxed approach, there followed the call for redundancies, a new four shift system, with little room for manoeuvre, and a demand for an increase in production of some 45 percent. St Piran was by then actively looking for buyers for the mine, and several large multi-national mining companies were showing an interest in Crofty.

In the event, 1980 saw about 10 percent of the miners made redundant, mostly voluntarily, and production remained at its former level. Tonnage milled amounted to 233,905, with 185,923 tonnes coming from South Crofty and the rest from Pendarves. This ore yielded 1,456 tonnes of tin metal. The average recovered grade was 0.66 percent, although Crofty's own ore was nearer one percent. With the tin price remaining static and costs continuing to rise, the management sought a six month moratorium on pay. The miners accepted this as they had the call for redundancies.

In April the first stage of Crofty's planned expansion was reached, when the Sub Decline conveyor was installed to the ore chute below 400 fm Level. While the shaft features were completed 400 Level was opened, with the cross-cut to Cook's Shaft being driven and some lode development carried out. A large part of 1980 and 1981 was spent in opening up 400 fm Level. The decline shaft sinking contractors were Jimmy Clemence, Alan Cooper and Bob Harvey Jnr. Pete Hughes remained shiftboss in charge of the sinking operations, becoming 400 Level shiftboss as it was opened up. The 380 Level waste crusher pit was mined out by the Sub Decline crews whilst sinking continued below 400 Level, the contractors being joined by John Clemence.

Elsewhere in the mine, Pryce's Lode in Tincroft section was developed on the 245, 260 and 290 fm levels and No.6 North Lode was opened up on 360 Level.

There was a tendency by 1980 to move from traditional shrinkage stoping with 'Cousin Jack' chutes built into boxholes, to long-hole stoping with footwall drives (side tyes) and draw points.

At the end of 1980 the number employed at Crofty had dropped to 536 and for the Company as a whole it was down to 608, compared to 677 the previous year. In 1981 Crofty mined 215,625 tonnes of ore and together with the 34,669 tonnes from Wheal Pendarves Crofty's mill treated 250,249 tons, which gave 1,380 tonnes of tin metal. The overall recovered grade was 0.61 percent, Crofty's ore being somewhat diluted by that of Pendarves.

During the year, plans were set in motion to totally re-equip, expand and modernise both South Crofty and Wheal Pendarves. Crofty was to have £1,000,000 spent on new machinery and better ventilation underground. The mine purchased 20 new rocker shovels (Eimco 21/Atlas Copco LM56), 24 new Clayton battery locos, 104 Hudson Wagons (40/50 cubic foot), 47 Holman 303 machines, 3 long hole drilling rigs and a new ventilation fan for Roskear Shaft. The mill was to be modernised at a cost of some £1,300,000 to increase throughput and improve recovery. £900,000 was earmarked for Pendarves, mostly to finance the deepening of the mine to the 7 Level.

A four shift system was introduced at Crofty, and for some time it caused more confusion than improvement. The four shifts ran 8am-4pm, 4pm-12 midnight, 8pm 4am and 12 midnight-8am. As the old night shift and afternoon shift workers had mostly been quite happy on their shifts for several years, the disruption caused problems. Men who had been twenty years on night shift were told they had to swing between days and nights. Afternoon shift men who had contentedly worked from 2pm-10pm for years were told they had to swing between 4pm-midnight and any one of the other shifts. Day shift were forced to work nights no matter what their objections. Many aspects of the new scheme were imperfectly thought through and chaos frequently accompanied the arrival on the level of the next shift. This was especially true of the arrival underground of 'early nightshift' at 8pm. On a few occasions violence followed the demand by the new arrivals for the wagons, rocker shovel and even the working place of afternoon shift. As is often the case, management were blissfully ignorant of the problems and showed little interest when the difficulties were pointed out to them.

During 1981 development continued in Tincroft and on Dolcoath North and South lodes, on 260, 290, 315, 340, and 380 Levels. Development by Roy Stevens and Timmy Hocking into the Roskear Complex area on 360 Level was 'mildly encouraging'. The Sub Decline conveyor was down to the 420 Level by the end of 1981, and 400 Level was developed 2,650 feet in the course of the year.

A sad episode occurred on June 9 1981, when Jack Baker, a young miner, was killed in a stope on Tincroft Lode above the 380 fm Level. The wide ore body at that point was being worked by conventional methods as a shrinkage stope, and there had already been some problems with rock falls. On the Thursday before the accident the contractor, Cyril Penrose, had been hit by a rock and had sustained a painful hand injury. On the Friday his replacement, Mat Wilson, was also hit by a rock fall and his shoulder and arm were seriously injured. On the Tuesday of the fatal accident David Curry, Cyril's mate, took Jack Baker to assist him. Close to the rearing ladderway, at the entrance to the stope, a large rock fell from the back and killed Jack. It was the third serious accident in that stope in four working days.

The total number employed rose during the year by ten to 546 and the overall including Pendarves rose to 624. During 1982 South Crofty raised 253,059 tonnes of ore and Pendarves broke 27,432 tonnes. A further 2,500 tonnes were treated from old burrows. The tonnage treated at the mill was an impressive 282,991 and yielded 1,650 tonnes of tin metal.

The management announced in 1982 that there had been a significant shift away from 'Cousin Jack' chutes to drawpoint loading of ore. The wide ore bodies in Tincroft-Pryces zone, especially at the 290, 315 and 340 levels, which had previously been stoped by conventional methods, lent themselves to long-hole stoping. This was the area where the new system was first exploited to the full, and it was only later that it was used throughout the mine.

During the year the Sub Decline was completed to below the 420 Level, with a small sump. The raise from the conveyor ore chute to the ore pass grizzley position was mined after the arrival of RTZ, two years later, when the first Sub Decline project was completed. An exciting discovery was made whilst deepening to the 420 Level. A wide lode was cut just short of the 420 turn off, and when the samples were assayed the geologists thought the shiftboss (Pete Hughes) was winding them up. The first samples right across the lode were 8 percent tin. Subsequently this proved an extremely valuable find on 360, 380, 400, 420 and 445 levels, and was named No.8 North Lode.

The modifications to the mill circuit were commissioned in March 1982, and seven day working for mill operatives was introduced. At Pendarves the shaft was completed to 7 Level and development was pursued on Tryphena and Harriet lodes. Diamond drilling toward the Great Flat Lode and Wheal Nelson was carried out, and there was talk of examining the western end of the old Dolcoath sett from Pendarves.

In August 1982 Charter Consolidated took over the mine and the management began to think in terms of even more expansion and investment. By the end of the year the number employed at Crofty had dropped dramatically to 506, although the Pendarves figure rose to 84.

There was a drop in Crofty's production in 1983 to 211,545 tonnes of ore raised. Pendarves generated 32,048 tonnes and there were 7,106 tonnes of ore from old burrows. The ore as a whole gave an average grade of 0.52 percent, with Crofty's remaining near to one percent. This ore produced 1,317 tonnes of tin in concentrate. One reason for this large drop in tonnage was a collapse in Robinson's Shaft on January 21 1983. Over 200 miners were laid off whilst the shaft was repaired. Timber lagging had failed at the 80 fm Level, causing damage to the shaft all the way down to 380 Level.

Another nasty accident occurred a couple of weeks before the shaft collapse, when the Underground Manager, George Curtis, fell some 150 feet down the shaft. His life was saved by a timber balk lying across the compartment, although he was seriously injured.

Once again developments in Tincroft and on Dolcoath South were encouraging, and on 400 Level No.4 and No.8 lodes were proving rich and wide. Exploration in Pendarves continued to produce mixed results, although the management there remained optimistic.

On November 1 1983 Dr Paul Mihalop resigned as Managing Director of South Crofty and C.J. Forristal became Director and General Manager. Mr Forristal, an Irishman, was a Charter man, and he took over a mine which by then was owned 60 percent by Charter and 40 percent by RTZ.

In 1984 production was again up, with 295,743 tonnes milled. Crofty had raised 247,311 tonnes and Pendarves and various old burrows 48,432 tonnes. The Company sold 1,817 tonnes of tin in concentrate, 1,519 tonnes being from Crofty.

During the year development continued in the principal sections, with drives into the Roskears, Dolcoath and North Pool (No.6) proving interesting.

On November 1 1984 RTZ took complete control of South Crofty Mine. Once again rationalisation, new capital expenditure, reorganisation, re-equipping, redundances and refurbishment of shafts were discussed. New Cooks Kitchen Vertical Shaft was to be totally refurbished and its configuration altered. A new Decline Shaft was to be started near Brea Village, and called the Tuckingmill Decline Shaft. With the tin price rising toward to the £10,000 per ton mark all was optimism and activity. The year ended with both the threat and the reality of redundancy for many miners and surface workers. Whole departments disappeared from the offices and no position seemed secure. The best miners were working long hours and earning higher wages than ever, but for others there was a pay-off and the dole queue. A definite plus as far as the mine itself and the miners were concerned was the appointment of Colin Jones as Mine Manager. Like Gerald Pengilly, Jones was a 'miners' manager', and will be long-remembered for his energetic style of management.

The number employed on average in 1984 was 596 and the average grade for all ore milled was down to 0.61 percent, with Crofty's ore at 0.9 percent.

1985 was one of the most dramatic years in the history of Cornish mining, a history which has seen more than its share of drama. The International Tin Council, representing a group of tin producing and consuming nations, spectacularly failed to fulfil its aim of tin price stabilisation. The ITC tried to avert wide fluctuations in the tin price by buying tin when the price fell and selling from is stockpile when the price rose. As the price rose so many hitherto uneconomic mines and dredging operations reopened, and others expanded production to take advantage. With world production increasing quickly there was soon an oversupply. With so much tin available the ITC had insufficient cash to buy it all. October 24 1984 saw the money run out. Early in the year the tin price had touched £10,500 and even in October the price was still a healthy £8,140. As the ITC's control disappeared the price crashed to under £3,000 a ton, which was a third of the break-even figure for Cornish mines.

Tolgarrick Tin Streams, which lay below Crofty closed. Other tailings and burrow treating companies followed suit. Geevor, Wheal Pendarves and Wheal Concord were soon to become history, and although Geevor reopened twice to tram previously broken ore, and then, in January 1988 began a brave but ultimately, short-lived attempt to carry out a full mining programme, by February 1990 only Wheal Jane (and Mount Wellington) and South Crofty remained.

Although mining at South Crofty in 1985 was completely overshadowed by the tin price crisis, until the crash the mine continued to operate normally, with considerable development taking pace in several areas. The Roskear, Dolcoath, Tincroft and North Pool zones were all producing good results and the discovery of Providence Lode and opening up of No.8 North Lode in the western end of the old sett also boasted morale at the mine. In November, despite the crisis, the Second Sub Decline Shaft project was started, with the section above the level mined out in preparation for the installation of an electric hoist, before sinking toward 445 fm Level.

RTZ had had ambitious plans for South Crofty, which included re-examination of all old workings, and involved a programme of sampling throughout the adit systems. The Company also examined the possibility of dewatering the Highburrow mines (Carn Brea, Tincroft and Cooks Kitchen) and even pumping old Dolcoath to the 420 fm Level horizon. A feasibility study made recommendations on the pumps needed and their location. The estimated volume of water involved made the scheme, in the light of the high tin price, potentially viable. The tin price crisis put paid to these long-term expansion plans.

In 1985 Crofty produced 194,918 tonnes of ore at an average grade of 0.9 percent. The Company sold 1,799 tonnes of tin metal. Those employed dropped to 469.

1986 began with the same feeling of despondency throughout the industry as had marked the last months of 1985. Negotiations with the government and other potential financial supporters continued as the miners and their families, together with all of the other workers in the industry began a campaign to bring the plight of Cornish mining to the attention of the world. The men of Geevor, Wheal Jane, Wheal Concord, Wheal Pendarves, South Crofty and all of the small treatment plants and ancillary industries held meetings, organised rallys, took part in marches, stuck up posters, distributed leaflets and did everything possible to fight the threat. All over the country there was an emotional response to this campaign, not lessened despite coal miners and others also seeing their traditional way of life being destroyed. At Exeter University, as at other educational establishments, posters both witty and pointed were erected on every notice board on the campus. Students whose parents had never done anything more arduous than checking their monthly bank and share statements became enthusiastic Cornish mine supporters. This happened throughout the United Kingdom as the enormity of the threat to Cornwall was perceived. All of this culminated in the great march through Westminster, on 29 January 1986, where hundreds of Cornish mine workers and their families, supported by thousands of others, proceeded through the capital in a display of unity only normally seen when the Cornish rugby team makes it to Twickenham.

1986 saw the Tuckingmill Decline Shaft well underway, with Thyssens struggling to cope with poor ground conditions, and being forced to use steel arches for support. This resulted in low monthly advances, 35.2m being the best achieved. The shaft is 3m high by 5m wide and had an initial gradient of one-in-seven.

In the meantime, the miners were further depressed by a fatal accident to one of the trammers. On Saturday April 13 1986, Wayne Shirley was driving a Clayton loco along the footwall haulageway on Pryces Lode, Tincroft, at the 290 fm Level, when there was a derailment. Wayne died before he could be taken to hospital.

In August the campaign to obtain government help proved successful, when the government gave way and it was announced that Carnon Consolidated, the wholly owned subsidiary of RTZ, through whom Wheal Jane and South Crofty were operated, would get an interest free loan of £15,000,000 whilst RTZ continued to meet the operating losses. Wheal Pendarves would have to close. Geevor and the rest of the industry received nothing. The offer that was made to Geevor was considered by the management too small to allow for the mine to become viable.

Despite the continuing problems in 1986 the mine raised 248,426 tonnes of ore at an average overall grade of 0.9 percent, which gave 2,118 tonnes of tin metal. Crofty's own ore grade was 1.2 percent. The workforce dropped still further to 407.

The increased productivity and improved grades continued in 1987, with the workforce of only 323 producing 213,612 tonnes of ore at an average overall recovered grade of 1.02 percent. The mine's ore grade was 1.3 percent. This gave 2,167 tonnes of tin metal.

The year saw the 'Great Trek West' into the Roskear and Dolcoath continue, with Roskear lodes to the north and south of Roskear Shaft being developed and Dolcoath North and South lodes being exploited. Dolcoath South Lode was being driven toward the old Camborne Consols Mine, under Camborne Town itself, and the grades and lode widths were encouraging and sometimes exciting. The lode was also extremely hard in places, and experienced miners, like Henry Kaczmarek stated that it was the hardest rock they had encountered at Crofty. The new levels of 400 and 420 were being opened up and on No.8 North Lode the grades were averaging between 2.5 and 5.6 percent tin, at 380 and 400. On 420 Level the newly discovered Providence Lode was proving good as were the lode drives on No.4 and No.8. During 1987 the miners were asked to follow a structure which was believed to be Providence Lode and turned out to be what became nick-named 'Gribble Granite Lode'.

There was still a mixture of shrinkage and long-hole stopes at South Crofty, although the trend continued toward the long-hole method of stoping. Looking to the future, there was a vigorous programme of diamond drilling carried out, not just to examine the new areas on the western fringes of the mine and to check the values below the mine, but also in the older areas, like East Pool and Wheal Agar. Once again, after a decade of moving downward and westward, the planners re-examined the Tolgus Tunnel area of Wheal Agar and particularly Great Lode. In August 1986 Kevin Ross became Mine Manager, having been Underground Manager since February 1985.

The Tuckingmill Decline Shaft was taken over by South Crofty's miners in April 1987, at the point where the Decline Shaft turns in a more easterly direction and steepened from a gradient of about one-in-seven to one-in-five. Eric Eckersall and John Clemence were the main contractors, and the deepening went on at an increased pace, with the August advance being 62.2m, November up to 73.3m and in January 1988 the shaft sinkers peaked at 83.8m. All work stopped at the end of March 1988, when the shaft had been sunk for a distance of 630m.

During 1987 the 445 fm Level was reached on the Second Sub Decline, and Jimmy Clemence and his mates cut the station and drove a cross-cut to No.8 North Lode. The crew then consisted of David Abrahams, David Eldred, Raymond Moyle and Bob Wilmott. Once 445 fm Level was started the sinkers pushed on down towards the 470 fm Level, reaching it by November 1988. The 470 shaft station was in the Great Crosscourse and expensive and time-consuming work had to be carried out to make the back safe.

The total tonnage raised at Crofty during 1988 fell from the previous year to 156,346 although the average recovered grade rose slightly to 1.07 percent. The workforce also fell again to 315 and tin metal production fell to 1,676 tonnes.

Short-term problems were caused to production by the changeover of New Cooks Shaft arrangement. North and south winders were introduced during the summer months, and Thyssens also finished the complete refurbishment of Cooks Shaft with ancillary work being carried at adit level and in other areas of the mine.

During the year exploration continued at all levels between 260 and 420, with Great Lode in Wheal Agar at 260 and 290, Providence Lode at 400, the old No.6 group of lodes (now re-designated North Pool Zone or NPZ) at 360 and 380, Dolcoath South Lode between 290 and 360 and the Roskears at 400 and 420 levels being developed. The Tincroft lodes, No.4 North Lode and Dolcoath North Lode were also not neglected. In August 1988 Andrew Lewis replaced Kevin Ross as Mine Manager, Ross returning to Wheal Jane.

1989 was a good year at the mine. The tonnage broken rose to 202,516 with an improved grade averaging 1.21 percent overall, although the ore from Crofty averaged 1.5 percent. Tin metal produced increased dramatically to 2,454 tonnes and the workforce also increased slightly to 330. Total revenue was £14,102,000 and there was a loss of £415,000.

In April 1989 sinking recommenced below the 470 fm Level and the present sump was reached in November. This position is 2,841 feet (866m) below surface, and is at the same horizon as the 550 fm Level at Williams Shaft, Dolcoath.

In 1990 the mine hoisted 200,742 tonnes of ore at an average grade of 1.5 percent (with Pendarves and burrow dirt the grade was 1.24 percent), which yielded 2,502 tonnes of tin metal. The workforce fell to 244. Revenue from tin was £9,120,000 and there was a loss for the year £2,752,000.

In February 1991 the government stopped the agreement to give to Carnon staged loans, and overnight the mine was again in crisis. The whole workforce were called to a cinema in Truro to be told by Brian Calver, Carnon Consolidated's Managing Director, that they were all redundant. He explained that a small workforce would be needed to remove broken ore and essential gear from Wheal Jane, and a similar small group of miners would be required at Crofty to remove sufficient good grade ore to pay the redundancies. Afterwards the recoverable gear would be removed and the mine placed on 'care and maintenance'. If no financial support was forthcoming the pumps would be turned off and the mine allowed to flood. Every retained worker, from the managing director down to the lowliest underground labourer would be paid a maximum of £4.24 an hour.

In the event things turned out a little different, and due to the tremendous efforts of those remaining, the mine was able to continue operating due to an improvement in the tin price and high productivity. The operating losses were covered by the sale of surplus assets. Gradually, the workforce expanded and production rose to a point where it became apparent that it was not going to close, at least for the time being. Wage negotiations began, leading to higher pay rates and enabling the men to earn sufficient to pay their mortgages and return their lifestyle to something like its former position. From a total workforce of 87 at Crofty when the men returned two days after the redundancy, the number increased by the end of the year to 192. To that 87 there would be added the 50 Wheal Jane millmen and 31 stripping out Wheal Jane. The Company as a whole employed 204 people in March 1991.

Through 1991 the main production effort was concentrated in Roskear and on No.8 North Lode. Large blocks of ore were removed by means of long-hole drilling and the grade was generally high. The total tonnage hoisted dropped to £152,993 in 1991, with Crofty's average grade up to 1.6 percent, producing 2,103 tonnes of tin. Crofty's revenue was £5,576,000, and there was a loss of £283,000. It would have been far higher were it not for the sale of land and other assets.

1992 began with a feeling of modest optimism. The mood among the miners was, 'We've survived so far, perhaps we have seen the worst of our problems!' as land sales continued to prop up the ailing finances of the mine there was a loss for the year of only £79,000. The miners gloomily noted, however, that there was still little essential maintenance and no main development going on, and they realised that this situation could not continue indefinitely. The workforce rose very slightly during the year, ending with a total of 197 including maintenance men, technical staff and millmen.

Once again mining was concentrated in Roskear, with some work on North Pool, Dolcoath South, No.4 North and No.8 North lodes. The mine was beginning to look neglected underground, as there was little time or money for basic maintenance or replacement gear. In October 1992 Kevin Ross returned to South Crofty as Mine Manager.

Crofty hoisted 168,149 tonnes in 1992, with an average recovered grade of 1.21 percent and a yield of 2,044 tonnes of tin metal. The total revenue was £6,030,000.

In 1993 there was an increased tonnage hoisted of 179,815, with a recovered grade of 1.24 percent and a tin metal yield of 2,232 tonnes. Revenue was £6,551,000, and there was a loss of £42,000. Once again land sales helped to cushion the mine from more serious loss. The workforce increased steadily to 231 with some departments returning to their former strengths.

Production in 1994 remained relatively static with 177,082 tonnes hoisted and a reduced recovered grade of 1.07 percent, giving a tin metal yield of 1,919 tonnes. The number employed rose to 270 by the end of the year. The mine lost almost 4^1/$_2$ million pounds in 1994

During the year there was a considerable effort on the periphery of the mine, with Dolcoath South between 340 and 290 levels being exploited beneath the old, abandoned Camborne Consols Mine; blocks on Pryces Lode in Tincroft being worked; North Pool Zone between 360 and 380 being worked and Nos. 4 and 8 North lodes being stoped at 380, 400, 420 and 445 levels.

By 1994 the Company's cash reserves were all but gone. Early in the year it was perceived by the management, that the only way forward was to have a share issue. £1,800,000 was seen as the figure required to give sufficient investment to secure the mine's future. The summer saw a tremendous advertising campaign to gain local and international investment. Shares were offered in minimum blocks of £200 for 200 ten penny shares. By the day of the offer closure local people and others with an emotional attachment to the Cornish mining tradition had requested over half a million shares, and two large corporate investors came in with some £650,000 between them. These two companies, Crew Natural Resources, from Canada, and Ocean Consolidated Incorporated, a Mauritius based company, effectively saved Crofty from immediate closure. At the same time Crew took a controlling interest in Carnon Consolidated and the Company's name reverted to that of the mine; South Crofty Plc.

At last Crofty could begin to replace some of the worn-out machinery and start to carry out routine maintenance, so essential to the efficient and economic running of a mine. The atmosphere of crisis management - often seen by the miners as panic management - gradually calmed down and for a while the planners were back in control. By the end of the year, with the price of tin still too low for profitable workings, the stopers were once again right behind the sub-developers, and the geologists and management were once again concerned for the future.

The mining performance between January 1995 and March 1996 rose slightly from the previous period, with tonnage for 14 months being 217,772, an average of 15,555 tonnes per month. The treated grade dropped fractionally to 1.22 percent, tin metal in concentrate was 2,305 tonnes and the workforce averaged 322. Once again the breakeven figure remained higher than the average tin price, and the result was a loss of £2,401,000.

The Chairman's Report was optimistic, it being seen as a period of consolidation, with 'a number of positive developments.' The Report showed that 79 percent of contained metal came from longhole stopes, 7 percent from shrink stopes and the rest from development. No.4 North Lode produced 33 percent of the tonnage, Roskear D Lode 23 percent, No.8 Lode 17 percent, Pryces Lode 10 percent and Dolcoath South Lode 9 percent.

Developments on Providence Lode and the North Pool Zone were to add to Crofty's immediately available ore reserve considerably. Preparations were also well advanced to clear the Second Sub Decline sump and re-start developments on 470 fm Level.

In March 1995 Crofty had begun the long task of replacing Robinson's Shaft, as the second egress, with Roskear Shaft. On 17 June 1996 the changeover was finally complete, when Robinson's was officially closed. A raise had been mined from 400 fm Level to the sump of the old Roskear Shaft, the holing taking place just below the 2000 foot Level. Wayne Brown put up the raise. The 2000 foot deep shaft, mined by the Dolcoath Company between 1923 and 1926, is 18 foot diameter and brick lined from top to bottom.

The new headframe, with shear wheels, stands 14m(46 feet) high, the diameter of the winding drum is 1.2m and the winding rope size is 18mm. The maximum hoisting speed is 1.5m per second. The headframe was designed at the mine and fabricated by a local firm.

1997 began with considerable optimism. High grades and production produced breakeven figures, and for a few months the old mine looked as though it might move into profit. But, the tin metal price began to fall inexorably. By Spring the price was averaging nearly a thousand pounds per tonne less than it had twelve months before. By June, after the price had gone down almost to £3,200 per tonne, the mine's situation began, once again, to look desperate. A memo issued on the 13 June 1997 announced the 'Temporary Suspension of Mining Activity on 470', and this was just one straw in the wind to signal impending crisis.

September 1997 found South Crofty Mine once again fighting for its life, and once again, outside factors, namely the price of tin metal and the pound-dollar exchange rate have caused the problem. The long-term ore reserves are sufficient for another generation of mining at Crofty. The grades are good and the tonnages are there, but economics conspire to render survival difficult. Many generations of miners have striven against great odds to win tin and copper from the hard rock of Illogan and Camborne parishes. It is to be hoped that the descendants of those long-dead men can continue the ancient tradition of mining in Cornwall well into the twenty-first century.

THE END

43. Development miners charging up a round on No.4 Lode at the 400 fm level. They are using ANFO explosives and 'Nonel' detonators. This type of non-electric detonator is used to avoid static electricity causing premature explosions. The holes are primed at the 'toe' using either dynamite or Powergel explosives. The holes are then charged by ANFO blown in by compressed air.

44. *Cyril Penrose and Nigel Durant longhole drilling on Roskear 'A' Lode at the 420 fm level. The drillrig is a Tamrock L500, and Nigel is drilling upwards at an angle of about 25 degrees from the vertical. June 1992.*

GEOLOGY

The surface workings of South Crofty Mine are situated on a series of slates and greenschist facies metasediments belonging to the Mylor Slate Formation, of Upper Devonian (Famennian) age, collectively known locally as 'Killas'. Intercalated with the killas are a series of dykes and sills originally of tholeiitic basalt, that also underwent low temperature metamorphism (between 345ma and 365ma) converting them to pyroxene/amphibole/feldspar/epidote/uralite 'greenstones'. At depths of around 148 fathoms (271 metres) below surface, the killas gives way to granite of the Carn Brea stock, which outcrops a few hundred yards to the south and forms the prominent hills of Carn Brea, Carn Arthen and Carn Entral close to the mine site.

The mine works a series of sub-parallel veins (termed lodes) that trend ENE WSW, dip sub-vertically and are of a complex discontinuous nature. Formerly, many of these lodes were worked in the Killas for copper and minor amounts of lead, zinc and iron. As the granite contact was approached this type of mineralisation gives way to higher temperature tin and tungsten mineralisation. Current workings are exclusively hosted within the granite, exploiting the tin content of the lodes.

The Carn Brea granite is a satellite stock of the Carnmenellis granite, itself a cupola of the Cornubian Batholith that extends from Dartmoor to the Western Approaches. The granite was emplaced around 290-280 ma during the closing stages of the Variscan orogeny (Late Carboniferous - Early Permian) at around 3-4km below the surface. The 'granite' is a two mica adamellite (monzogranite) with strong Ilmenite Series affinities. Isotopic data shows it to be an S-type continental derived body. Its high U/Th content and strong thermal activity have resulted in it being classified as a HHP (high heat producing) granite. The rock is typically coarse grained, carrying phenocrysts of perthite and albite and varies from white to pink in colour. Small bodies of pegmatite and aplite are associated with the granite and it is also intruded by a later series of quartz porphyry dykes termed 'Elvans'. To the North of New Cook Kitchen Shaft, along the line of the main Camborne-Redruth road lies a large Greenstone dyke. No outcroppings of this rock are known from within the present mine workings.

The lodes occupy a series of fracture zones (complex normal and reverse faults) related to stresses developed due to intrusion within the killas and cooling within the granite. These fractures acted as pathways for mineralising fluids of magmatic departure depositing the early hypothermal tin-tungsten mineralisation, and for later phases of mesothermal and epithermal mineralisation related to convecting meteoric and connate fluids.

These fracture zones now host complex multi-phase lode structures, some of which persist for 2km or more along strike and for dip heights of over 600m. Within the present workings five main phases of mineralisation have been identified:

1.   An early black tourmaline (schorl) phase, with thin (tin bearing) stringers of schorl emplaced throughout the fracture zones. The tungsten bearing (greisen type

mineralisation) quartz floors and pegmatites of Pegmatite Lode and the North Pool Zone are of similar age.

2.(a) A blue tourmaline ('blue peach') phase. This phase carries the majority of the economic tin mineralisation in the form of fine grained cassiterite which may be in discrete layers or in disseminated grains. This phase shows evidence of very rapid crystallisation and often displays brecciation textures related to explosive decompression.

2.(b) A chlorite ('green peach') phase. In this phase, that often overprints 2.(a), dark green crystalline chlorite is the dominant gangue mineral. It often carries coarsely crystalline cassiterite, as disseminations and seams, which may form the classic crystals of 'sparable' type. It is likely that much of this cassiterite has been remobilised from existing vein material.

3.   A tin-barren fluorite phase. This phase occupies sections of the lodes with 'caunter orientation', where the lodes have been faulted by later tensional wrench faults. These intralode fault segments (having the same strike as the E-W trending caunter lodes) have been infilled with a fluorite/haematite/earthy chlorite/quartz paragenesis, replacing the earlier tin rich phases of mineralisation.

4.   The caunter lode phase. These lodes represent later mesothermal/epithermal mineralisation emplaced in E-W trending fractures developed in a rotating stress field. These lodes are typically poor in tin, carrying a gangue of earthy amorphous chlorite/haematite/fluorite/quartz along with copper/lead/zinc/bismuth base metal mineralisation. Where they cross the earlier lodes they fault them, often with considerable displacement.

5.   The crosscourse phase. Crosscourses are infilled wrench faults. Most post-date phases 1-4, though faults of this type can be found across all phases. Many have a rough N-S orientation related to Permo-Trias wrench faulting. The faults carry an epithermal paragenesis of chalcedonic silica with earthy chlorite, haematite and minor amounts of marcasite and occasional copper and bismuth sulphides. Displacements along crosscourses vary from a few centimetres (they are typically of the order of a metre) to over 100 metres in the case of The Great Crosscourse. Many lodes also show intralode shearing related to this phase and carry the same paragenetic sequence as infilling/replacements within the lode, e.g. No.4 Lode.

The Great Crosscourse is a major wrench fault system that forms a recognisable surface feature for some 5km running from North Cliffs back inland past Brea village. The Red River flows along part of its course. The fault system may pre-date the granite and it has been active over a very long period. It is a series of dextral wrench faults forming a zone some 100m wide. The ground between the shears is heavily kaolinised and crossed with extensional chalcedony infillings along larger planes. It effectively divides the mine into two sections and was used as a boundary by many former mines. Lodes on either side of the crosscourse cannot be equated, although there have been suggestions that this can be done in the past (e.g. Roskear A = No.8 Lode, Roskear B = No.4 Lode) the number of lodes on each side is unequal and recent work on similar lodes (No.8 and Roskear A) show that there are major differences in pay shoot orientation as well as prominent mineralogical differences. The movement on the crosscourse could be considerably more than previously anticipated, though at present there are no firm indications as to the total movement involved.

The thirty or more lodes within the South Crofty sett can be divided into four main types:-

Type I Lodes:
These are lodes predominantly showing phase 2.(a) (blue peach/tourmalinite) mineralisation. They include the No.1 Lode, No.3 Lode and its branches, No.6 North Lode, No.8 Lode, Dolcoath South Lode, North Lode and Roskear A Lode.

Type II Lodes:
These lodes show a higher proportion of haematite/chlorite/fluorite enrichment and as well as having phases 2.(a) and 2.(b) present, they show areas consisting largely of phase 3 type mineralisation. They include No.2 Lode, No.4 Lode and its branches, No.6 Lode, No.9 Lode, Dolcoath North Lode, Pryces-Tincroft Lode System, Roskear B Lode, Roskear D Lode and Roskear South Lode. No.7 or Reeve's Lode.

Caunter Lodes:
No. 7 or Reeve's Lode.

Mineralised Zones:
No.2 Complex, 3abc Complex, 3b Pegmatite Lode and the North Pool zone (NPA, NPB, NPB2, NPC, NPD).

The lodes are heavily influenced by the position of the granite/killas contact, both in terms of distribution (the lodes tend to diverge and branch in the contact area) and mineralisation type. Evaluation of a variety of lodes has demonstrated a 'ponding' effect in terms of tin grade on approaching the contact, with cassiterite being rapidly deposited as this thermal threshold was reached.

N Leboutillier BSc (Hons), PGCE, FGS

Development of South Crofty Lodes
It would be difficult to list and describe all of the lodes worked at South Crofty, and it would be almost impossible to detail the many names used for the same lodes or to explain the relationships between lodes that apparently are associated. Originally, the tiny mines that worked the lodes near to the surface were known by the names of the tenements or the particular field or croft where the work commenced. Thus, Wheal Dudnance was a lode that gossaned in Dudnance tenement; Long Close Mine was located in the field in Brea tenement called the Long Close; Tincroft was the operation in the field called 'ye Tyn Croft in Penhellick'; and Penhellick Lode was the one that was worked from the surface at Penhellick Vean.

Since about 1920 the names and numbers given the lodes worked at South Crofty have been more or less standard. Crofty's Main Lode was originally called 'Middle Lode' and is the downward extension of Tincroft North Lode, which is faulted at the 160 by Pryce's Lode and heaved upward about 40 fathoms, before descending as Main Lode. It is also the western extension of East Pool's Great Lode, which was an important lode in the early years of this century. As Tincroft North Lode it was worked from just below the surface as a gossan lode, and as Main Lode it has been worked down to the 335 level. Robinson's Shaft intersects it between the 205 and 225 levels. This north dipping lode courses E 20 degrees N and underlies 10 to 30 degrees N.

No.1 North Lode was worked from the 225 level downwards, but in Robinson's section it has not been driven below the 335 level. In New Cook's section it has been developed, with outstanding results, to the 380 level, the drive west on 360 being particularly rich.

No.2 North Lode was the saviour of the mine in the mid-1920s, and has been worked between the 225 level and 380. It is a north dipping lode that was extremely rich in Robinson's section down to 310 level, but thereafter its values moderated. On 380 it is worked west of Cook's main north cross-cut.

In 1921 on 260 level the north cross-cut from Robinson's Shaft intersected what we now call No.3 North Lode. It has been extensively stoped between 245 and 335 levels, with work also having been done in places at the 360 and 380 levels. Lodes known as 3a, 3b and 3c are also worked at the deeper levels, with No.3b being particularly rich in places. It is believed that No.3b has a relationship to East Pool's Rogers' Lode, but it peters out as it approaches the point of connection, and there is no certainty about it. East of Robinson's cross-cut, between 290 and 360 levels, a large number of the crown and floor pillars have been removed, leaving a vast empty gunnies.

Closely related to the No.3 series of lodes are the great complex ore bodies known as the pegmatite lodes. Wolframite, arsenopyrite and cassiterite are all found in these pegmatite lodes, and at Crofty the two principal examples occur between No.2 and No.3 lode at Robinson's section and between No.3 and No.3c at Cook's. The largest of these ore bodies is that worked between 315 and 360, just to the east of Cook's cross-cut, and is upwards of one hundred feet wide in places. Robinson's Complex has been worked between 290 and 335 levels.

The principal lode at South Crofty is the No.4 North Lode. In 1927, whilst driving Robinson's 290 cross-cut north from No.3 Lode, a south dipping lode was intersected, which was later called No.4 North Lode. It assayed at 48lb (2 percent) per ton over its three feet width, but scant notice was taken of it as the management wanted the miners to push on into the Trevenson sett. Although No.4 Lode is as erratic as the rest of the mine's lodes, nevertheless it has shown payable values on all levels it has been worked, throughout the width of Crofty's sett. Only on 380 are there significant distances on the strike of No.4 that are not of sufficiently high value to stope.

No.5 North Lode was discovered in 1928, when the 290 north cross-cut was driven 100 feet beyond No.4 Lode. It is a south dipping lode, and, as its underlie is steeper than that of No.4 Lode, it moves closer to the latter as it goes deeper, and also as it goes eastwards. Some very high values have been encountered on No.5 near to the cross-cut, but below 335 the lode is, for the most part, inseparable from No.4 Lode. It has not been found in Cook's section.

Although No.6 North Lode has been cut in the main cross-cuts north from Robinson's Shaft, little of value has been discovered that far west. In the area to the north-west of

Taylor's Shaft however, very high values have been encountered. It appears to have been worked by East Pool and Agar Mine, and between 290 and 335 levels it is extensively stoped, with drives into the payable area on 360, 380 and 400 levels recently completed. No.6 Lode, North Branch, has been worked between the 290 and 335 levels, with some of the crown pillars recently removed. Close by are other related ore bodies, of varying value. No.6 is a north dipper. For recent work on these lodes see the comments on North Pool Zone, below.

No.7 North Lode is almost certainly Reeve's Lode. It caunters the main ENE strike of Crofty's principal lodes, and is clearly seen in the cross-cuts north of Robinson's Shaft on the 290 and 310 levels. Some exploration has taken place in Cook's section, but it appears to be barren at the depths at which the modern mine has encountered it. This was one of the first lodes worked by the old Penhellick Vean Mine, as it gossans as a copper lode near to the main Pool to Tuckingmill road. It has had a variety of names and is possibly the one known originally as Penhellick Vean Lode, in the late 17th century. By the second half of the 18th century it was called Penhellick Lode, and it dipped north into Trevenson sett as it was worked deeper, so that after 1854 it was worked by North Wheal Crofty. Until about 1840 it was called Caunter Lode, but about that time it was again renamed after one of the Adventurers of East Wheal Crofty, Phillip Reeve. It is generally known now as Reeve's Lode. It is not to be confused with the lode known in the 19th century as Penhellick Lode.

No.8 North Lode has been worked mainly on 290 and 310 levels. In Robinson's section it is closely related to No.9 Lode, which it joins to the east, but in Cook's section it lies well to the south of No.9. The lode now known as No.8 North Lode was discovered by the sinkers of the First Sub Incline Shaft, close to the 420 level turnoff. It is dealt with below.

The most important lode north of No.4 has been undoubtedly the No.9 North Lode. It was first cut in 1953 by the 290 cross-cut from Robinson's. It lies 1,603 feet north of the shaft and, when discovered, was found to average nearly ten feet in width. Its values are very erratic, and although it has produced large quantities of good tin, it can be notoriously unreliable. This wide, south dipping ore body, consists for much of its length of groups of stringers that split and come together with great frequency. Horses of ground are common, as are branches from the main ore body.

To the north of No.9 are various lodes which are known as No.9 Fault, No.10, No.11 and No.12. Good values have been encountered in places on these lodes, but none has been developed.

Close to No.2 Lode on 290 level, there is a very wet lode that was dammed off at the time of the mine's closure in 1921. In the late 1930s this lode, known as 'Wet Lode', was drained in preparation for stoping. It has been extensively stoped on 260, 290 and 310 levels.

Inside East Pool sett, various ore bodies have been developed, including the Great North Lode, and the so-called 'New North Lode'. Ground long since abandoned due to the flooding of East Pool Mine in 1921, has been reworked. Considerable time has been spent in driving toward the 'Tolgus Tunnel Lode'.

In the Dolcoath and Roskear sections, to the west of the Great Crosscourse, many lodes have been explored, and some have proved of value. About a dozen ore bodies have been looked at to some extent, and Roskear South Lode, Dolcoath North Lode and Dolcoath South Lode have proved the best prospects. Extensive stoping has taken place in these areas, particularly of late, on the Dolcoath North Lode, and more recently on Dolcoath South Lode.

To the south of Crofty's Main Lode are several ore bodies of note. The Second South Dipper Lode, in the extreme west of the sett, just east of the Great Crosscourse, has proved to be very valuable, particularly on 315 and 340 levels.

South of New Cook's Shaft the No.1 South Lode on 340 has been developed to the Great Crosscourse but without spectacular results. On 315 level there has been limited exploration of the lode.

Tincroft South Lode has proved both rich and wide between 290 and 380fm levels. It is closely associated with Pryce's Lode, which has been worked practically from surface for or the last three centuries. Pryce's Lode has been a consistent producer of copper and tin, and over recent decades enormous gunnises have been created, which bear witness to the large tonnages of ore removed. It was on this lode that longhole drilling and drawpoint mucking was first developed on any scale at Crofty.

At the beginning of the 1980s, Pryce's and No.4 North Lode contained the largest ore reserves on the mine, supplemented by considerable tonnages in North Pool (No.6), No.9 and in Dolcoath. In 1985 Pryce's-Tincroft contained 33 percent of the mine's ore reserve (tin metal), Dolcoath South 12 percent, No.4 North 12 percent and No.6 North (NPZ) 11 percent. At about that time, attention was turned to the area beneath Roskear Shaft, in the belief that rich tin ground lay there, and by November 1985 diamond drilling had confirmed this.

There was a rapid and radical response to the tin price crisis of 1985, when mine planning underwent a total change of emphasis. Production moved from the low grade, high tonnage Pryce's-Tincroft lodes to the high grade lodes of No.8, Dolcoath South and Dolcoath North lodes. The period following the crisis also saw the intersection and proving of the Roskear 'A', 'B' and 'D' Lodes.

By 1990, the three Roskear Lodes accounted for about 20 percent of the tin ore reserve, Pryce's-Tincroft 16 per cent, North Pool 9 percent, No.4 North Lode 8 percent and Dolcoath North and South Lodes 20 percent. The emphasis was shifting toward the Roskear and Dolcoath sections.

North Pool also began to acquire new importance as close examination by the mine geologists, especially Paul Gribble, revealed that the old No.6 and No.6 North Branch Lodes were only a small part of a far more complex ore zone containing high grade stockwork mineralisation. What had been suspected by the miners and had puzzled the geologists for decades was finally explained and fairly sophisticated planning and mining methods were employed to exploit this zone, now known as the NPZ.

The early 1990s saw great emphasis placed on development and stoping of the Roskear Lodes from the 400 and 420fm levels. In 1991, some 70 percent of all tin metal came from the Roskears, with even Pryce's-Tincroft and Dolcoath lodes producing very little ore, and this general picture continued through most of 1992. During 1993, 445fm level saw major development work, with No.8 North Lode opened up and the drive into the Roskears pushed ahead. In the years 1993 and 1994, approximately 25 percent of all the mine's tin metal production came from No.8 Lode above 445 level. The geologists believe that the Roskears, together with No.4 and No.8 Lodes, will provide the bulk of the mine's tin metal in the immediate future.

The low tin metal price coupled with a current high break-even cost, make the option of extensive lateral development on successive levels limited. The most cost-effective option, for the immediate future, remains to deepen the mine workings, centred on the proven ore bodies of No.4, No.8 and the Roskear Lodes.

M Hodgson MSc, MIMM, Euro-Geol

APPENDIX

The following is a list of the identified mineral species observed in the current South Crofty workings:

Cassiterite	Stannite	Wolframite
Scheelite	Chalcopyrite	Chalcocite
Bornite	Chalcanthite	Brochantite
Bismuthinite	Arsenopyrote	Erythrite
Zippaeite	Johannite	Pyrite
Marcasite	Melanterite	Haematite
Siderite	Specularite	Limonite
Tourmaline	Fluorite	Chlorite
Quartz	Chalcedony	Calcite
Orthoclase	Coffinite	
Dolomite	Elateritic Hydrocarbon	

SOURCES/REFERENCE MATERIALS

L.T.R., em., 69 c.m. 34 - Acc'ts. Exch. K.R. bdle. 261, No. 9.
Speculi Britanniae, pars Cornwall, John Nordon.
Henderson MSS RIC, Truro.
Praed Papers (GHW) CRO, Truro.
Tehidy Manor lease agreement (HB 5/11).
HB 5/165 RIC, Truro.
HB 5/166 RIC, Truro.
HB 5/148 RIC, Truro.
HB 5/149 RIC Truro.
HU 13 (1625-1;63) CRO, Truro.
Lanhydrock Atlas (1696) copy at RIC, Truro.
Tehidy Estate Papers, Tehidy Mineral Office, Camborne.
22 M/EB/42 Vyvyan Acc'nts, CRO, Truro.
Mary Coates MS No.15 (1619) CRO, Truro.
22 M/EB/31 Vyvyan Papers (9-14), CRO, Truro.
R.T..Gunther, Early Science in Oxford, vol. 3 pp.497-9.
Kerrier D.C. Plans in Council's possession.

Tehidy Estate Map by Doidge (1737) DDX 101/5 CRO, Truro.
Praed Estate Map of Trevenson & Penhellick Vean (1740) GHW (Praed) 1/3. CRO, Truro.

Penhellick Work Acc'nt Book (1712-19) J. 1788, CRO, Truro.
Pool Adit Cost Books (1721-37) J. 1784-5 CRO, Truro.
Pool Adit Valuation of Materials etc (1749) J. 1419 CRO, Truro.
Pool Work, Penhellick Work, Pool Adit, Trevenson Mine and Wheal Dudnance for 18th century; all Cost Books, Accounts and Reports not used at CRO are to be found at RIC and Tehidy Mineral Office.

East Wheal Crofty Cost Books	(May 1834 to Feb 1845) DD.SC. 1. CRO, Truro.
	(May 1849 to Dec 1852) DD.SC. 2. CRO Truro.
	(Jan 1853 to May 1854) DD.SC. 3. CRO Truro.
East Wheal Crofty Charge Book	(May 1852 to July 1852) DD.SC. 4. CRO, Truro.
East Wheal Crofty Tributers' Book	(Jan 1840 to Feb 1854) DD.SC. 7. CRO, Truro.
EWC Index to Tributers' Ledger	(Nov 1852 to Feb 1854) DD.SC. 8. CRO, Truro.
EWC Tributers' Ledger	(Nov 1852 to Feb 1854) DD.SC. 9. CRO, Truro.
South Wheal Crofty Cost Books	(Dec 1863 to Dec 1870) DD.SC. 10. CRO, Truro.
	(Jan 1871 to May 1876) DD.SC. 11. CRO, Truro.
	(June 1876 to Nov 1882) DD.SC. 12. CRO, Truro.
SWC Pay Books	(Dec 1881 to Nov 1887) DD.SC. 14. CRO, Truro
	(Nov 1887 to Sept 1895) DD.SC. 15. CRO, Truro
SWC Tutworkers Setting Books	(Feb 1872 to Feb 1874) DD.SC. 16. CRO, Truro.
	(Mar 1874 to July 1882) DD.SC. 17. CRO, Truro
	(Aug 1882 to Nov 1890) DD.SC. 18. CRO, Truro
SWC Tributers Ledger	(May 1890 to Dec 1895) DD.SC. 21. CRO, Truro

EWC (1822-54) Reports, Agents' Reports, Tehidy Agents' Reports and Accounts, formerly at Tehidy Mineral Office, Camborne.
SWC (1854-1906) Agents, Pursers, Committee and Adventurers' Reports formerly at Tehidy Mineral Office, Camborne.
South Crofty Ltd. All Agents, Managers, Pursers and Secretaries' Reports, together with all production figures, accounts, development and assay reports, and all other material relating to the period 1906-1980 were at either Tehidy Mineral Office, the South Crofty Mine Offices, or are in the possession of the author.

BIBLIOGRAPHY

Barton, D.B. - Copper Mining in Cornwall & Devon (1961 Barton)
The Cornish Beam Engine (1969 Barton)
A History of Tin Mining in Cornwall (1967 Barton)
Essays in Cornish Mining History Vol 1 (1968 Barton)

Borlase, W. - Natural History of Cornwall (1758)

Carew, R. - The Survey of Cornwall (1602)

Collins, J. H. - Observations on the West of England Mining Region (1912 Brendon)

Dines, H. G. - The Metalliferous Mining Region of Southwest England (1956 HMSO)

Donald, M. B. - Elizabethan Copper (1955)

Earl, B. - Cornish Mining (1994 Cornish Hillside Publications)

Fiennes, Celia - The Journeys of Celia Fiennes (1698)

Jenkin, A. K. H. - The Cornish Miner (1927 Allen & Unwin)
Mines & Miners of Cornwall vol x (1965 Truro Bookshop)

Harris, T. R. - Dolcoath: Queen of Mines (1974 Trevithick Soc.)
Arthur Woolf (1966 Barton)

Henwood, W. J. - Metalliferous Deposits of Cornwall & Devon (1843)

H.M.Government Reports. - Enquiry into State of Copper Industry (1799)
Report to Parliament on Cornish Mines (1842)
Report to Parliamentary Commissioners on all British Mines (1864)

Hunt, R. - British Mining (1884)

Lean, T. - Duty Performed by Steam Engines in Cornwall (1839)

Lemon, Sir Charles - Statistics of Copper Mines of Cornwall (1837)

Lewis, G. R. - The Stannaries (1908)

Meyerstein, E. W. - A Key to Cornish Mining (1907)

Morrison, T. A. - Cornwall's Central Mines: Northern District 1810-95 (1980 Hodge)
Cornwall's Central Mines: Southern District 1810-95 (1983 Hodge)

Noall, C. - The St Just Mining District (1973 Barton)

Norden, John. - Topographical & Historical Description of Cornwall (1584)

Pryce, W. - Mineralogia Cornubiensis (1778)

Richardson, J. B.- Metal Mining(1974 Allen Lane)

Rowe, J. - Cornwall in the Age of the Industrial Revolution (1994 Cornish Hillside Publications)

Spargo, T. - Statistics & Observations on the Mines of Cornwall & Devon (1861-65)

Symons, R. - Gazateer of Cornwall(1884)

Thomas, R. - A Survey of the Mining District from Chacewater to Camborne (1819)

Thomas, W. - Cornwall Mining(1923)

Tredinnick, R. - A Review of Cornish & Devon Mining Enterprise 1850-56 Inclusive (1857)

Trounson, J. H. - Historic Cornish Mine Scenes At Surface (1968)
The Cornish Mineral Industry (1989 Exeter University Press)

Watson,J .Y.- Compendium of British Mining (1842)

INDEX

Clemens,Ernest 102
Clemence, Jimmy 181, 188
Clemence, John 188
Climax Rock Drill Co.Ltd 110
Climax Lightweight Machine 121
Climax Stoper 125, 137
Climax 142, 149
Climax Imperial 102
Climax Disc Valve 131
Climax Vixen 100
Clitters Mine 102
Club, Miners' 44, 45, 51, 62
Clymons,John 39
Coalbrookdale 21, 22, 24
Collins,Henry 39
Colliver, Will. 62-65
Compressors 76, 87, 88, 106
Cooks Kitchen Mine 10, 11, 17, 19, 23, 27, 33,
    42, 82, 83, 91, 164
Cooper, Alan 181
Copperhouse Foundry 94
Cornwall Copper Co. 28
Coster, John 12, 13, 15, 23, 28
Cornish Engine Preservation Soc. 159
Contrino,.G. 163
Cornish Consolidated Tin Mining Ltd 102
Couch, D. H. 146
Cousin Jack Chutes 182, 183
Crane family 10
Crew Natural Resources 190
Crothers, Martin 106-109, 113
Crowst time 46
Curnow, W. J. 144
Curry, David 183
Curtis, Geoge 184

D

Dangerfield & Co. A. 101
Daniel, F. R. 121
Daubuz, Mr & Mrs 35
Davies family 109
Daw, John 64
Deacon, G. C. 99
Delabole Slate 178, 181
Delme-Radcliffe, P. A. 175
Denyer, J. B. 162, 171, 175
Diamond Drills 112, 113, 136 ,160, 167, 183
Dick's Whim 41
Disease, Miners' 63,109
Doering Drill 72
Doering, F. B. 72
Doidge, Will. 15,17,19,25
Dolcoath 20, 26, 27, 33, 42, 46, 57, 71-6, 86, 87,
    91-6, 106, 109, 133-9, 143-5, 149, 162,
    175-8, 183, 186, 188, 191.

Downing, Donald 138, 139
Drilling Machines 72-8, 87, 89, 92, 100-5, 109,
    147, 149
Druids Lodge 136
Dudnance 10, 11, 19, 25, 35
Dungey, C. J. 178
Dunstanville, Lord de 34, 35
Dunstone, James 39
Dutch Indies 128
Dutch 140
Dynamite 73, 76
Dyer, Rich.12

E

East Cornwall & Kennel Gunpowder Co. 103
Eastern Wheal Crofty 31
East Hill,Tuckingmill 42
East Penhellick Mine 29
East Pool Mine 56-8, 60, 68, 74, 75, 79, 82-6,
    106-12, 116-20, 129, 147, 150, 155, 164, 168,
    170-5, 178.
East Seton Mine 160
Earthquake 44
Ebsworth, N. E. J. 175, 176
Eckersall,Eric 187
Eddy, Bill 107
Eddy (Eudy), Henry 29
Eimco Rocker Shovel 143-5, 151, 182
Eldred,David 188
Eliots Metal Co. 91
Elizabeth 1st 1, 10
Elsan Toilets 165
Employers' Liability Act 76
English Copper Co. 28
Epsley, Thom. 13
Evans, T. Wallace 101, 102, 131, 135, 154
Exeter University 186

F

Faber Merlin (Hong Kong) 175
Factory Act 71
Fair Meadow, Redruth 83
Fane, R. G. V. 33
Fane, Vere 35, 42
Fiennes, Celia 14
Forristal, C. J. 184
Foxes & Portreath Co. 35
Franks, F. W. 124, 131
Freemans & Co. 28
Frue Vanners 89, 90, 93, 165

G

Gadsden, P. O. H. 176
Geevor 108, 143, 162, 185-7
General Strike 123

Pengilly, G. C. 166, 170, 171, 175-8, 185
Penhall, John 88-93,96
Penhellick House 11
Penhellick, New 25, 26
Penhellick, Old 25 ,26
Penhellick Vean 9-19
Penhellick Veor 10, 11
Penhellick Work 9, 10
Penrose, Cyril 183
Penrose family 109
Penwith & Kerrier Stannary 9
Phillips, J. M. 76, 80
Phillips, John 43, 47
Phillips, Will. 15
Philp, Thom. 102
Phoenix Mine 102
Plume of Feathers 30
Polish Miners 147, 152, 153, 159
Pool Mine 9, 13, 15, 19, 23
Pool School 9
Pool, The 168
Poynter,John 12
Pool Adit 12-25
Pool Health Centre 36
Pool Village 13, 14, 33
Portreath 78
Praed family 9, 11, 12, 19, 26, 29, 34, 36
Praed, James 35
Praed, John 14
Praed, Will. Markworth 21, 29
Praed, W. T. 35
Provis, Hen. 19
Provis, Mr 76
Pryce, Will. 12, 13, 17, 33
Pryor, Thom. 154-8

R
Radnor 10
Radnor, Earl of 25
Raper, J. J. 175
Rashleigh, John 26
Red River 9, 10, 15, 17, 34, 71, 176
Redruth Miners'Hospital 139
Reed, Walter 27
Reeve, Philip 35, 42
Relubbus 94
Reynolds family 34
Reynolds, J. J. 43
Reynolds, Will. 35, 47
Richards family 109
Richards, James 43
Richards, John 37
Richards, Joseph 96
Rich, Harry 146-8, 150, 153
Riches, Mr 136

Robartes family 36
Robartes, Lord 83
Robartes, T. J. A. 61
Roberts family 109
Roberts, Joseph 37
Rock Drills 72-5,169
Rodd, E. H. 60, 62, 63, 66, 67, 71
Roe & Co. 28
Rogers, John 10
Rogers, Joseph 136, 137
Roscroggan Mill 175
Rosewarne & Hearland Mine 59
Ross, Kevin 187, 188, 190
Rowe, James 64, 65
Royal Commission 109
Rowe family 109
Rowe, Ted 141, 142
R.T.Z. 183-5, 187
Rubisz, B. 151
Rule, Bert 143, 144
Rule, Nicholas 42
Rule family 109
Rule, Mr 47
Rutter, Will. 42, 55, 59, 61-5.

S
Salmon, Verdun 165
Sandys, Vivian & Co. 94
Saunders family 109
Savory, Thom. 14
Schools, Local 46
Scorrier 41
Scottish Oils 152
Sedgemore, Fred. 115, 125, 139
Sedgemore, Jimmy 125
Sedgemore, Rich.Thom. 138, 139
Shaen-Carter, G. V. 175-7
Shirley,Wayne 186
Shortman,Bert 144
Siamese Tin Syndicate Ltd 171-3
Sicily/Sicilians 153, 166
Silicosis Act 148, 150
Silver Bullet Machine 147
Silver 3 Machine 149
Silver 303 149, 169, 182
Sim's Whim 41
Simms, James 43, 59, 61
Skiproad 66, 76
Smith, Charles 138
Smith, Sir Gilbertson 153
Somerset 13
South Frances United 83, 94
South Penstruthal Mine 77
Spanish Miners 152
Spargo, Thom. 63

Vyvyan, Sir Rich. 14, 30
Vyvyan, R. R. 72
Vyvyan, Sir V. 77

W
Wales 14
War Damage Act 145, 146, 148
Watt, James 30
Webster, Artie 135
Webster, Tom 124
Weeks, J. P. 175
West End, Redruth 83
West Frances Mine 91
West Penhellick Mine 29
Westminster 186
West Seton Mine 164
Wheal Abraham 94, 158
Wheal Agar 72, 82-4, 116, 117, 160, 164, 187
Wheal-an-Gare 11, 19, 25
Wheal Alfred 158
Wheal Basset 83
Wheal Concord 185, 186
Wheal Crofty 17, 20, 33, 34, 59, 74
Wheal Dudnance 17, 19, 20
Wheal Gerry 144

Wheal Grenville 117
Wheal Horse 17
Wheal Jane 94, 185-9
Wheal Knight 17
Wheal Nelson 183
Wheal Pendarves 175-8, 181-8
Wheal Sisters 102
Wheal Susan 34, 53
Wheal Vernon 17
Wheal Vor 13
White, W. T. 96
Widow Maker 131
Williams Bros. 41
Williams Directory 65
Williams family 109
Williams, Fred.Martin 61, 62
Williams, Harvey of Bootle 140, 159
Williams, Jeremiah 63, 64
Williams, Tom 138
Wilmott, Bob 188
Wilson, Matt. 183
Wilson, Ted 125
Wire Rope 71
Woon Antron 10